THE HUNGRY PLANET

THE HUNGRY PLANET

The Modern World at the Edge of Famine

GEORG BORGSTROM

THE MACMILLAN COMPANY, New York

COLLIER-MACMILLAN LIMITED, London

Contents

Preface

MAN threatens to deprive himself of a future by re-fusing to recognize his predicament. Insanely we try to talk ourselves out of reality. We refuse to acknowledge the rising human tidal wave. We profess to believe that our civilization will be the first in history to attain immortality. We are convinced we know the secret of perpetuating our way of life with the aid of science and technology. Yet our fate is to be read as in an open book. We are dazzled into inactivity like the rodent facing the gaze of the snake. We do not seem to want to face facts or to make a courageous effort to regain control of our destiny by overcoming our demographic illiteracy. What we must do is start the great rescue operation of mankind.

The most heartening sign of reawakening was the assertion by President Lyndon B. Johnson, in his State of the Union address (1965), dedicating his Administration to facing "the issue of the population explosion and the scarcity of resources." If the present book may shed light on this crucial dilemma of our days it will well serve its purpose.

The book originated as a series of broadcasts and therefore in no way pretends to give full coverage to the multitude of difficulties facing man in various continents. Due to the national-istic turmoil of Africa, the imminent food crisis of that vast continent and of its narrow resource margins, despite numerous ambitious programs, make a general survey difficult. Nor was the *danse macabre* of Europe analyzed—next to Asia the world's most overpopulated region. For more than four centuries Europe has, like an octopus, taken a grip on almost every continent and sucked out its riches. One after another of the arms of the octopus are now being cut off. Only in a completely new context, a new superstate, whether of Atlantic design or embracing most of the white race, inclusive of the United States and the Soviet Union, will Europe survive, regain strength, and overcome its recurring crises. Another alternative is a world state, which, however, looms in a far more distant future.

As things now stand we seem to face the alternative of nuclear annihilation or universal suffocation. It is five minutes to twelve but there still remains the choice put forward to mankind by the late Sir Winston Churchill in his last major speech in the House of Commons: "Immeasurable reward or Supreme disaster." Our tragedy is that we think we have made our choice in favor of reward, but it is becoming increasingly clear that man is heading for disaster. Only one recourse remains open—namely, to mobilize our talent, ingenuity, brain power, and resources to fight the only war that still can be fought and won—that of our survival. We desperately need a General Staff to wage this global war— paradoxically enough also the road to peace.

We need to move back to reality from our excursions among abstract symbols. Completely defiant of all facts, we still preach about an "abundant world" when only a few strongly armored oases remain on the globe. A whole generation became the victims of a colossal failure of our education in not conveying pertinent, accurate knowledge about our predicament. The focusing of our learning and general education on the Western world has given us an entirely wrong perspective; it is a poor guide in a world rapidly dwindling in size and truly becoming one.

Finally, there are to be noticed signs of a late awakening from our century-long demographic lethargy. Charlie Chaplin in his *Modern Times* tries in the department store to run up the escalator, all the time moving downward. He failed. But until quite recently we made ourselves believe we were going to succeed in such a futile undertaking, even when our great human escalator is persistently accelerating its downward movement.

East Lansing, January 1965   GEORG BORGSTROM

Introduction

THERE are countless books on how to deal with the population increase in the world—the so-called population explosion. Economists, agricultural scientists, and geographers vie with each other to provide comforting details of the world's enormous food potential, and all kinds of calculations are being made and publicized as to how many more billions the world can feed, but these estimates stop at twelve, fifteen, or twenty billion. This does not take into account visionary speculations about transforming the Arctic and Antarctic into giant food-producing hothouses heated by atomic power. None of these fantasts seem to be worried by the fact that the melted ice would submerge most of our large capitals and drown a major portion of the human race.

A a rule, the fact is completely overlooked that—despite the enormous sums invested, the impressive technical progress we have made, and the extraordinary efforts by governments, by international bodies, and by scientific and technical communities —mankind has by and large failed in its supreme effort to feed adequately those billions of people *now* living on earth. Of these, at least one billion are undernourished, and the diets of an additional eight hundred million are deficient in one or several key nutrients.

The warning voices that have been raised have gone unheeded.

Dreams and unrealistic planning have been favored over reality. The great issue of our age is not the Iron Curtain or the Bamboo Screen, but the Hunger Rampart—the enormous and constantly widening gap separating the 450 million well-nourished inhabitants of the globe from these one and a half billion who are underfed or malnourished.

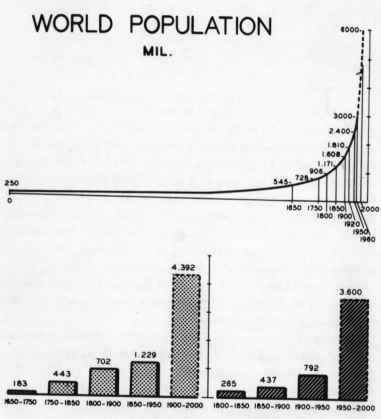

FIG. 1 Growth of world population since the days of Christ. Bars in lower part show the increment per 100-year periods (in the left section) and per 50-year periods (in the right section). Graphs prepared by the author from U.N. Demographic Yearbook and various estimates in textbooks as to earlier size of total human race.

In 1960 the world population passed the three billion mark (in 1964 in excess of 3,250 million). Few have clearly visualized the consequences of having an addition to the world's population of what amounts to a whole new United Kingdom every tenth month or almost a whole United States each third year and a new Soviet Union every fourth year. In the first sixty years of this century the world's population has doubled, and we can look forward to a second doubling before year 2000.

This rising flood of people threatens to deprive the human race of its future. The increase is not the result of any magical rise in the birth rate. Since the turn of the century most countries show a decline in this respect. A few countries, including the United States, show an increase in the postwar period. A drastic reduction in birth rates is important in order to save mankind, as well as civilization—or on the whole any values, including religion. But even if a strict birth control could be implemented, its long-term effects would not be felt for decades to come. We will be faced with an excessive feeding burden in this very century. Despite all our medical and technical progress, still only 5 per cent of the world's deaths are due to old age. This is the picture that is being unrolled before our eyes, making it obvious to everyone what the experts have known for quite some time and warned about—that the human race long ago exceeded the limits of what the world can feed. Contrary to all facts, we continue to talk about an abundant world, whereas the truth is that the world is desperately short of almost everything: food, shelter, homes, clothing, soil, utilities, forests, water—even the lack of physical space is felt in many places.

If the world's population continues to expand at the present rate, it will double itself every 35 to 40 years, and this means that within 120 years the present production of foodstuffs will have to be increased eightfold if the present standards are to be maintained—and yet these are inadequate for more than half of the present number of people. If the minimum requirements of the entire present population were to be met, food production would have to be doubled immediately. Does anyone really believe that the magic required to meet such enormous needs is feasible? If we were to ration what the globe totally carries in food in such a way that each individual received an equal share, this would mean universal starvation. It has taken the energetic West five centuries to treble its wheat production. In the latest century, with all the aid of modern science and technology, the increase in this progressive part of the world has been a modest 60 per cent.

Early critical analyses in the eighteenth and nineteenth centuries warned about this calamity. Particularly Thomas Malthus, the holder of the first professorial chair in economics in the British Isles, had been ridiculed for his anticipation, on purely mathematical grounds, that the world could easily double its population in twenty-five years. This was considered almost inconceivable and incredible. And yet in this very moment many key areas of the world are doubling their numbers in around twenty years.

Most of our efforts to master the present population increase have been on a Lilliputian scale. We need a broader program of general education and a mobilization of the world's brainpower to facilitate a clear understanding of these issues and their true dimensions. We must be realistic and acquaint ourselves with the facts, which for too long have been veiled in a mist of catchwords and glib "reasoning." Laymen and the learned alike are miserably uninformed on these matters and resort to easy-going, evasive diagnoses. We must be made to realize and appreciate the fact that the menace is now becoming truly universal and is certainly not confined to the teeming millions of Asia. Our own civilization is in clear danger. We, the peoples of the West, are facing serious calamities in our inevitable adjustment to reality, much more so than will ever be the case in that part of the world which we arbitrarily label underdeveloped though it happens to comprise some of the world's oldest and highest civilizations.

The Real Costs Unaccounted For

We in the West have never written up the books of our administration nor arrived at the total sums of our enormous squanderings: the real costs, measured in terms of board feet of forests, cubic feet of water, acres of arable land, and tons of minerals. Our tragic mistake has been our failure to recognize that Nature is not acquainted with our abstract money evaluations nor does it pay attention to or fit into our methods of percentage calculations.

What counts are the absolute figures as represented in wasteland, eroded soils, polluted waters, eradicated plants and exterminated animals, and in desiccated, waterlogged lands or swamplands. The West never did strike a balance in making up its debit and credit accounts. The hazards of the future will in all probability be greater for us, having just lived through our Golden Age, during which we thoughtlessly squandered our natural resources, taking consolation in the fallacy that we would always be able to grab land and wealth somewhere else and that our supremacy would be retained, giving us the first world priority rights. We will have to pay dearly for this Play of Pretense which we have conducted so dexterously but at the same time with such ominous consequences.

We are behaving like children richly endowed with toys and gadgets—but who do not realize that we are involved not in a game but rather in a struggle for survival. Our present implements are by and large not adequate for this world of reality. Surely there must be worthier goals for human endeavor than nuclear annihilation and universal suffocation. It is now the great responsibility of scientists to flash the red light to this human drive ahead. For too long a time we have shown green no-danger signals.

Scope and Magnitude of Measures

The desalinization of seawater and its effective use in agriculture involves problems infinitely more complex and far greater in their dimensions than those described by science writers in Sunday editions of major newspapers. If this kind of irrigation were to be more than a mere sprinkling along the fringes of the continents, gigantic closed tunnels—not pipelines—would have to be built and enormous energy quantities allotted for the pumping of the tremendous water quantities up and out over the continental land masses. Plans were recently drawn up for the irrigation of southern Texas, the groundwater reserves of which will have been so reduced by the year 2000 that desalting of the waters of the Gulf of Mexico will then have become not only inevitable but the only recourse, unless measures are now taken to curb the present mining of Pleistocene water. Merely for southern Texas this would imply the erection of no less than 15,000 plants, each in size equaling the largest chemical plants of present-day United States.

If the future millions are to be fed through agriculture, a considerably broadened use of chemical fertilizers will become indispensable. It is largely along that line that Europe managed to feed its added population in the latest hundred years. By the end of this century the amount of fertilizers that will have to be distributed around the world in terms of weight will by far exceed the total weight of the human race at that time, and yet this would only cover about three or four of the key substances that crop plants require and not the whole range of nutrients which by then will have to be taken into account.

Collateral Space Limitations

If India and China were to publish books on the same scale as does England, it would mean an annual production of close to two billion volumes, and that figure does not take into account periodicals, films, etc. The House of Knowledge is also threatening to burst at its seams. If the people of South America, Asia, and Africa were to start traveling to the same extent as we North Americans do, world transportation would have to deal with four billion additional travelers. Witnessing how most countries have been unable to deal adequately with the increase in traffic that has taken place since the war ended, one realizes the hardships ahead for countries forced to deal with such massive hordes of humans. The new international airport of London when working to capacity can dispatch four thousand passengers per hour, a fraction of what a big railway station is able to take care of in far less space. No wonder there is talk about the need for two to three additional airports for London in the immediate future.

Similar examples could be presented in great numbers. It is astounding, to say the least, to find how little thought is being devoted to these and similar problems. It almost seems as though we lacked the courage to face reality. Nor do we seem capable of interpreting the danger signs, even when they are almost self-evident. Instead we talk ourselves out of reality. Or, possibly the truth is that we have already capitulated. Sometimes one wonders whether we really are serious about our solemn assurances of technical assistance to "underdeveloped" areas.

We talk about the four freedoms, apparently quite oblivious of the fact that the world's resources of forest, water, and land are quite inadequate to provide the present population with the requisite minimum of food, housing, fuel and paper. Education, research, and politics need to be adjusted to reality and forced to leave the world of fantasy in which they have lived for too long.

We insist on talking about the Big Four without giving a thought to the fact that England and France are now tenth and twelfth among the nations of the world. The Big Four are: China, India, the Soviet Union, and the United States; then come Japan, Indonesia, Pakistan, and Brazil. Here one can see the contours of a new world order. The expression "great power" no longer means the same as before: in effect only those countries are powerful which have natural resources in excess of their immediate needs, and in this sense only the U.S.S.R., Canada, Brazil, and the Congo qualify.

The Inundation Wave and the Illusion of the West

We are horrified at the Chinese communes, yet we are drifting toward similar living conditions. The frightening visions of Aldous Huxley and George Orwell are beginning to take shape before our eyes. In some respects they look mild and humane compared to what seems to be materializing in reality. Mass collectivization is on its way, not unexpectedly, also in the overpopulated parts of Western Europe and the United States. A single vote that once may have been influential in the parochial world swiftly becomes deflated in a world community of immense masses. One vote among a million carries little force. No one listens any longer to an individual, unless he represents a powerful, multi-headed organization. One voice among the 420 millions of India is impotent, yet we go on pretending that traditional democracy is viable under these grim conditions. The inundating wave of humans is rising fast. It is threatening to stifle all that is human, and we of the West seem to think that alms are enough. That is a fallacy of illusion that may destroy us.

War and Peace

To start paying attention to these essential questions will in itself pave the way for peace and disarmament. There are good grounds for asserting that, if the politicians had recognized the urgency of striking a balance between natural resources and population and the need for a more even distribution, the two world wars that our generation has known might have been averted. Only by tackling these questions *now* can a third war be averted. It is getting very late.

The popular notion that it is the hungry countries that take recourse to war is quite false. A starving people do not have the resources and other prerequisites for war, and history substantiates the opposite view: it is the countries that are threatened with hunger and a lowering of living standards that resort to war, for example, Japan's invasion of Manchuria, Italy's African conquests, and Germany's plundering of Europe, to cite examples only from our own time. When William Vogt's *Road to Survival* was published in 1948, *Time* in its review stated that if the United States ever would reach the unlikely position of not having enough food for its population because of land shortage, there would be only one remedy: to go out and grab the land it needed!

Cynical hopes that war will get rid of excess populations are unfounded. The two great wars in this century did little in this respect. Their combined casualties of forty to fifty million are less than the present net annual increase of sixty-five million. All the bombs now in store would not suffice for mass extermination, and to achieve the latter by bombing would be more than our economic resources could stand. It seems that man may be unable to show restraint in procreation. That leaves the field open for tryouts more unpleasant even than those the world so far has experienced. Faced with the threat of death by suffocation from numbers, future oppressors may resort to mass extermination for which cheap and effective means are already available in nerve gases and bacterial toxins. Therefore, in the name of humanity as well as sanity, one must earnestly appeal to everyone to acquaint himself with the facts of this fateful question. Similarly, scientists should be urged to stop telling fairy tales about the world's abundance and almost limitless resources. There can be no more urgent task than that of spreading knowledge of mankind's truly precarious situation. Public education on the broadest possible basis is called for—from the first grade right up through our academic institutions. Although it may be one hundred years too late, we might still have a chance to save man and, possibly, civilization. But without a large-scale educational drive, our frantic rush downwards with a constantly accelerated speed cannot be slowed up or, better still, switched into a smooth climb for prosperity, progress, and human betterment.

CHAPTER 1

Fifteen Billion Extra People

THE world population is at present growing at a rate of sixty-five million people annually. This means that a number almost equal to the population of the entire United States is added each third year. This amounts in effect to a daily increase of almost 177,500—or a city about the size of Springfield, Massachusetts or Nashville, Tennessee. The growth is not the result of a sudden mysterious upsurge in the number of births. Compared to the start of the century, most countries show a decline. The United States exhibits an unprecedented postwar increase, making us holders of the world record in net growth in the developed world.

Furthermore, the battle against death has been advancing victoriously in all areas of the world, including the underdeveloped part. Ceylon may serve as a case in point. In three years, from 1945 to 1948, the island reduced its death rate—thanks primarily to successful measures against malaria—by as much as it took Western Europe three hundred years to accomplish. In spite of more or less spectacular progress in reducing the death rate around the globe, the fight against diseases and death has barely begun. An overwhelming number of people still die from infectious and contagious diseases which we now possess the means to curb or eradicate. This explains why in China, India, and Latin America more than one-third of the population—in many cases close to half—consists of children below fifteen years of age.

TABLE 1

Percentage of Population Below 15 Years of Age (1960)

Taiwan	45.1	India	37.3
Mexico	44.4	U.S.	31.2
Peru	44.0	Japan	30.0
Brazil	41.9	Sweden	22.0

Against this background we have every reason to look to the future with grave concern. Even if the commendable efforts to introduce an effective birth control are successful, mankind will still face a considerable expansion of its population in the immediate years ahead and will almost surely exceed six billion before the year 2000.

In this twentieth century so far, more than one and a half billion people have been added to the world population. The total net growth during the nineteenth century amounted to half that amount, or 702 millions. Merely during the latest twenty-four years—from 1937 to 1961—937 millions have been added. In 1964 the three-and-a-quarter-billion line was passed. It is therefore a safe estimate that before this century comes to a close, the globe will carry in excess of six billion inhabitants even provided an energetic and purposeful worldwide family-planning policy is implemented. If not, the population figure might easily reach seven to eight billions. Already by the year 2025, the fifteen-billion mark will be passed if unforeseen catastrophes do not interfere or radical countermeasures are not adopted.

There is a great deal of talk about optimism and pessimism in reference to the possibility of feeding the world. Basically, there can be no such difference of opinion; it is only a question of degree—when do we pass the danger line? The only thing that counts is reality itself. The indisputable fact remains that we already possess on this earth more people than we are able to provide for adequately. At the same time that we are facing this formidable task, we have to perform the feat of satisfying the needs of twice as many human individuals in less than forty years. Man has almost reached the point where, for all practical purposes, he is depriving himself of any history.

Asia

Asia constitutes one of those regions where the population increase will create almost staggering problems. Only fifteen years from now, by 1980, there will be another billion people, in addition to the one and a half billion already living there now. If these two thousand five hundred million were to aspire to a standard comparable to the rather modest one of present-day Japan—actually very low, judged in western terms—the following additional quantities of various key commodities would be required per year:

TABLE 2

Additional Quantities of Selected Items Required per Year in Asia

5,000	billion gallons of water
90.4	million tons of rice (world crop now 172 million tons)
11	million tons of wheat
198.4	million tons of vegetables
66	million tons of food fish (world catch now 35.3 million tons)
14.3	million tons of meat
300	million living quarters
10	million hospital beds
120,000	elementary schools (for 1000 pupils each)
1	trillion kilowatt hours

Every single day an additional 500,444 tons of wastes would be piling up and would need to be disposed of and thousands of miles of highways and railways would have to be built.

Traditional Computations of Population Density

Geographers have used various methods to measure population density. Sometimes the simple figure indicating number of people per square mile is used, without taking into consideration if the available land area consists of mountains, marshlands, deserts, or tilled land. With this simple method we find that the population density of Asia is 64 people per square mile, compared to 10 in the Soviet Union, North America, and South America. In the remainder of the world the comparable figure is Europe 63, Africa 9, Oceania 2.

An admittedly superior method is to put the number of people in relation to the tilled acreage. By this method it becomes feasible to indicate how many acres of land producing food and feed are at the disposal of each human individual, or, conversely, how many people are fed from each acre of cultivated land. Some elucidating examples showing the great discrepancies on earth in this respect are given in the table below.

As the table indicates, several West European countries rank in the same range as Asia's hunger countries. In reality, however, the plight of these European countries is alleviated by their making use of extensive pasture land, besides the tilled land. They further lean heavily on substantial transoceanic acreages for their feeding. Fisheries are another significant means of providing food and feed. Vast additional acreages would be required to substitute food from land animals for the important contributions rendered by the sea to the feeding of these European countries, not the least in terms of feeding-stuffs. In this particu-

TABLE 3

Number of People in Relation to Tilled Acreage (1958–59)

	Number of People per Acre Tilled Land	Tilled Acreage in Acres per Person		Number of People per Acre Tilled Land	Tilled Acreage in Acres per Person
Japan	7.4	0.14	India	1.1	0.91
Netherlands	4.4	0.23	WORLD	0.80	1.25
Egypt	3.9	0.26	Mexico	0.70	1.43
U.K.	2.9	0.34	Nigeria	0.60	1.67
China	2.5	0.40	U.S. and		
Peru	2.4	0.42	U.S.S.R.	0.38	2.63
Indonesia	2.0	0.50	Argentina	0.28	3.17
Norway	1.7	0.59	Australia		
Brazil	1.4	0.71	and		
Italy	1.2	0.83	Canada	0.17	5.86

lar regard they differ from the Asiatic areas that largely are forced to use their regional fish catches for direct human consumption.

This type of population density calculation can still be rated as deficient, owing to the fact that the nutritional standard does not enter the picture. It is well known, and evident to the nutritionist, that more agricultural products are required to keep a North American going than a Brazilian or an East Indian. It takes a substantial amount of feed to produce the animal products a North American consumes. This obvious nutritional relationship has not been reflected in the conventional population density calculations of the geographers. There is reason to believe that this is due to the lack of an acceptable and simple method which would allow such comparisons.

ARES PER CAPITA
TILLED LAND

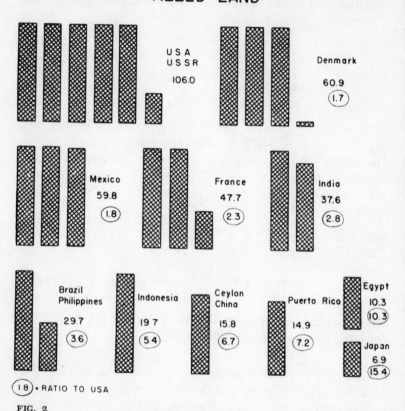

USA
USSR
106.0

Denmark
60.9
(1.7)

Mexico
59.8
(1.8)

France
47.7
(2.3)

India
37.6
(2.8)

Brazil
Philippines
29.7
(3.6)

Indonesia
19.7
(5.4)

Ceylon
China
15.8
(6.7)

Puerto Rico
14.9
(7.2)

Egypt
10.3
(10.3)

Japan
6.9
(15.4)

(1.8) ● RATIO TO USA

FIG. 2

The Human Circus

Crude estimates, showing that the world population—if nothing
unexpected happens—could easily reach fifteen billion around the
year 2025, overlook the fact that man has a whole range of livestock which are needed for traction or for food production. To
a smaller extent, pets also have to be fed from available food

resources. The human sector in living nature is thus already much larger than the present world population figure of three and a quarter billion indicates. Are there any methods by which it would be possible to estimate what this huge human circus is carrying around? Yes, various calculations of this kind have been made. Some of them will be discussed in chapter 4, "The Biological Budget of Mankind." Two alternative possibilities will be analyzed here.

The total weight of all human beings may be computed on the basis of certain standard figures for the average weight of humans at various age levels. On such a basis it can be inferred that the present world population weighs around 180 million metric tons. If, in the same manner, the number of livestock belonging to different categories of animals which are listed in available statistics (thus not all) but including traction animals, are added up, their total weight amounts to 925 million metric tons. In other words, these animals represent a living mass weighing five times as much as that of the total human race. Even in this case, certain assumptions must be made as to the average weight of each animal, etc., but on such a basis it can be stated with reasonable accuracy that the living mass of presently registered livestock equals about fifteen billion people.

Population Equivalents

The implications of these computations become even more obvious when another method is employed, and this by posing the question, What do these livestock animals actually amount to as consumers and measured by human standards? In these computations all these animals have been converted into what I have termed *population equivalents*. This has been done in the following simple way: Recognizing what modern animal feeding has established as minimum protein requirements of various species of livestock, their total protein consumption has been computed; what the nutritionist calls the *average standard man* (an individual weighing 154 pounds [70 kilograms] and with a protein requirement of about 2.5 ounces [70 grams] daily) has been adopted. Using this as a unit, it then becomes feasible to appraise each category of livestock in terms of number of standard men they represent as protein consumers, i.e., population equivalents. These computations reveal that the United States is not only carrying a feeding burden of 195 million humans, but in order to provide food for its people the country also has to furnish nourishment for the livestock animals. Measured in terms of their protein consumption they correspond for the United States to 1,300 million human beings and this in spite of the mechanization of agriculture having drastically reduced the number of horses. The total reaches 1,495 million when the human population of 195 million is added. Presently the North American continent is, in these terms, exerting a population pressure on its plant production, and more specifically on its protein resources, corresponding to that of more than two billion people. The figure for Canada is 168 million and for Mexico 396 million. The U.S.S.R. exhibits a biological pressure on its agricultural resources very near to that of the United States, 1,370 million— see table below.

TABLE 4

1960–61 POPULATION EQUIVALENTS
(IN MILLIONS)

	Livestock Population Equivalents	Man	Total Population Equivalents
U.S.	1,300	195	1,495
U.S.S.R.	1,150	220	1,370
Mexico	360	36	396
Canada	150	18	168

The Imbalance of Latin America

It is thought-provoking to bring into this discussion the dynamics of our own Western Hemisphere. Various commentators on the Latin American issue have repeatedly stressed the ominous fact that, in the fifties, an important crossroad was reached when the southern flank first outbalanced the northern part in number of humans. Recognizing that, on the whole, this southern part has 50 per cent more individuals in the age group below fifteen years—and this appears to become more accentuated as time moves on—we see prospects of a human mass as great as that of China, before the year 2000. Disturbing as this may appear, the situation is seriously aggravated when the total living mass of the human biosphere is taken into account, in the way this study advocates. With its dominant "colonial" agriculture, organized for feudal purposes and not for the feeding of masses, the ratio between livestock and man is almost twice that of North America. If we take into consideration the population equivalents in North and South, (see Table 5) North America in 1940 was already far behind South America—1.4 billion as against 2 billion. Instead of adjusting to the needs of their burgeoning population they have persisted in their outmoded pastoral agriculture, inherited from the Spaniards and the British. This, more than anything else, justifies branding Latin America as "out of date." In 1960, the discrepancy had become still more absurd— 1.7 billion as against 2.9 billion. We need not here discuss the fact that in the south the living mass of the hogs and poultry per unit is not rendering as much meat, milk, and eggs as in the north. The fact remains that the balance of the human biosphere is heavily weighted in favor of the south in this Western Hemisphere.

This poor undernourished southern part of the hemisphere already carries a feeding burden of close to three billion—almost that of the entire human race today. No wonder they are in a feeding crisis—which threatens to become chronic. It can be seriously questioned if there is any other part of the globe where the nutritional revolution is going to cause a greater upheaval than it will when the adjustment to the realities of the Latin Americans' existence takes place and the true needs of *all* the people have to be recognized.

TABLE 5

The Western Hemisphere 1940–60

POPULATION EQUIVALENTS (IN MILLIONS)

Country and Year	Livestock Population Equivalents	Human Population	Total Population Equivalents
Anglo-America—1940	1,249	144.4	1,391
Anglo-America—1960	1,482	195.3	1,677
Increase	233	50.9	284
Latin America—1940	1,892	129.7	2,021
Latin America—1960	2,661	201.0	2,862
Increase	769	71.3	841

Scandinavia

Although Scandinavia is a small part of the world (see table below), it is, however, an interesting fact that Denmark's livestock as consumers, measured as indicated above, surpasses the human population figure of the United Kingdom. With its present nutritional standard, Sweden has a population pressure which corresponds to that of fifty million people, and the entire Scandinavia, of 162 million, seven and a half times more than simple population figures show.

TABLE 6

Population Equivalents of Scandinavia (1958–59)

	Population (millions)	Livestock* (millions)	Ratio Livestock/ Man	Total Population Equivalents (millions)
Denmark	4.5	61.4	13.6	65.9
Finland	4.4	25.1	5.7	29.5
Norway	3.6	16.4	4.6	20.0
Sweden	7.5	39.2	5.2	46.7
Total	20.0	142.1	7.1	162.1
Percentage of Entire World	0.7	1.0	—	1.0

* incl. poultry

The World at Large

If we add up such data for the entire globe, a world emerges populated not alone by 3.3 billion people. In order to fill the nutritional needs of these billions and in order to produce their food, a livestock population is maintained which is equivalent to almost fifteen billion human beings. Clearly, it is an entirely different question to what degree these immense needs of food and feed are actually met. As is well known, among the livestock many animals are also underfed or starving. But these data give us a gauge for the pressure that man exerts directly and indirectly in order to satisfy nutritional requirements. In summary, our earth carries in total a feeding burden exceeding that of 18 billion human beings. Figure 3 shows the distribution of this living mass on continents and the ratio of livestock to man in each continent, clearly indicating that Asia and Europe are below the world average owing to their excessive population pressure.

Still, we have not accounted for all living things that man controls and earmarks for his existence, such as wild animals and plants. The multibillion armies of bacteria and fungi in the soil are, strictly speaking, consumers and part of this enormous human biosphere—the total living mass which must be fed in order to provide for man. In chapter 4, "The Biological Budget of Mankind," an effort will be made to appraise the significance and impact of this living mass toiling within the human sector.

The interesting aspect of this kind of computation is that it offers a means of gauging nutritional standards in geographical

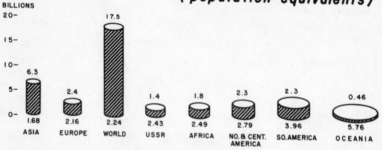

RATIO-BASIS OF CONTINENTAL BIOMASS
(population equivalents)

BILLINGS

RATIO-LIVESTOCK/MAN

FIG. 3

as well as agricultural terms. To a certain degree, the number of livestock reflects the quality level of the diet as reflected in production of animal products. They also facilitate a comparison between various countries on a commensurate basis. Japan with its 96 million inhabitants is not so overpopulated as this figure may make one believe. The livestock which form a part of the living mass operating within the human biosphere is equivalent to a number of protein consumers corresponding to 56 million people—in other words, a living mass in numbers as well as living weight far less than that of man.

A New Population Density Concept

These population equivalent figures comprise the total live-stock population required directly for the production of animal-product foods and indirectly for traction purposes. By employing these figures, population density can be computed in an entirely new way and can be given a broader and more realistic meaning by relating the total living mass of the human biosphere to available land resources. Pastures have then to be taken into account as they provide some of the food to the livestock. This slightly reduces the degree of accuracy of the computations. Grazing acreage unfortunately means very different things in the agricultural statistics for various countries. But for all smaller, fairly homogeneous countries, nations, or provinces such calcula-tions remain both meaningful and elucidative. For extensive areas such as the United States, the Soviet Union (one-sixth of the earth's land surface), India, and Indonesia they are less valid. These arbitrary boundaries of national units or states have unfortunately played far too great a role in geographical analyses.

At any rate, along these lines one arrives at a new concept of population density, based on the relationship between the total living mass within the human sector and the disposable acreage of tilled land, pastures, and available water. A few figures from my calculations have been selected and listed in the table below. See also Figure 4 as compared to Figure 2. They are based on statistics for 1957–1958, and by and large they are still (1964) valid—at any rate for comparative purposes.

I indicates the rank of the country in the complete list of all nations arranged on the basis of these new calculations of population density.

II indicates their rank according to the conventional calcula-tion method; number of people per area of tilled land.

TABLE 7

Population Equivalents in Relation to Agricultural Acreage (Tilled Land + Pastures)

I	Country	II	Population Equivalents per Acre	Acres per 100 Population Equivalents	I	Country	II	Population Equivalents per Acre	Acres per 100 Population Equivalents
2	Taiwan	2	13.7	7.3	33	Poland	40	3.9	25.6
4	Egypt	5	11.4	7.8	37	Brazil	26	3.5	28.5
5	Netherlands	4	11.1	9.0	37	Italy	28	3.5	28.5
7	Japan	1	9.3	10.7	39	New Zealand	18	3.4	29.4
10	Denmark	42	8.5	11.7	46	China	13	3.0	33.3
13	W. Germany	14	7.2	13.9	49	Peru	14	2.2	45.4
17	India	32	6.2	16.1	53	Mexico	41	1.8	55.6
20	Switzerland	2	5.4	18.5	58	Argentina	52	1.5	66.6
21	Philippines	26	5.2	19.2	60	U.S.	49	1.3	76.9
23	Nigeria	43	5.1	19.6	—	WORLD	—	1.3	76.9
25	England (U.K.)	10	4.9	20.4	65	U.S.S.R.	49	0.93	107.5
26	Indonesia	17	4.8	20.8	68	Australia	55	0.35	285.7

The Biological Ranking of Nations

We can now proceed to the question, How is this enormous living mass in excess of 17.5 billion population equivalents distributed over the globe? China, in spite of its 1,528 million, must yield the top position to India, which reaches 2,193 million. These countries are in reality the "Big Two." The U.S. and U.S.S.R. each respond to almost 1.5 billion. These nations are in effect the "Big Four" in biological terms and represent together more than one-third of the human biomass, or 6.1 billions. (Figs. 4, 5a and 5b.)

The traditional ranking between nations is thoroughly reshuffled through such a biological appraisal. Japan, which in number of inhabitants occupies the sixth place (96 million), moves down to the world's twenty-first country in terms of its total living mass—150.4 million population equivalents. Brazil emerges as a major power and becomes fifth in rank with more than one billion population equivalents, followed by Argentina with more than half a billion. The cattle of the pampas contribute largely to this upgrading. Other notable cases are Mexico with 396 million equivalents and Ethiopia with 265 millions. This latter country ranks in terms of human population as the world's twenty-fifth country, but attains the eleventh position when livestock is taken into account. France, England, and West Germany reach more than a quarter billion each.

These figures may be utilized for a more realistic appraisal of concepts like population density and population pressure. A series of interesting observations could be made on the basis of these figures. The most striking one is, however, that the pressure which the living biomass exerts on the vegetation-cover as well as on other natural resources in relation to available acreages becomes almost identical in Scandinavia and in densely populated countries like Indonesia, Japan, and others.

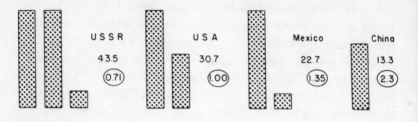

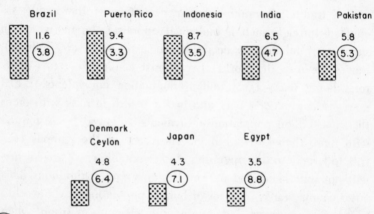

(3.8) = RATIO TO USA

FIG. 4 The total living mass (man + livestock) measured as population equivalents in relation to the feeding basis (tilled land + pastures). Compare these data with conventional agricultural density data—man in relation to tilled land—as in Fig. 2.

Various Livestock Categories as Consumers

Considerable interest is also attached to the relative part played by various livestock categories as consumers in the global household. In spite of mechanization, horses still amount to about 609 million population equivalents. Cattle have naturally a dominating position and correspond to 8.4 billion, i.e., nearly three times the world population; thus they account for almost two-thirds of the total livestock biomass. The total protein consumption of the hogs in the world household is equivalent to 1,794 million population equivalents and surpasses as such the total human biosphere of both the U.S.S.R. and the United States, taken separately. Sheep add up to 881 millions. (Fig. 7.)

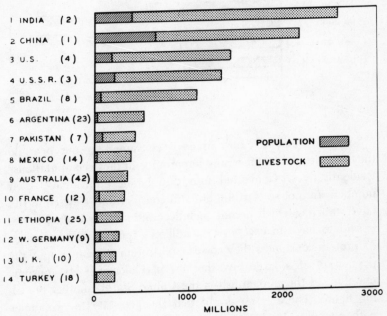

POPULATION PRESSURE IN POPULATION EQUIVALENTS

FIG. 5a The figures in parentheses refer to the rank of the individual country on the basis of human population solely in reference to tilled land (traditional agricultural density). (Note that in Fig. 5b a different scale has been employed.)

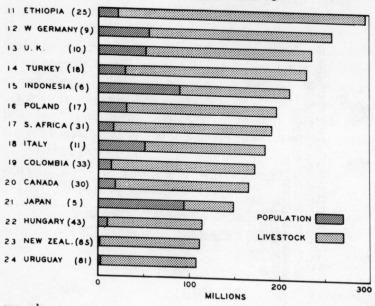

FIG. 5b

Somebody may ask how much is consumed by our pets—do they constitute a factor of any importance in these computations? Evidently, yes. Converted into population equivalents, their numbers are not so startling but still considerable. Few countries have statistics which permit such accounting. The United States is said to have in excess of 25 million (1964) registered dogs. As protein consumers they correspond to four million people, the population of a large city the size of Chicago. Cats consume one-third of the canned fish in the United States, another revealing figure. There is no doubt that the necessity to economize with adequate food resources was an important factor behind the elimination of dogs in China. *No Dogs in China* was the striking title of a recent book on modern China by an English reporter. (See list of references on China in chapter 7.)

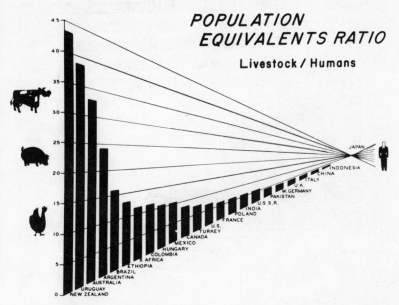

FIG. 6 The relationship between human beings and livestock, calculated on the basis of population equivalents in various countries. One extreme is represented by New Zealand, with a ratio of livestock to man of 43:1, with Japan at the other end with a ratio of 0.6:1.

The Demographic Illiteracy

Against the background of the facts presented above, there is reason to pose the question why so few people have acquainted themselves with the true biological feeding balance of the world. This responsibility rests primarily with the scientists. They will be forced to abandon their specialized disciplines and take the initiative in confronting mankind with the harsh facts of reality. They cannot persist in dwelling in a world of abstractions. To an alarming degree opinions have taken the place of facts, and gospels are substituted for knowledge. There is no wonder that

WORLD BIOMASS

(HUMAN SPHERE) 1958-59
MIL. POP. EQUIV.

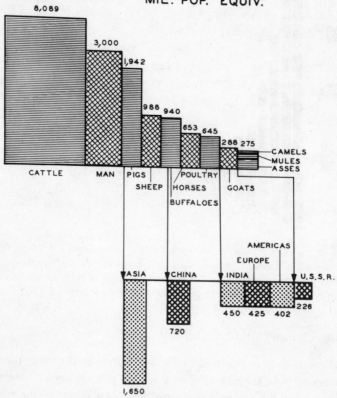

FIG. 7 The living mass which directly is part of the human biosphere. Besides man are the various livestock categories required for traction and other work but largely for the raising of animal products (milk, meat, eggs, etc.). Indirectly, man is enjoying the support of a far greater biomass, represented by the lengthy biochains of oceans and fresh waters, terrestrial wildlife, as well as soil organisms and a wealth of microorganisms.

public information on these matters in general is so scanty and defective.

The demographic illiteracy among leading politicians of the world is disturbing if not frightening. The President of Pakistan (Ayub Khan) as well as India's ambassador to the United States appealed in vain to the United States for aid in carrying out birth control programs in their respective nations. The incapability—or, what is even worse, the unwillingness—to recognize the realities of overpopulation and their imminent consequences is almost criminal. A cartoon in a U.S. newspaper recently showed two young children playing. One of them told the other that his neighbor just had an addition to their family. "Is that what they call the population explosion?" the other one asked. "I haven't heard anything," was the curt reply. This is more or less the way the politicians behave, even those who pride themselves on being responsible and progressive.

This is a problem of such complexity and magnitude that patent solutions or wiseacres fail to offer remedies. There is little evidence of statesmanship in the handling of these matters. In most cases the first step in any process for action has not been reached—recognition of the problem as such. On the whole, however, it is rather alarming to witness how these major and ominous problems of our time are sidetracked—their existence or gravity unrecognized. The conflicts of Laos (1.7 million), Israel (2.2 million), West Berlin (2.3 million), and Kuwait (220,000) are inflated to world dimensions, while the sufferings of the burgeoning billions are ignored. Even South Vietnam (14 million) and Yemen (5 million) are insignificant in comparison with a world that adds 65 million to its population each year. The trifles get the attention, and for their sake world war is incurred or risked. The talents of the politicians seem seriously inadequate to cope with the major problems of our day, such as mobilizing world action against hunger and poverty. One almost gets the impression that world leaders already have capitulated, and this seems to apply to both the power blocs—that of the East as well as that of the West.

Since the first Swedish edition of this book appeared (1962) things have been moving on this front. Most leading Asian politicians—the first to seriously feel the undermining effect and economic pinch of overcrowdedness—have expressed themselves in favor of effective birth control. This is true of Nehru (India), deceased in 1964, Ayub Khan (Pakistan), Nasser (Egypt), and Ceylon's female prime minister, Sirimavo Bandaranaik (resigned in 1965).

The Pope has stunned the world by acknowledging the gravity of the situation and hinting a coming reconsideration of these matters by the Catholic Church. A number of Catholic laymen and medical experts as well as several clergymen, bishops, and even cardinals have voiced support of planned parenthood, evidently with the contraceptive pill in mind. Several Protestant groups in the United States gave their support to family planning as early as the thirties. The National Council of the Churches of Christ in the United States of America, a federation of twenty-five major protestant denominations, gave their wholehearted endorsement to birth control in 1956, reaffirmed unanimously in February, 1961. There is now (1965) growing evidence of a better understanding of the urgent need for universal birth control. The pill, when used on a major scale, is, however, too complicated and costly a device. The simple uterine spiral appears to offer greater possibilities for use among the masses, requiring little education in use. It can also be made available at low cost.

Planned parenthood on a global scale that really reaches billions is a formidable challenge to public education and mass media. No task could be more urgent. It is sobering, however, to remind ourselves that population control is no new phenomenon in human history. It has been practiced in almost every advanced civilization. The devices for this purpose were not always barbarian, as were cannibalism, human sacrifices (e.g., the Aztecs), or weeding ("mabiki" among the Japanese—exposure of newborn infants, particularly females). Contraceptives were known to the Egyptians as well as to the American Indians. They were commonly sold in Europe in the eighteenth century. We are not the first in human history to realize the limitations of man's existence and the need for restraint and adaptation.

References

BARNETT, A. *The Human Species.* Baltimore, Pelican Books, 1961, 339 pp.

BOUTHOUL, G. *La Surpopulation dans le monde.* Paris, Payot, 1958, 269 pp.

BROWN, H. *The Challenge of Man's Future.* New York, Compass, 1954, 210 pp.

BROWN, H., BONNER, J., and WEIR, J. *The Next Hundred Years.* New York, Compass, 1960.

CHANDRASEKHAR, S. *Hungry People and Empty Lands.* London, Allen & Unwin, 1954, 306 pp.

CIPOLLA, C. *The Economic History of World Population.* Baltimore, Pelican Books, 1962, 117 pp.

COOK, R. C. *Human Fertility: The Modern Dilemma.* New York, Sloane, 1951, 380 pp.

CRAGG, J. B., and Pirie, N. W. (ed.). *The Numbers of Man and Animals.* Edinburgh and London, Oliver and Boyd, 1955, 152 pp.

FAGLEY, R. M. *The Population Explosion and Christian Responsibility.* New York, Oxford, 1960, 260 pp.

FRANCIS, R. G. *The Population Ahead.* Minneapolis, University of Minnesota Press, 1958, 160 pp.

FROMONT, P. *Démographie Économique: Les rapports de l'économie de la population dans le Monde.* Paris, Payot, 1947, 222 pp.

GEORGE, P. *Introduction à l'étude géographique de la population du monde.* Paris, Presses Universitaires de France, 1951, 284 pp.

HAUSER, P. M. *Population and World Politics.* Glencoe, Illinois, The Free Press, 1958, 297 pp.

————. *Population Perspectives.* New Brunswick (N.J.), Rutgers University Press, 1960, 183 pp.

HAUSER, P. M. (ed.). *Population Dilemma.* Englewood Cliffs, (N.J.), Prentice-Hall, 1963, 187 pp.

MEIER, R. L. *Modern Science and the Human Fertility Problem.* New York, Wiley, 1959, 263 pp.

PEP (Political and Economic Planning). *World Population and Resources.* London, 1955, 339 pp.

SAUVY, A. *L'Europe et sa population.* Paris, Les éditions internationales, 1953, 221 pp.

————. *Fertility and Survival.* New York, Collier Books, 1963, 237 pp.

SAX, K. *Standing Room Only: the Challenge of Overpopulation.* Boston, Beacon, 1955, 206 pp.

STUART, A. J. *Overpopulation—Twentieth Century Nemesis.* New York, Exposition Press, 1958, 240 pp.

THOMPSON, W. S. *Population Problems.* New York, McGraw-Hill, 1953, 488 pp.

VOGT, W. *People! Challenge to Survival.* New York, Sloane, 1960, 257 pp.

WRONG, D. H. *Population and Society.* New York, Simon & Schuster, 1961, 148 pp.

YATES, P. L. *Food, Land and Manpower in Western Europe.* New York, Macmillan, 1960, 294 pp.

ZIMMERMAN, A. *Catholic Viewpoint on Overpopulation.* Catholic Viewpoint Series. New York, Hanover House, 214 pp.

CHAPTER 2

The True
Hunger Gap and
the Calorie Swindle

Mostists writers on the subject of the world's food supplies confine themselves to calculating man's total calorie requirements and the capability of agriculture to meet these demands. This dangerous oversimplification is also encountered in most textbooks on agriculture, economic geography, and nutrition. Figures are presented that give a reassuring picture of the world abundance in food and how much more can be raised. These rosy analyses completely overlook the fact that, despite two postwar decades of tremendous efforts, we have not been able to satisfy even the minimum needs of the human race. Only a minor fraction of those now living come close to opulence.

Taking Denmark and Holland as patterns for the world, these "experts" offer entirely unrealistic calculations of the enormous quantities of food that would be obtained if, all over the world, the production level of agriculture were to be raised to that of these two countries. They completely disregard the obvious fact that neither of these two countries would be able to manage as they do without importing considerable quantities of feed, or without their fisheries. If the world really were to follow such foolish advice and copy Holland, for instance—a net-importing (imports exceed exports) country—the earth would need to acquire a food- and feed-producing satellite one-third the size of the present globe. Furthermore, world fisheries would have to treble their present catch to provide mankind with an amount of fish corresponding to what Holland is now procuring from the oceans. Nonetheless, calculations of this kind are used to convince people that the world would be able to feed from twelve to fifteen billion.

As the computations above have shown, we have already reached this level. As was pointed out in the previous chapter, a biomass of this gigantic size is in operation merely to supply the present population of the world, which is nowadays forced to be largely satisfied with a vegetarian consumption. Only one tenth of what the human race eats consists of animal products— meat, milk, eggs, and fish—yet such delicacies are, by and large, the privilege of a few hundred million.

A number of striking examples could be set forth to demonstrate what could be achieved if one could concern oneself merely with filling the calorie requirements of man. The United States, for instance, could dispense with much of its agriculture and convert the land thus freed into parks for the recreation of its zooming population. The present corn acreage would in effect suffice to provide ample and adequate amounts of calories to fill the present U.S. needs. The total tilled land in the United States could easily supply the world's present population, now exceeding three billion, with all the calories it needs if the northern zone were to grow sugar beets and the southern region sugar cane.

This kind of reasoning is based on a fallacy and reveals serious confusion about fundamental concepts. It should be obvious, even to the layman, that apart from the intolerable monotony of such a diet, it would inevitably lead to a nutritional catastrophe. People, as living beings, are certainly not mere internal-combustion engines. Recognizing only the fuel value of our food is an error and greatly misleading. Of course man needs energy, but that need has never been the really serious problem of man, despite what atomic physicists try to make us believe. Energy is not a limiting factor in food production. In three days the sun supplies the earth with more energy than is totally accumulated in all the deposits of coal, oil, and uranium.

Protein Shortage: The Most Serious Threat to Human Nutrition

In his food man needs protein—the living substrate of the cell's protoplasm—and in addition his protein intake has to satisfy very narrow specifications as to molecular structure. Man, furthermore, requires a number of vitamins, also special fats and, it would appear, certain specified carbohydrates. The proteins, however, are key compounds. It is more than a coincidence that, during recent decades, protein deficiency diseases have come to prevail in most continents and must be regarded as the chief nutritional deficiency of the world. Before we make an effort to outline in more realistic terms the true dimension of the protein shortage situation, we must deal with another aspect of what might be designated the calorie fallacy.

The True Calorie Disparity

The average calorie intake of the hungry masses of India is said to be 1,800 to 2,000 calories a day per person, while contemporary expert opinion puts the normal requirement of a full-grown person of 154 pounds (70 kilograms) weight at about 3,000 calories, recognizing that some of this is inevitably wasted and some is never used up by the body. Taking into consideration the fact that the East Indians are relatively short in stature (consequently weigh less) and also that there is a greater proportion of children among them as compared to the United States and Western Europe, the actual requirement of an East Indian at the present time may be estimated as from 2,400 to 2,500 calories. Thus, the gap between the present underconsumption and an adequate but still minimal diet requires an additional 400 to 500 calories a day per person. This would involve an increase of approximately 25 to 30 per cent in the amount of grain grown in that country.

We will not discuss at this stage whether or not it would be feasible for India to do this and to what degree this extra grain could be raised; instead, let us scrutinize these figures and see if they hold true. Even the Indians consume certain animal products, above all milk and fish, and a little meat and eggs as well. Now, for every calorie of animal foodstuffs produced, five to eight primary calories are required, represented by plant products and other feeding-stuffs that the animals need for their maintenance as well as for their food-producing activities. On such a simplified basis, the number of calories required to feed the various categories of livestock, in terms of primary calories, can be computed. The intake of an East Indian is therefore not restricted to the 1,500 to 2,000 calories he actually puts into his mouth, but comprises also the primary calories needed to procure these animal products. In this way the total amount of calories disposed per day reaches 2,400 or more. The most telling aspect of this, however, is not so much the fact that India's figure has to be readjusted in this way, but that the corresponding data for Americans and West Europeans must be revised upward in a similar way and this has much more far-reaching consequences.

The calorie consumption of most of the peoples of the Western world is thus not confined to the 3,000 calories they eat every day, but is more in the region of 9,000 to 10,000. The average

American disposes of about 11,000 primary calories a day, while the New Zealander requires 13,000. Here we encounter the true disparity between the peoples of the world—the true Hunger Gap. And it should be obvious that in order to fill such a gap, far greater efforts are called for. Measures are needed of quite another magnitude and scope than those generally intimated. It can safely be said that discrepancies of such tremendous dimensions could never be eliminated even if agricultural miracles and worldwide equalization of distribution were accomplished. The enormous disparity between the "have" nations and the "have-nots" in terms of total calorie disposal are shown in Figure 8 and are based on calculations adjusted in the manner indicated.

The Privileged

There is an upper class of some 450 million, out of the world's 3.5 billion, which occupies a privileged position as far as nutrition goes. We like to think that we owe our abundance to our greater skill and ingenuity, completely forgetting that we owe it equally, or maybe even to a greater extent, to our good fortune in the great lottery of history, which has given us a disproportionate share of the world's agricultural land resources. When the Europeans overflowed their boundaries, they took possession of this vast double continent of North and South America, as well as of Australia, parts of Southeast Asia and South Africa. Millions of acres in undeveloped countries are devoted to providing this luxury client with such items as sugar, cotton, coffee, tea, oilseeds, and bananas.

These luxury nations, to which the United States clearly belongs, constitute the privileged nations of the world. At present, their peoples dispose of as many calories per day or per year, as do the 1,300 millions at the lower end of the scale, such as the peoples of China, India, and Indonesia. Politically, this enormous chasm between the two groups provides an explosive situation, while economically the repercussions of this widening gap will become more and more serious. Wages and prices cannot in the long run remain unaffected by the fact that it costs three times as much to maintain a Westerner, whether he be professor, laborer, or engineer, than it does to feed even adequately an East Indian or Chinese. It is worth noting that most students of these calorie needs, as mentioned at the begin-

PRIMARY CALORIES AND POPULATION BALANCE

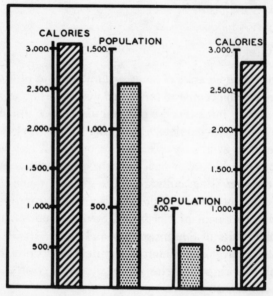

FIG. 8   The true gap between the malnourished and the well fed. The pair of bars to the left refer to the poorly nourished nations, ranking at the lowest level of caloric intake, while the pair to the right apply to the well-fed nations ranking at the top. The first group makes use of $3,000 \times 10^9$ kcal to supply 1.3 billion people, while the second group disposes of $2,800 \times 10^9$ kcal to the benefit of only 300 millions.

ning of this chapter, have not recognized the true relationship between calories and man's nutritional needs, but have satisfied themselves with using simple, standardized consumption figures, the real validity of which they have made no attempt to examine.

The True Role of Fish

Fisheries is a good example of the risks of this unilateral approach to the calorie problem. In reality, fish do not account for more than 2 to 3 per cent of the total calorie consumption of man. In this respect fish do not deviate much from any other animal product when they are judged individually. Even such fish-eaters as the Japanese get scarcely 3 per cent of their calorie intake from seafoods. Regarded in this way, fish does not stand out as particularly significant even when constituting an important part of the daily diet. To overcome this wrong perspective, tables have been computed to show how large a proportion of the animal protein intake in individual countries is consumed in the form of fish; but even these figures are inadequate. Even in this respect one striking evidence is provided by Japan. The Norwegians eat almost as much fish per head as the Japanese, yet fish accounts for only about one-fifth of the Norwegian intake of animal protein, while in Japan fish is a staple item and constitutes almost 70 per cent of the animal products consumed.

Any such relative analysis of the role of fish in the food balance must recognize that fish represents one important source of high quality animal protein and is in this respect fully comparable to milk, meat, and eggs; likewise it is superior to most plant proteins whether cereals or pulses.

Fish Acreage

A more striking and more adequate picture of the true role of fish is obtained by posing the following question: How many acres in each particular country would need to be tilled and devoted to an intensive production of feeding-stuffs in order to produce an amount of protein equal to that provided by fish? In most cases, milk is the best comparison, particularly because in computations of this nature it is desirable to deal with minimum figures in order to avoid any exaggerated claims. As to acre utilization, milk is in general the most economic and efficient animal product. In order to raise a corresponding amount of protein in meat or poultry this would normally call for still larger acreages. Milk is therefore a good choice for this kind of appraisal of the role of fish, as defined in agricultural terms.

Calculated in this way, it becomes evident that Norway would require an extra acreage amounting to two-thirds of its present tilled land in order to produce enough additional milk to provide the amount of protein which the Norwegians presently are consuming in the homeland (not exporting) in the form of fish and shellfish, and which they are furthermore disposing of in the feeding of their domestic livestock. This fish feed reaches the consumers' tables in the form of eggs and pork, produced by poultry and hogs fed on fish meal or related fish products. Some milk is obtained this way.

The corresponding figures for fish acreage for some other selected countries are:

TABLE 8

Fish Acreage of Selected Countries
(in Percentage of Tilled Land) ·

	%		%
W. Germany	28	Holland	69
UK	38	Japan	154

The latter figure, when interpreted, means that Japan is so dependent on fish that the "fish acreage" represents in food protein terms more than one and a half times the area of the present tilled land (see Figs. 9 and 10).

These estimates constitute concrete examples (see diagram) of how misleading these simplifications in terms of calories can be, and how a true picture emerges only when one goes into the question of protein. We are entitled to speak of success in our fight against hunger in the world only if we can supply people's minimal needs of protein. It is most unfortunate that, so far, agriculture's one-sided point of view, dominated by quantity or tonnage, has colored all arguments as well as planning in this sphere. It is high time that nutritionists, underlining nutritive quality, get their say in these vital world matters.

FISH ACREAGE I

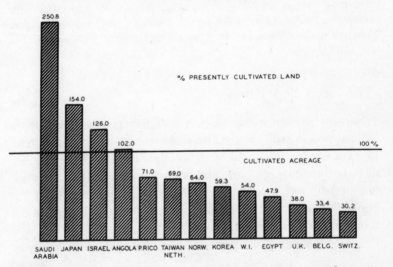

FIG. 9 Acreage required in respective countries to produce via present agriculture an amount of animal protein, in most cases milk protein, equivalent to what fish now is providing via food and fodder. Note particularly countries such as Japan, Israel, Netherlands and Norway.

FISH ACREAGE II

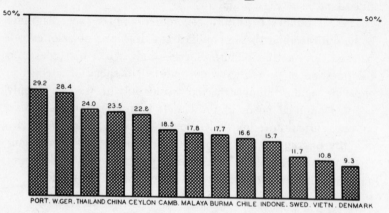

FIG. 10 Acreage required in respective countries to produce via present agriculture an amount of animal protein, in most cases milk protein, equivalent to what fish now is providing via food and fodder. Note particularly countries such as Portugal, West Germany, China and Ceylon.

"Fish" and Population

Norway consumes enough fish and fish products to supply 685,000 people with their entire requirements of animal protein. In addition, 450,000 could receive their protein from fish indirectly through eggs, pork, and poultry produced from livestock fed on fish meal, etc. Thus 1.2 million, roughly one-third of the population, stand in debt to fish for their standard. Judged in the traditional way, by calories, the figure would be only 75,000. The following table gives comparable figures for some other countries.

Deceptive Yield Increases

It is urgent that the public be alerted to this deceptive calorie and quantity thinking. Even the layman would understand that

TABLE 9

1958–59	I Number of People Pro- vided with Animal Pro- tein Through Fish or Fish Products (in thousands)	II Number of People Indirectly Provided with Animal Protein Through Fish Being Fed to Livestock and Poultry (in thousands)	III Total Number of People Fed by Fish (I and II) (in thousands)	Per- centage of Total Popu- lation
China	196,500	2,729	199,229	30
India	103,571	1,451	105,022	26
U.S.S.R.	21,000	420	21,420	10.2
U.S.	6,840	2,247	9,087	5
Japan	60,610	2,630	63,240	67
Indonesia	45,000	455	45,455	51
England	4,982	1,537	6,519	12
Portugal	7,244	103	7,347	81
Denmark	486	166	652	14
Norway	583	249	832	23
Sweden	1,258	138	1,396	19

a person cannot live on sugar and flour and remain healthy. Western agriculture has been dominated by this yield concept based on quantity. Progress has been gauged in terms of increased yields per acre or in tons per working hour. These are important measurements but they are far from enough, especially when it comes to the decisive question of food production and nutritional needs. It is most unfortunate that increased yields to such a great degree have been attained at the expense of quality. This is particularly true with regard to protein. Quality has frequently deteriorated considerably in this regard, showing up in declining levels. Both grain, potato, and root crops have been made to fill up their cells with more starch and sugar, while on the whole the relative content of protein has dropped, even when in a few cases the acre-yield may have been sustained or has even been raised. This trend becomes particularly hazardous when the protein level falls below the acknowledged nutritive minimum of approximately 12 per cent, which according to modern nutrition is a must for both man and non-ruminant animals.

Thus, today, the present production of wheat and corn in the United States has to be supplemented with approximately two-thirds of its present production of soybeans if the protein content of these two crops is to be brought up to the protein level

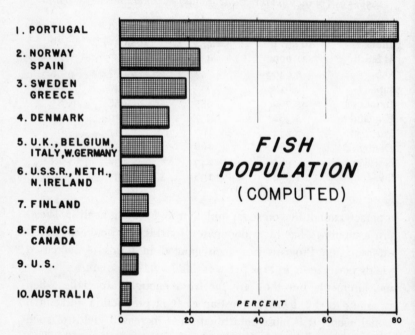

FIG. 11   Fish population in non-Asiatic countries. (Author's computations, 1959–60.)

that was common only fifteen years ago. Hybrid corn has to be sent to a feed mill in order to be mixed with protein foods to make it into an acceptable hog food. The West European of today has to put a slice of cheese on *his* bread and butter to make it as nourishing as his grandfather's. Postwar wheat yields in the United States, frequently the highest ever recorded in this country, and the resultant surpluses, are partly due to new wheat varieties, most of which contain 20–25 per cent less protein compared with the wheats grown when World War II ended.

Many of the yield increases registered by modern-day agriculture have similarly been attained at the expense of something else. We would have been better aware of this deterioration if we had substituted one crop for the other, rather than filling up grain with more carbohydrates and thereby "diluting" the proteins and arriving at less relative amounts. In some cases the nitrogen as well as the protein level has been raised, but only rarely at the same rate as total yield and this generally only in the initial phases of improvements in a low-yielding agriculture.

Sugar beets provide at least three times as many calories per acre as wheat, and about ten times as much in weight. Thus if one substitutes the sugar beet for wheat on land in good fertility, one may obtain, without doing anything further (and certainly without in any way improving on the fertility of the soil), amounts of calories three to four times higher, as well as a total crop weighing ten times as much. These factors have so far been little understood by the layman. Indeed, ignorance of their true nature has even dimmed the thinking of trained persons.

Calories and Colonialism

The dissatisfaction exhibited by many colonial peoples can also be traced back to the same kind of hazardous thinking in terms of calories. These people were often supplied with cheap fats and sugar by the colonizers, but at the same time they were frequently deprived of protein foods or meat-producing pastures. The expensive but valuable animal products were placed beyond reach of the purchasing power of the new proletariat. The present ferment in Africa is to no small degree a consequence of this calorie swindle.

One example: The Kikuyu tribe, that initiated the Mau Mau insurrection, was deprived of its traditional pasture lands, the grazing grounds for its numerous cattle. These used to be tapped for blood, approximately each tenth day; this was their chief source of indispensable animal protein, safer and more plentiful than meat or milk. These pastures were ploughed up by the white "colonizing" invaders to allow the creation of sizable tea plantations. No wonder these tribesmen set the tea-plant nurseries on fire.

Part of the failure of the colonial policies must undoubtedly be attributed to the lack of understanding about the nutritional consequences of introducing such radical changes in traditional forms of husbandry. These changes in themselves were by and large the result of the calorie illusion, thanks to which people were satisfied to calculate food needs merely in terms of energy, as if man were just a combustion engine and did not even need oil. Still less did anyone seem to bother about the fact that the machinery of the human body needs to be continually renewed and repaired. This is done primarily with the aid of protein and its constituents, the amino acids. Such mistakes in the early days of modern nutrition are understandable. In other words, these dietary changes were not introduced in bad faith. But it remains unforgivable that even today, agriculturists in most parts of the world are repeating these mistakes. They even go one step further and place these accomplishments on record as successes. Customary agricultural planners do not recognize these fundamental issues and persist in reckoning only in tons and calories. Economists follow suit and move one step further away from reality into the abstract world of money symbols. A great deal of this deception could have been avoided if prices had been based on nutritive value such as protein or vitamin content.

Mankind should benefit by its errors and gradually employ more constructive methods, but we persist in placing quantity ahead of quality, as though more tons per acre were more important than what kind of tons are obtained. The calorie swindle is no feat in the history of mankind; in fact it represents a dangerous oversimplification which, for each day that passes, is costing the human race enormous suffering.

References

BELSHAW, H. *Population Growth and Levels of Consumption: With Special Reference to Countries in Asia*. London, Allen & Unwin, 1956, 223 pp.

CÉPÈDE, M., and LENGELLE, M. *Économie alimentaire du globe*. Paris, Médicis, 1953, 654 pp.

CÉPÈDE, M., HOUTART, F. and GROND, L. *Population and Food*. New York, Sheed and Ward, 1964, 461 pp.

GUERRIN, A. *Humanité et Subsistance*. Paris, Dunod, 1957, 485 pp.

ROYAL STATISTICAL SOCIETY. *Food Supplies and Population Growth*. London, Oliver & Boyd, 1963, 85 pp.

CHAPTER 3

The Protein
Crisis

IT has already been pointed out how hollow and oversimplified calorie concepts are. For too long they have been allowed to dominate thinking and discussion with regard to world feeding. It is more urgent than ever to take a thorough new look at the world, this time through "protein glasses." Concepts such as agricultural production, nutritional standard, and the possibilities of satisfying man's needs take on a different aspect when protein is brought into focus.

Total Amount of Protein in the World Household

The world population consumes totally about 85 million metric tons of protein annually. Almost two-thirds of this quantity, 61 million metric tons, comes from plant products such as grain, beans, and potatoes. More than 24 million metric tons, close to one-third, is represented by milk, meat, eggs, and fish. In terms of calories, however, nine-tenths of the human intake is derived from the plant kingdom and a pitiful one-tenth is derived from animal products. In terms of protein, a significant shift toward animal products is evident, these accounting for no less than one-third of the total world protein consumption.

TABLE 10
World Food Consumption

| | RATIOS | |
	Animal Products	Plant Products
Calories	1/10	9/10
Protein	1/3	2/3

This greater dominance is primarily due to the fact that animal protein is better qualified to provide building stones for man's body protein. In other words, its structure is better suited for

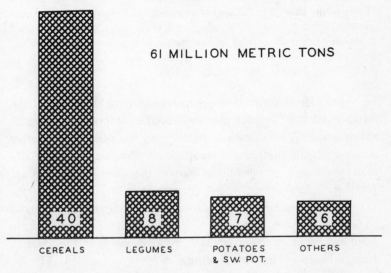

FIG. 12   Plant protein consumed by man. (Author's computations.)

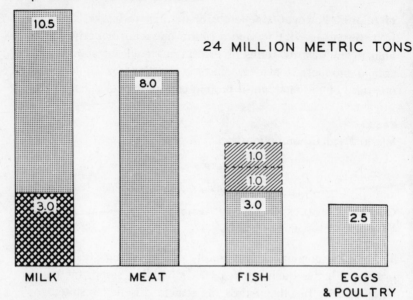

FIG. 13 Animal protein consumed by man. (Author's computations.) The specially shaded lower part of the milk bar indicates what approximately is fed to animals as whey and skim milk. The top sections of the fish bar indicate one million metric tons converted into animal feed as fish meal and the approximately one million tons lost in eviscerating, filleting, and through spoilage.

the particular nutritional requirements of man. There is in the build-up of most animal protein a better conformity to that of man's needs. The so-called amino-gram, meaning the relative amount of the individual components, the amino acids, lies closer to man's specifications than is the case for most plant proteins. In several cases, animal protein is in addition cheaper (as less is required) in quantity, more readily available, and easier to compose into a diet. It is in effect no easy task to compose plant proteins in such proportions that the relative requirements of individual amino acids are fulfilled. Finally, animal protein is readily digestible in man's gastric system, while plant protein is encased within an impenetrable cell wall, the breakdown of which requires elaborate processing such as milling, fermentation, toasting, etc. But much more decisive for this disproportion between calories as compared to the protein feature we are discussing here, is the somber fact that the world's privileged, about 450 million people, dispose of the lion's share of this protein. Besides, no less than around 150 million metric tons of protein, or three times more than the total amount of plant protein with which the world's billions have to be satisfied, are needed to produce the 21 million tons of this terrestrial animal protein that largely goes to a minority. As in the case of the calories, losses of plant protein are involved in its transformation into animal protein. These need to be taken into account. All livestock, such as cattle, hogs, and poultry, have protein requirements which must be filled—both for life maintenance and for the production of milk, eggs, and meat.

Owing to the lengthy production chains in the oceans, approximately 1,500 million metric tons of primary protein—in phytoplankton and seaweeds—is involved in the making of the food fish and shellfish contained in the present world catch (36 million metric tons in 1962). An additional 500 million tons of protein is entangled in the intricate production machinery of the seas in order to render all the fish that is converted into meal, solubles, and other feeding-stuffs.

The Undernourished World

Through computations of this kind, one arrives at figures which in broad terms reveal how much *primary protein*, or plant protein, is in effect needed to keep individual nations going. Such data tell that the United States alone disposes of as much primary protein as a number of poor countries like India, China, Indonesia, and Ceylon, taken together, have to be satisfied with. In other words, the 195 million Americans revel in an amount

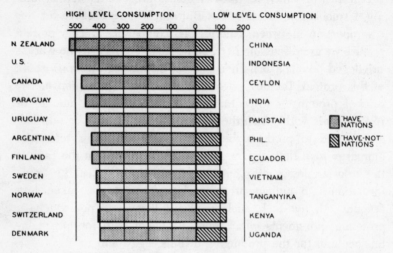

PRIMARY PLANT PROTEIN

HIGH LEVEL CONSUMPTION   LOW LEVEL CONSUMPTION
500 400 300 200 100 0   100 200

HIGH LEVEL	LOW LEVEL
N ZEALAND	CHINA
U.S.	INDONESIA
CANADA	CEYLON
PARAGUAY	INDIA
URUGUAY	PAKISTAN
ARGENTINA	PHIL.
FINLAND	ECUADOR
SWEDEN	VIETNAM
NORWAY	TANGANYIKA
SWITZERLAND	KENYA
DENMARK	UGANDA

"HAVE" NATIONS
"HAVE-NOT" NATIONS

FIG. 14 Figures indicate g/day—amount of primary protein required to provide each person with his daily food. The huge gap between the well-fed and underfed countries is most evident.

of protein which in other parts of the globe has to be portioned out to more than 1.5 billion, almost half the world population.

Another example which illustrates the enormous gap between the well-nourished and the undernourished world is the following: If the total world catch of fish and shellfish (oysters, shrimp, and lobster)—everything that China, U.S.S.R., Japan, Europe, the United States, and all other nations extract from the sea—were used merely to feed the United States, this country would not receive from this source more protein than is now being consumed in the form of meat—less than half of our animal protein intake. In fact, fish provides about one-fifth of the total animal protein consumption in the world and is actually the only form of animal protein that reaches the masses among the billions. Milk, meat, and eggs are to a greater extent the monopoly of privileged nations. Thus it is sheer parody when international organizations with great satisfaction point to the increased world production of milk and meat during the latest decade, indicating improved world feeding. The fact that some Americans and West Europeans eat more steaks, pork chops and eggs, and drink more milk may be most gratifying, but it remains a sore point, if not an insult, to the hundreds of millions on earth who have

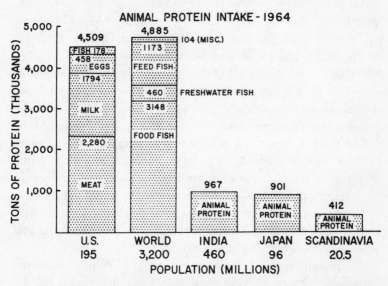

FIG. 15   The consumption of animal protein in selected countries. The total annual catch of food fish by all nations of the world does not yield totally more protein than what the United States per year consumes as meat and half of its milk intake. This reflects the (1) high nutritive standard of the United States and (2) the current overestimation of the resources of the sea. Note further that the 460 million people of India are limited to an amount of animal protein equivalent to what Japan's 96 million obtain. Japan's more favorable position is to more than 60% the result of their world-wide fisheries. The luxury of the 20.5 million Scandinavians is measured by the fact that they gulp down a total protein quantity constituting one-half that of Japan's 96 million as well as that of India's 460 million.

never seen such delicacies and are bound to a near-starvation diet. Many hundreds of millions never in their whole lives get the opportunity even of a square meal and at best only see meat as strips in a soup.

Protein the Best Gauge for Nutritional Standard

It is indisputably feasible to put together a satisfactory diet filling all man's needs and wants, based on different plant products, e.g., soybeans, sunflower seeds, peanuts, and Chinese cabbage. At the same time it should be made clear that this undertaking requires a great deal of thoughtfulness as well as acquaintance with the findings of modern nutritional science. In addition, several basic relationships are too often overlooked in the popular vegetarian debate. The acreage gains claimed to be within reach by resorting to a true vegetarian diet for all mankind are certainly not so large as is maintained, owing to the simple fact that the livestock utilizes substantial quantities of feed which man's intestinal system cannot handle. Extensive acreages of pastures and even some tilled land cannot—with known agricultural techniques—be effectively utilized in any other way than for feed production.

The protein intake, be it plant or animal protein, remains the most reliable way of measuring nutritional standard. Only by satisfying the minimal protein needs of the human race is man entitled to speak about waging a serious battle against world hunger. It is highly unfortunate that one-sided agricultural viewpoints or abstract money symbols have been allowed to dim thinking and to distort rational planning in this field for a long time. A revision is long overdue. Nutritionists should be given their say in these matters and should be permitted to draw up new and more adequate guidelines for agricultural production as well as for economic planning. Even if Brazil were to make use of its total coffee acreage, it would not under the present agricultural conditions be able to produce the protein quantities which that large nation now so desperately needs. If Brazil's protein standard were to be raised to that of Italy's—in effect nothing spectacular—and if this were to be achieved through peanuts, an acreage would be needed twice the size of the present coffee acreage. This means that the present total tilled acreage would have to be increased by one-third. If the brave assumption were made that the acre yields could be doubled, this task would still be gigantic. This is correspondingly true of Mexico. The acres now used to raise crops for the United States (pineapple, sugar, limes, beans, strawberries) and for Spain (chick peas) are all needed to feed the country adequately. Similar examples can be given from other countries, such as present-day Egypt and Ceylon.

If the 65 million people which constitute the present annual net growth of the world's population were to be provided with

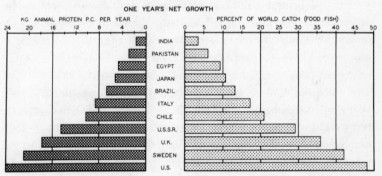

ANIMAL PROTEIN REQUIRED TO FEED 65 MILLION
ON DIFFERENT NUTRITIVE LEVELS

ONE YEAR'S NET GROWTH

FIG. 16 Required increase of world fisheries in order to provide the added population for one single year with protein on the present nutritional level of the above-indicated countries. To the left, the present consumption in kilograms of animal protein per person and year in those countries; to the right, required percentage increase of world fisheries (1962).

a satisfactory diet—something along the line of the present average Italian diet—the world catch of ocean fish would have to be increased by one-fifth. In four years a doubling of the world catch would thus be required. For the more modest Japanese standard a doubling of the world catch each eighth year is indicated. The United States and even West European standards could not be met. United States standards would demand a doubling of the world catch each second year. Still nothing would be done for the many hundreds of millions who already are starving.

Adequate Knowledge, Inadequate Resources

Medical research and modern food preservation may pride themselves on having relieved mankind of the scurvy plague. Beri-beri, rachitis (rickets), and other diseases caused by vitamin shortages are fairly well under control. The science of nutrition has started to penetrate the field of metabolic disorders and is constantly employing new successful advances which even hold promise of bringing remedy to various mental disturbances. In other words, our nutritional knowledge is mastering most of our major difficulties. But it is equally evident that we are failing—not so much in the application of our results, as in our capabilities of providing adequate quantities, and in the right places. The endemic goiter, from which millions of people are still suffering, is emerging not as a simple iodine deficiency disease but as a direct result of unsatisfactory diets, inadequate in several other respects, such as in vitamin A. This single field of research deserves millions of dollars in appropriations and still more millions for the mass distribution of, for instance, fish oil or synthetic vitamin A.

Kwashiorkor

We will now proceed to a discussion of the overshadowing problem—the global protein shortage. This is a case where we have completely failed to take countermeasures and to introduce remedies in time, despite all scientific endeavors and technical progress. As a matter of fact, it seems likely that we have aggravated instead of alleviated the sufferings. The widespread protein deficiency diseases bear witness to our failures. A series of disease symptoms, described in reports from several continents and latitudes, have become more and more amalgamated and interrelated as evidence has accumulated that they all belong to the protein deficiency syndrome. Peculiar words such as *marasmus, kwashiorkor, infantile dystrophy, weaning damages, sugar babies,* and *Annam obesity* are a few of the many terms which gradually have found their way into the news media. They are all designations for various symptoms of protein deficiency.

At the start of this century the Mexicans wrestled with what was called *serpent skin* among infants; the skin peeled off, diarrhoeas were common, and death ensued. In Indonesia, French physicians fought an uneven battle to save swollen babies. In several colonial regions in Africa, at different times, kwashiorkor appeared, meaning "red baby." This has become a predominant designation for protein deficiency disease. In the beginning there was a clear tendency to assume that infections were the real cause of these afflictions. Nowadays, it is fairly well established that in most cases these are secondary. Medical treatment for a few weeks with first-rate protein—milk solids (powdered milk), fish meal, and other similar food products—restored health rapidly and almost in a miraculous way.

Jamaica's "sugar babies" also were and still are victims of protein deficiency. The hunger is abated with sugar-carbohydrate or belly-filling foods. Large sections of the colored people in South Africa cannot afford other food than so-called "mealy" (a starch-rich flour mixture). This results in widespread undernourishment as well as malnutrition. Correspondingly, the urban population of the Congo (Leopoldville) and French West Africa have to satisfy themselves with cheap calories (sugar, cassava, etc.), and they suffer widely from protein deficiency. History carries records of numerous tragic happenings of a similar nature, where man failed to safeguard the nutritional frontiers of mankind. They were far too easily subjected to a breakthrough with "cheap," calorie-supplying foods. The Norwegian explorer Fridtjof Nansen described the hard destiny which befell Siberia's aborigines when they substituted bread and sugar for their traditional fish and game diet. Similar developments are known from the Laplanders in the North to the Indians in the high plateaus of the South American Andes as well as from the Australian aborigines. These incidents are, however, much more limited in their effects than the worldwide protein crisis which now is unraveling itself in almost every continent. Shortage of protein is no longer restricted to isolated ethnic groups but is insidiously invading our own high-level civilizations, spreading in the urban slums among the underpaid masses of the industrial nations. They resort to macaroni, flour, and sugar to make ends meet, having to forego in adequate quantities milk, pork chops, beefsteaks, eggs, and other high-protein foods.

There are many indications of a relative protein deficiency in our own diet. Arthritis is a case in point. This is seriously affected by the relative shortage of methionine and vitamin B_6. The poor become the first victims of protein deficiency, whether they are underpaid agricultural labor, office girls, industrial workers, or retired people.

The Scourge of the Tropics

The most extensive deficiency regions are primarily to be found in warmer latitudes. This is no coincidence. High temperature brings about a rapid degradation of the organic nitrogen reserves in the soil. The heavy rainfalls common in the wet tropics leach the soil and diminish to a considerable degree the protein return from nitrogen fertilizers. The naïve overrating of quantity to the detriment of quality—metric tons of gross weight instead of metric tons of protein, be it in grain, milk, or other foods—has made the situation even worse. Furthermore, spoilage is a constant menace, taking great tributes not the least among protein foods. Both insects and microorganisms are constantly on the rampage under these warm conditions.

Scientists in the United States recently studied the situation in Haiti and found that 7 per cent of the children suffered from kwashiorkor, while no less than two-thirds of all children under fifteen years of age showed other unmistakable symptoms of protein deficiency. We who belong to the world's privileged class and eat beefsteaks and pork chops in plenty, drink milk in unlimited quantities, and have as many eggs as we want, find it difficult to understand that this is a prerogative of a very small minority among the billions of the world.

Nutritional Equalization—A Revolutionary Program

Nutritional equalization will probably be the next step in the development of mankind. This will have far more revolutionary effects than the various strivings for equality symbolized by the French and Russian Revolutions. Historians have too frequently overlooked the economic factors which both capitalists and Marxists profess and to which they give priority as driving forces. World events are to no little degree subordinate to nutritional conditions. Human endeavor and progress depends to a considerable extent upon adequate food. Conversely, lack of feeding resources continue to drastically limit and retard development, as they have been instrumental in the rise of major human migrations and large-scale hostilities.

The more profoundly I study these questions, the more it becomes evident to me that the proteins have always had a key position in world economy. The methods of appraisal advocated in this book and further analyzed in a number of scientific treatises, and the computations made on that basis, seem to offer possibilities for a more realistic discussion and planning. New perspectives are gained and reality seems to be brought into clearer focus. For this very reason, the true scope of the protein crisis becomes evident if we calculate how large an additional acreage of tilled land would be required to raise the nutritional standard at various assumed levels, chosen among now existing countries. It goes without saying that yield increases are alternatives to expanded acreage.

For a whole range of countries it is evident that an improved nutritional standard seems highly unlikely—even unattainable— on the basis of available soil resources (in most critical cases extremely limited—mostly far below anything we as Americans enjoy). It can be seriously argued whether we have not permitted the human race to grow so far beyond the reasonable potentialities of the globe that we are now forced to limit ourselves to satisfying only the minimal needs established as imperative to health by nutritionists—well aware of the fact that the closer we move to these minimum values, the greater becomes our susceptibility to disease, and the greater the risk of setbacks. Mankind is moving into the twilight of semihunger and of extreme scarcity. For a few decades abundance may remain the legacy of a few fortunates with excessive resources. Frugality has already become the lot of the billions. We must seriously question whether advanced civilization can be maintained without a reasonable excess in the production of food as well as other commodities (fiber, wood, etc.).

UNICEF

The aid of UNICEF (United Nations Children's Fund) to children is primarily a protein supplementation program. There are in the world today at least 950 million children, 600 million of which are undernourished or malnourished. At best, one-tenth of these receive aid through this United Nations organization. Available funds do not allow a broader program. As this is primarily a protein operation, United States surpluses have been of subordinate avail (pp. 349–51). UNICEF has been forced to seek contributions from all over the world in the form of dried milk, condensed milk, fish meal, eggs, and plant proteins of special composition, such as INCAParina and others. Most recently the "surpluses" of the English egg producers caught their interest.

Five leading Mexican nutritionists established, in an investigative survey published in 1961,* that "the most serious social challenge facing our Government is the enormous problem of malnutrition among the broad masses of the people. For centuries millions of economically weak families—in other words, such with meagre economic, educational, or social resources—have been suffering from malnutrition. Even today, they obtain hardly more than 60 per cent of the calories that are required by an adult in order to manage to perform normally in working. Furthermore, the food they get is of a very low biological value. This is the reason that large groups of our people in a conspicuous way look tired, gloomy, and incapacitated. They lack sense of responsibility, they fail to take creative initiatives, nor do they have ideas of their own. In one word, they are devoid of all ambition. It is true that they do need much to get along, but on the other hand they are not productive. They endure their nutritional misery with a stoic indifferent fatalism."

The undermining ravages of undernourishment—real protein deficiency—can hardly be described in better terms. To the many uncritical interpreters who, in the declining infant mortality rate around the world, see evidence of an improved nutritional standard, these indisputable facts about the devastating effects of

* F. Gomez, R. Ramos-Galvan, *et al., Studies on the Use of Deodorized Fish Flour in Malnutrition.* Preliminary report from group for research on infantile malnutrition. Hospital Infantil, Mexico, D.F. 1961. Translation made by this author from original text in Spanish.

malnutrition—although not usually leading to immediate death—ought to be a thought-provoking refutation. A cynical argument has been advanced: If malnutrition and undernutrition had caused people to fall dead or to succumb rapidly, the nutritional problem of the world would never have reached its present dimensions and become such a potent menace to the human race and to civilization. The ghastly apparitions in the concentration camps, surviving on 800 to 1,000 calories daily, bear witness to how far into the shadows of semistarvation man can be forced without being relieved through death. But those who maintain that such an existence can be termed human have little knowledge of the importance of nutrition to human health nor do they appreciate human values.

The Mexican nutrition experts continue:

Anyone who looks superficially at these malnourished people could possibly get the idea that their laziness, indolence, filth, and fatalism are characteristic features; but we pose the question: Could any human individual show any noticeable reaction when the body tissues are worn out, when the body is permanently tired and the stomach is empty—or in the best of cases is filled with an amorphous mass of corn and beans, inadequate or deficient for the performance of a normal day's work?"

Both primary and secondary schools as well as colleges and universities should offer elementary education in the symptoms and effects of malnutrition. This should put an end to the many naïve lamentations by tourists after having visited undernourished nations, as well as to the strongly opinionated statements by journalists, executive presidents in industrial enterprises, and not the least, by officers (captains and first mates) of the merchant navies—describing the laziness, apathy, and lethargy of local populations toward their own depravation and misery. Education is needed in our own midst, not merely to remove racial prejudices. Misunderstandings about the ravages of hunger and malnutrition urgently need to be resolved.

References

BOURNE, G. H. *World Review of Nutrition and Dietetics*. Vols. I-V, Hafner Publ. Co., London, 1960–1964.

BROCK, J. F. and AUTRET, M. *Kwashiorkor in Africa, WHO Monograph Ser. no. 8.* 1957.

Communications Inter-African Conference on Nutrition. Vol. I-III, Angola, 1956.

FAO. *Protein Malnutrition in Brazil*. Rome, 1956, 40 pp.

GILLMAN, J. and GILLMAN, T. *Perspectives in Human Malnutrition*. Grune and Stratton, New York, 1951, 584 pp.

Proceedings 5th Intern. Congress on Nutrition, 1961. Federation Proc. 30 (1), *Part III*, 415 pp.

TROWELL, H. C., DAVIES, J. N. P., and DEAN, R. F. A. *Kwashiorkor*, Arnold, London, 1958, 308 pp.

See references under chapter 2 pertinent also to this chapter.

CHAPTER 4

The Biological
Budget of
Mankind

Against the background of the facts presented in the previous chapter, a closer analysis of the biological budget of mankind is called for. In spite of all technical progress, man is above all a living being inexorably dependent upon what the plant kingdom produces. The Bible has given us a most depictive expression for this fundamental law of nature: "All flesh is grass." All vegetarians and meat eaters alike, as well as most of the living world, depend on the green plant cover. A Chinese scientist and thinker has called this "man's green thraldom."

The Delusion of the One-Hundredth

To what degree does man utilize these resources which the green plants provide, thanks to the energy they capture from the sun? Most plant physiologists maintain that we exploit these assets poorly. They conclude that man makes use of only one-hundredth of the energy which the plants collect from the sunflow. This appears to be rather reassuring, even though we are not entitled to the absurd conclusion that because of this we could expand a hundred times in numbers and still be in position to take care of our needs.

Man is in fact already the most numerous among large mammals. There are probably not more than ten, maybe twenty, thousand tigers or lions and hardly twenty-five thousand elephants living today on earth, but the number of humans exceeds three billion. The only higher animal which can to a certain degree compete with man in numbers is the rat, who in effect lives in the shadow of man.

Man's consumption of nature is far more overwhelming than the calculation of 1 per cent seems to indicate. Unfortunately, the calculations of the plant physiologists are misleading. They were computed in the following way: On the basis of an average consumption of 2,200 calories per person—which is approximately the world average of today, when taking into account the large number of children and the undernourished millions—this figure was then multiplied with the total number of people now living on earth, to arrive at the total amount of calories, which proved to be about one hundredth (or 1 per cent) of the edible plant production according to available estimates. But it was not taken into account that in order to produce one calorie of animal products through livestock an average of seven plant calories are required. Thus man is making use of a considerably higher proportion of the world's total available primary plant calories. The plant physiologists overlooked this nutritional aspect. The hogs, cattle, and poultry that produce meat, milk, and eggs must be kept alive. The only accurate and correct way to compute man's true disposition of the calorie riches is to go back and find out how many primary calories man is earmarking for his own purposes. This would show the degree of man's interference as well as his impact in the plant kingdom.

Primary Calories

When adding up in this way the computed primary calories which individual nations actually are using, one arrives at a total sum of calories which is six times higher than the amount of calories which are directly eaten by man. This may also be expressed in the following way: If it were feasible to feed man

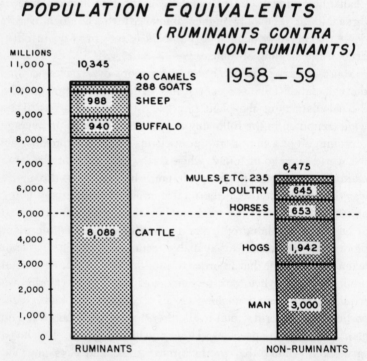

FIG. 17 The ruminants have vastly expanded the human biosphere by the capability of their rumen to (1) synthesize protein; (2) make use of cellulose and other organic compounds not available to man's more gastric system; and (3) finally by grazing lands which otherwise would not be utilized in regular till for the direct production of human food.

exclusively on plant products and we thus all became vegetarians, the computed sum of primary calories would theoretically provide for seventeen billion people, within the realm of possibilities under the present stage of the techniques. This is, however, not possible—for both nutritional and agricultural reasons. As already clarified, the world on the whole is already almost vegetarian, since only one-tenth of the human diet consists of animal products. But in order to produce this one-tenth, a primary plant production is utilized which should suffice in theory to cover the needs of more than thirteen billion people with regard to both calories and proteins. Furthermore, the human stomach is not capable of utilizing a considerable portion of the plant calories built into the primary plant products of the earth, such as cellulose and lignin.

This accounting of man's biosphere is, however, by no means complete. It is well known that insects, fungi, and pests grab at least one-fifth of the world's crops before they are harvested or become available as foods. In addition, a few nations in the luxury class indulge in a tertiary production; that is, their livestock is fed animal products such as skim milk, buttermilk, fish, and meat meal.

The discussion so far has referred to the total photosynthesis of the globe. But one would like to know more specifically what proportion man is taking on land in contrast to the oceans—in other words, to distinguish these two major realms from each other. We then have to recognize the lengthy conversion chains in the seas, involving many more links than those on land. In order to produce one pound of cod, no less than 50,000 pounds or more is required in terms of primary plant products such as phytoplankton or seaweeds. On the other hand, in order to maintain the productive capacity of the land, armies of billions of bacteria, fungi, protozoa, and other living organisms in the soil must feed.

If all these circumstances are taken into account, the 5 to 6 per cent are in reality much higher—close to one-tenth of the total organic mass which through the sun's energy is mass-produced in the cells of green plants through photosynthesis is taken by man. In addition, man extracts from the forests a great deal for fuel, lumber, and paper, which take a continual toll from the annual plant production. In view of the fact that the present food production needs to be doubled to give every human being now living on earth an acceptable minimal diet, such an accomplishment would imply new global mortgages of gigantic dimensions. On top of this, the world population is in for a second doubling during this very century, as underlined several times already. Consequently, mankind would then, as early as the year 2000, require about 40 per cent of the earth's total plant production for its immediate dietary needs. As already hinted, man would in reality need more than this, particularly as there seems to be little likelihood for implementing a worldwide efficient birth control in such a brief period. We can therefore safely conclude that the now living generation has already reached out so far as to be forcefully reminded of the limitations of the globe. Man is already experiencing serious repercussions in his moving so dangerously close to the ultimate subsistence margins of our own "spaceship." At any rate, we begin to discern the obvious need of exercising restraint in order to avert calamities. It should be added that what improved agriculture eventually may do for expanding the total photosynthesis of the earth is of a much lower order of magnitude than the increase in population. Improved techniques therefore cannot be expected in any dramatic way to extend the limitations of man's existence.

Controls

The calculations above are based on production years and do not take into consideration the possibility that a certain amount —and perhaps a growing percentage—of the original plant production may occasionally return into circulation within a shorter period than one year. But by and large the figures presented here describe in a rather accurate way man's dominance in the living world. These findings have been confirmed through several alternative analyses. Already the simple weight figures presented on page 8 indicated that the total weight of mankind amounts to about one-fifth of that of the livestock which, according to world statistics, are utilized in food production, this including traction animals. The total weight of livestock inclusive of traction animals amounted to 925 million metric tons. This leads to figures of about the same order of magnitude as those we have reached on the basis of the primary calories. This points to the fact that the present biomass—all living creatures which are directly within the human sphere, measured on the basis of their consumptive requirements—corresponds to almost fifteen billion people.

A second method of checking these figures is by converting the various livestock animals into population equivalents in the way outlined in chapter 2. In this way the ratio between human beings and livestock—3.1 billion as against 15 billion (1961–62)—turns out to be 1:5. This would mean that man's total biosphere consumes six times more than man himself does. However, such a huge machinery can never operate without losses; we may therefore safely assume that from 7 to 8 per cent is a more likely minimum figure for the human share of the total photosynthesis.

The Photosynthesis of the Land Area

Thus far our discussion has taken into consideration the photosynthesis of the entire globe. It is, however, a well-known fact that the oceans provide but a minor part of the food intake. Recent measurements indicate that the oceans produce about twice as much photosynthetic matter as the land area. Consequently, if our calculations are revamped, taking this factor into account, fish and other seafoods must be subtracted when we consider the terrestrial balance. The figure for the human sector in the plant budget of the land surface runs beyond 19 per cent (see Table 11 and Fig. 18). No wonder that wildlife is becoming pressed for space and almost everywhere is affected by man. Besides, this latter figure of approximately one-fifth

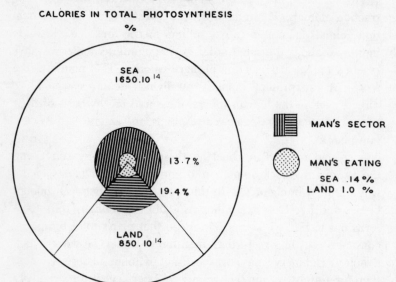

HUMAN BIOSPHERE

CALORIES IN TOTAL PHOTOSYNTHESIS
%

SEA
1650.10^{14}

13.7%

19.4%

LAND
850.10^{14}

MAN'S SECTOR

MAN'S EATING
SEA .14%
LAND 1.0 %

FIG. 18 The human biosphere as part of total photosynthesis on the land and sea area respectively (as to postulations for these data, see text).

reflects in a more telling way the supremacy of man in living nature, manifested indirectly in numerous ways. This demonstrates to what extent man has been able to fulfill his mission to people the earth. Living nature has every reason to fear his advance. In this context it should be pointed out that in many countries agricultural land comprises almost all vegetation, as in the overflowing valleys of China and India, and in large sectors of the narrow coastal shelves and valleys of Mexico, Italy, and Japan. In countries such as West Germany and England, the tilled acreage is presently more than half the total land surface.

These calculations are based on the assumption that about half of the photosynthesis of the plant kingdom yields products which can be utilized by man and animals. If, for one reason or another, one would want to adjust this generally accepted figure of 50 per cent upward, it would naturally affect accordingly all the figures given above. However, this would not change the conclusions drawn as to the general magnitude of mankind's biological budget, to any significant degree.

The Calorie Budget of the Sea

The calorie budget of the sea has also been grossly misjudged. If we compute the fish catch in the North Atlantic on both sides of this mighty basin and place the resulting figure in relation to the total photosynthesis of the North Atlantic, we discover that the present catch level merely allows 3.14 conversion links in the producing chain. It is an established fact that the cod requires five and the herring two links (see chapter 17).

If a reasonable average is chosen for the number of links in the conversion chains of present-day fisheries, three seems to be an acceptable figure. This means that on the average the landed fish belong to the category of secondary carnivores; thus one finds that the present world catch of fish is engaging no less than 14.5 per cent of the total photosynthesis of the oceans. In other words, out of the primary production of the oceans in terms of phytoplankton and seaweeds (algae), not far from one-fifth is already now involved in man's feeding! How false is the notion that fish play an insignificant role in the world household! On the contrary, most fishing constitutes a major ecological factor in the living communities of the oceans.

Almost ten times more protein (1,500 million metric tons) is involved in the aquatic production of human food than the amount of primary protein entering into animal production of the world (149.1 million metric tons—see Table 11, p. 65). If the fish landed for the making of feed (fish meal) also is taken into account, this ratio becomes 13.5:1. For this total aquatic catch a quantity of primary plankton and seaweed is required which, with regard to its protein content, is equivalent to no less than 64.5 world wheat crops or 111 rice crops. These figures are almost inconceivable, but nevertheless they strikingly bring home the enormous magnitude of the productive machinery on which man is dependent in the oceans and freshwaters. This also explains the hollowness of all talk about the ocean resources as limitless. Our modest fish landings have wide repercussions in the living world of the seas. There is no question that man in ecological terms already is the biggest monster ruling there.

The Protein—Nitrogen Balance

Protein requires access to nitrogen for its synthesis. The nitrogen balance of the soils is therefore of paramount importance. In spite of impressive accomplishments by the fertilizer industry, the nitrogen-fixing bacteria and other natural nitrogen sources yield directly or indirectly the greatest proportion of the nitrogen involved in the protein synthesis of plants. This can be computed along various lines which all lead to the same total sum.

Let us take a look at one such calculation. One metric ton of nitrogen incorporated into a commercial fertilizer renders enough extra protein to fill the needs of about forty people. Presently world agriculture is using thirteen million metric tons of nitrogen each year. In theoretical terms, this means that 520 million people would get their protein this way—about one-sixth of the world's population. In reality, however, a complete return

TABLE 11

A. Man's Food-Protein Balance

(MILLION METRIC TONS) (1958–59)

	Man's Food Protein	Primary Protein Involved in Producing
Plant Protein	60.1	60.1
Animal Protein	25.3	—
—terrestrial	21.3	149.1
—aquatic	4.0	2,000
—food	3.0	1,500
—feed (fish meal)	1.0	500

World Crop	Protein
Wheat	31.0
Rice	18.0

B. Photosynthesis of Land Area and Man's Food

(IN 10^{14} KCAL) (1958–59)

Calories	Globe	%	Land	%	Sea	%
Total in photosynthesis	2,500	100	835	33.3	1,665	55.7
Primary Calories Involved in Producing Man's Food	410	16.4	169	19.9	240	14.5
Calories Incorporated in Man's Food	24	1	23.64	2.79	0.36	0.022

can never be expected, but this does give a fairly accurate idea of the significance of the present nitrogen-fertilizer industry of the world in the biological budget of mankind. In other words, this measures man's contribution through chemistry to this crucial defense-line of protein.

But this is not the whole story. The total picture needs many adjustments in order to be complete. First of all, this additional computed production of protein does not constitute a net gain or something achieved on top of nature's own production. A considerable portion of this nitrogen fertilizer is in effect used to compensate for man's robberies from the soils, both historically and in present times.

Partly, and in some cases completely, nature's own large-scale nitrogen fixation has been jeopardized. Each year man has removed in definite form—and through urbanization now in a more final way than earlier—considerable amounts of nitrogen. These riches were in the past returned into circulation through farm manure and human waste from the farm and village. This phenomenon is also clearly evident in the diminishing quantities of compost and manure now being returned to the soils. There are few industrial countries—maybe only Holland and parts of Japan, some sections of the eastern United States and Western Europe—which have caught up with this process and have managed to stop further depletion and have even raised the productive level. Urbanization on a major scale has accentuated this withdrawal, which is becoming almost a one-way traffic.

In view of the population growth, we have good reason to ask ourselves if we will be able to meet the demands of the nitrogen budget. Can we actually continue to rely on compost, manure, nitrogen fixation through bacteria, leguminous plants, and marine products for five-sixths of the nitrogen needed in the protein synthesis? Space does not permit a full penetration of this intriguing problem. It will merely be pointed out here that for several reasons it seems highly unlikely that more than half of the nearly three billion people which will be added to the world population before the end of this century will be able to rely on natural nitrogen sources. Therefore 37.5 million metric tons of additional nitrogen will be needed besides these thirteen million which are now put into circulation each year.

Fertilizers are key factors in the enormous transportation needs which are accumulating. In addition to nitrogen, phosphate, potassium, and lime, further magnesium and several trace elements are required. Before the end of this century this annual transportation burden will be in the range of 500 million metric tons annually. This is far above the total weight of the human race at that point (360 million metric tons). Yet this gigantic load allows only a very modest level of fertilizer use, approximately one-fifth of what Japan and one-third of what Holland presently is practicing.

Huge Losses

Another crucial aspect of the nitrogen budget are the evident losses—a kind of wastage we can ill afford but about which we have only scanty information and dim concepts. It is amazing to find that the nitrogen cycle of the earth is so little known and poorly studied that we still lack insight into essential causal relationships and—what is worse—cannot present a detailed balance for the globe. Theoretically, thirteen million metric tons of nitrogen should yield 98 million metric tons of plant protein. The world household consumes at present 84.6 million metric tons (see Table, p. 65). If this is converted into primary protein, based upon a conversion factor of seven, we arrive at about 200 million metric tons of terrestrial plant protein. This indicates that artificially added nitrogen ought theoretically to satisfy nearly half the protein requirements of the world, but as we have seen above, commercial nitrogen fertilizers provide protein to only one-sixth at the most. A considerable amount of nitrogen is known to be lost in the denitrification processes of the soils; other losses are those due to leaching or involved in the feeding of the soil bacteria, fungi, and insects. Maybe ways will be found in the future to eliminate or reduce some of these losses but they will obviously never disappear completely even if we manage to improve on the utilization efficiency of this nitrogen account. Other forms of food production which in principle are less wasteful of nitrogen than are present methods may have to be considered (see chapter 18).

Budget-conscious Outlook

These and similar calculations justify the statement that it is urgent that we fully comprehend our biological reality and acquaint ourselves with the true consequences of man's domination. It is high time that economists made an effort to return to the concrete level of real values in order to formulate a valid world budget—and not only in terms of nitrogen. They can no longer remain in the lofty world of abstract symbols such as dollars, rubles, and francs.

Many assumptions can be made as to the reasons for this kind of escapism. For my part I have come to the conclusion that biologists, agriculturists, and nutritionists are the first to blame for these misjudgments about the world and its feeding potentials. These professional categories should be better equipped in conceptual terms to give correct and understandable information about such matters. Some have undoubtedly tried to do this, but the overwhelming number have committed the same mistake of not facing reality, and preferring to devote their time to their respective specialties, not even cognizant of the broad and complex issues engulfing their own disciplines.

It is not sufficient, however, to know only the facts. Everybody, even the layman, must become budget-conscious. This is a highly urgent challenge to all public education as well as to universities to teach everybody the true costs required to keep the human race going, our society functioning, and civilization alive. The basic study of this great issue ought to be compulsory to all, but, thus far, there are few textbooks on any educational level which enter into these fundamental questions and provide the pertinent facts.

References

BORGSTROM, GEO. "The Human Biosphere," (22 pp.), *Proc. UNESCO Symposium on Global Impacts of Microbiology.* Stockholm, (1963) 1965, 590 pp.

HILL, R., and WHITTINGHAM, C. P. *Photosynthesis.* London and New York, Methuen, 1957, 420 pp.

NITSCHIPOROWITSCH, A. A. *Die Photosynthese der Pflanzen.* Berlin, Deutsch. Bauernverlag, 1951, 31 pp. (Translated from the Russian.)

PEI-SUNG, T. *Green Thraldom—Essays of a Chinese Biologist.* London, Allen & Unwin, 1949, 127 pp.

PIDDINGTON, R. A. *The Limits of Mankind.* Bristol, Wright, 1956, 154 pp.

SPOEHR, H. A. *Photosynthesis.* New York, Chemical Catalogue Co., 1926, 393 pp.

TERRIEN, J., TRUFFAUT, G., and CARLIS, J. *Light, Vegetation and Chlorophyll.* New York, Philosophical Library, 1957, 228 pp. (Translated from the French.)

CHAPTER 5

Ghost

Acreage

IT is a well-known fact that most countries do not subsist merely on agriculture but depend upon the importation of food and feed and in addition obtain essential protein from oceans, rivers, and lakes. This should be self-evident, but private and national economies with their vested interests enter as disrupting or blurring factors into these simple relationships. Nevertheless, economic and nutritional measures are commonly discussed and analyzed as though they concerned agriculture alone. There are many factors which might explain this state of affairs. One important reason for the lack of understanding of these fundamental forces is the fact that there have so far been no data, readily understandable, whereby one could on a commensurate basis compare trade, fisheries, and agriculture. In short, there has been no common denominator, aside from the misleading standard of the dollar, pound, franc, ruble, etc.

A method was presented in chapter 2 whereby it became possible to evaluate the true role of fisheries in individual countries, based on the prime function of fish as supplying animal protein. By calculating the acreage necessary to produce in the most acreage-saving way for each country an amount of animal protein equivalent to what presently is obtained through fisheries and with present techniques in the agricultural production of this very same country, we arrived at what I have termed the *fish acreage* (see chapter 2, pp. 31–32). This constitutes one basic element in what this author has chosen to call the *ghost acreage* of a country. This is the computed, non-visible acreage which a country would require as a supplement to its present visible agricultural acreage in the form of tilled land in order to be able to feed itself. If part of this acreage is taken up by grazing lands or pastures, the calculated ghost acreage would be correspondingly larger.

The second element of the ghost acreage is represented by *trade* acreage—calculated as the acreage, in terms of tilled land, required to produce, also with present techniques, the agricultural products constituting the *net importation*. The traditional trade balance sheets are based upon either metric ton figures or monetary values. Both concepts are, however, less suited for a realistic appraisal of the feeding capacity and overall food balance of a country. As is well known, weight varies considerably with the water content, which renders the traditional adding-up of various kinds of food on a weight basis as nutritionally absurd. Unfortunately this is still frequently done with industrially manufactured foods of various kinds. Such data may be of interest in relation to transportation costs and when it comes to procuring tonnage for shipment, but such total sums poorly reflect the nutritional significance of shipment loads.

For more than thirty years the food prices both on the world market and in individual countries have rarely reflected the true production costs. Production regulations, subsidies, tariffs, taxes, and subvention purchases have long ago replaced free competition in this area—fortunately, it may be fair to add. At the same

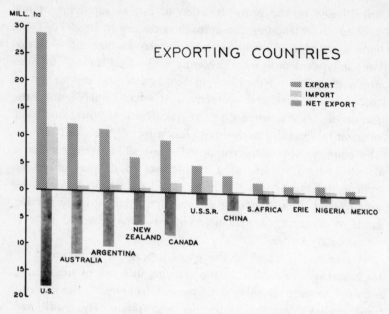

FIG. 19   Trade acreages based on 1958–59 figures.

time, however, monetary appraisals of food and feed have
become far removed from what would be acceptable from a
nutritional point of view. As a contribution to a discussion along
new and more meaningful guidelines, I have therefore introduced
this acreage concept. In the first place, this was done to place
protein in its key role in human feeding. Protein raised through
soils is in general the most acreage-demanding constituent. Besides, protein content and value have hardly ever been the prime
yardstick in determining prices, although in so many cases it
holds the first line in determining the nutritional value to man
and to livestock.

In order to make these calculations more reliable, and with
the aim of offering real guidance, trade acreages are computed
separately for each individual country. Even in this connection

it is true that when it comes to huge countries such as the United States and the U.S.S.R. these figures become less relevant and need to be supplemented with corresponding regional analyses, such as for example the Soviet Far East, European U.S.S.R., the Rocky Mountain States, the New England States, or the Pacific Region of the United States. Only when referring to a region reasonably uniform in topographic and climatic respects do such analyses take on full meaning.

Another complication arises from agricultural products which cannot be produced in a given country (such as coffee and bananas in the United States) and are imported. In trade statistics food importation is sometimes split up between supplement-

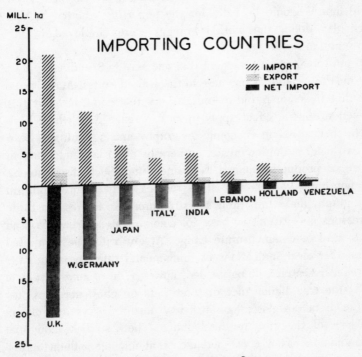

FIG. 20 Trade acreages based on 1958–59 figures.

ing and substituting products, often given the designation supplementary and complementary—the latter not normally grown in the country. This distinction is important.

It should be underlined that the trade acreages comprise all categories of agricultural products (the nutritive values as well as their demand on acreage), also non-food items such as fibers and tobacco, as they all dispose tilled land and pastures. In other words, they affect the acreage available for the raising of food in the exporting and importing countries. On the whole, however, acreages for nonfood items are minor compared to those used for food and feed. Another complication refers to commodities that are complementary and not supplementary. Also in this case the total acreage is minor, but no reasonable yield figures would be valid for the importing country. In this particular detail the world averages were employed in my computations.

From the above it is evident that one acre in Scandinavia does not mean the same as one acre in the United States. Acre figures are directly comparable in only a very few countries. But this objection does in effect apply to most acreage data which have so far been used in economic geography and agriculture. Even in two neighboring countries, an acre of tilled land may not, in terms of production, mean the same thing. Such discrepancies do not imply, however, that in regions with a fairly uniform topography and comparable soil structure, acre figures constitute a reasonably satisfactory basis for comparisons and can be used as a kind of commensurate gauge. At any rate, the computed data offer clear indications of fundamental differences. Further detailed research will be needed, however, in order to evaluate fully the true significance of these data on ghost acreages.

Let us take a closer look at a few illustrative results from an analysis of the kind outlined above. These studies show that Scandinavia has a ghost acreage of almost 6.7 million acres—almost an entire additional agricultural Sweden in terms of tilled land (see Table 13, pp. 82–83)—this is the case in spite of the fact that Denmark through its export deliveries, primarily to Western Europe and the United States, places at the disposal of the world household a net acreage of 1.1 million acres. This means, among other things, that the total food export of Denmark would not suffice to cover more than one-third of these net import needs of Scandinavia as measured in acreages. It seems appropriate again to stress the fact that such acreage figures far better measure the real significance of this trade in food and feed, as these calculations pay attention to and directly reflect the nutritive values as well as the demand on acreage for their production.

The fish acreage of Scandinavia, for example, amounts to almost three million acres, or half the tilled land of Sweden. The total ghost acreage of Sweden exceeds 36 per cent of the tilled land of the country, an almost identical land area. Importation accounts for 24 per cent. It is worth noting, that in this case these figures come close to the estimates made in the conventional way on the money value of the trade. This might, therefore, even provide argument for questioning the need of approaching this field from the nutritional angle along the principles advocated here. For a number of countries, however, the discrepancies between the two approaches becomes considerable.

Presently this author is devising methods whereby the use of commercial fertilizers and the energy inputs are computed in corresponding terms and added to the ghost acreages. Furthermore, it has proved most useful to present the unfilled nutritional needs of man in similar, unequivocal terms. The question is then posed: What acreages would in respective countries be required to fill the gap between minimal nutritional needs and the present conditions of undernutrition or malnutrition? In countries where comprehensive dietary surveys are lacking, one can by this method readily establish what acreage with the present state of the techniques would be needed to improve the nutritional standard to a defined level such as that of Japan, Brazil, or Italy.

Contrary to all analyses so far presented, the ghost acreage of Japan has increased continuously since 1952, primarily owing to the rapid increase in the importation of wheat, soybeans, and feeding-stuffs. In principle these imports constitute a large-scale influx of proteins. Japan's balance sheet at the turn of the latest decade looked this way: the fish acreage was equal to 1.54 of the tilled land of Japan (see chapter 9); the net importation accounted for a *ghost acreage* equaling the entire tilled acreage of the country. Both these figures have grown since 1958–59. The *ghost acreage* of Japan consequently zooms to 2.55 Japan in terms of the present tilled land. In addition to the tilled acreage there are available for food production within the borders improved pastures, which constitute merely 0.27 of the tilled land. A simple chart presenting the feeding balance of the Japanese nation is given in Figure 29, p. 159. (See also Table 19, p. 160.)

This means that Japan obtains less than one-third of its food from its own soils (28 per cent). Approximately the same quantity is taken from abroad and a little less than half (44 per cent) from the sea through fisheries. Anyone starting to add up calories in the conventional manner would soon find that agriculture is accounting for more than half of the calorie intake. If we consider protein and recognize the relatively large acreage required to produce this precious commodity, we obtain a strongly modified and more realistic picture of Japan: (1) the enormous degree of dependence upon territory other than its own; (2) the key position of its fisheries; and finally, in relative terms, i.e., tilled land, (3) the modest role of its agriculture.

Holland is another illuminating example. It is looked upon as a food-exporting country, which it is. But this is often interpreted to mean the country has a food surplus from which it generously delivers to other less fortunate nations. The Dutch are pictured as magicians of the soils who feed more people per acre than any other nation. These notions are misconceptions.

TABLE 12

Ghost Acreage in Relation to Tilled Land

One (1) is the relative figure given to tilled land in every country listed.

Country	Fisheries	Net Import	Ghost Acreage
Switzerland	0.33	3.22	3.55
England	0.38	2.90	3.28
Belgium	0.33	2.58	2.91
Israel	1.31	1.38	2.69
Japan	1.54	1.01	2.55
West Germany	0.28	1.33	1.61
Holland	0.47	0.99	1.46
Norway	0.66	0.64	1.30
Egypt	0.48	0.14	0.62
Ceylon	0.23	0.30	0.53
Portugal	0.29	0.08	0.37
China	0.23	0.03	0.26

Another illustrative example is Israel, which feeds only one-third of its population from its agricultural acreage despite all impressive accomplishments. The very narrow margin for new soils, and their critical dependence on water, set obvious limitations to the productive capacity of the country. Irrigation is, even when expanded and superefficient (depending on the rainfall and condensation in the watershed area), mainly the river Jordan systems. Fisheries contribute one-third of the feeding acreage and the net importation another third.

In these tables only a few examples have been chosen of particular interest from one viewpoint or another. But they all serve to demonstrate the role of the ghost acreages. They also bring out the hollowness of conventional self-sufficiency concepts.

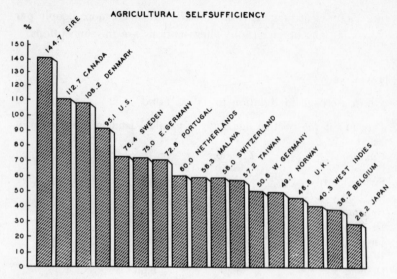

FIG. 21 The feeding of a country rests on a tripod—agriculture, fisheries, and trade. In this study all three have been computed in terms of acreages referring to each country respectively. Net exportation reduces the agricultural acreages. This chart shows in these terms to what degree agriculture provides the feeding basis of a country.

Figure 21 shows the degree to which a number of listed countries depend on their agriculture for feeding their peoples. Fishery and net trade fill in, or in the case of net export, reduce the operational basis of the country.

Population density figures may also be modified to take into account these ghost acreages. There is in this particular respect a great deal of glib talk and confused reasoning when discussing "miracles," such as Japan, Holland, Ceylon, and others—how they manage to "feed" so many from so little acreage. The graphs (Figs. 22 and 23) refute the validity of these reasonings, as in all these cases substantial contributions are made through net importation and fishing. Without fisheries it would in most cases not be feasible for any of the Southeast Asian countries to maintain their trade deliveries of such items as rice, copra, tea, and rubber.

Nutritional Acreages

All the computing done so far and discussed above has been based on the assumption that each country is meeting the needs of its inhabitants. This is a fallacy. Dietary surveys are available for a number of countries. Several of these point to the presence of extensive undernourishment and nutritional deficiencies. In those cases, where the results of such surveys present comprehen-

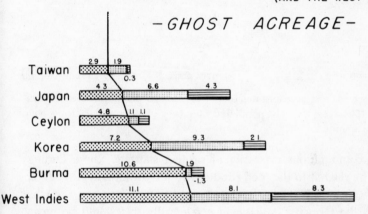

ARES PER P.E.-UNIT, ASIA
(AND THE WEST INDIES)

—GHOST ACREAGE—

Taiwan	2.9	1.9	0.3
Japan	4.3	6.6	4.3
Ceylon	4.8	1.1 1.1	
Korea	7.2	9.3	2.1
Burma	10.6	1.9	-1.3
West Indies	11.1	8.1	8.3

Agriculture   Fish   Trade

FIG. 22 Ghost acreages calculated as acreage per population equivalent. The most densely populated countries of Asia and Europe have been included.

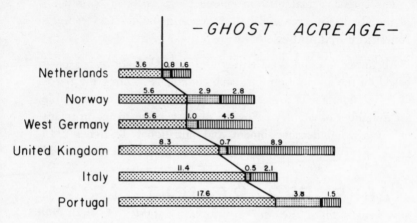

ARES PER P.E.-UNIT, EUROPE

−GHOST ACREAGE−

Netherlands	3.6	0.8 1.6	
Norway	5.6	2.9	2.8
West Germany	5.6	1.0	4.5
United Kingdom	8.3	0.7	8.9
Italy	11.4	0.5 2.1	
Portugal	17.6	3.8	1.5

Agriculture ▦   Fish ▥   Trade ▥

FIG. 23 Ghost acreages calculated as acreage per population equivalent. The most densely populated countries of Asia and Europe have been included.

sive computations primarily of protein shortage, these findings can be related to the food production of each individual country. In this way it becomes feasible to add to the ghost acreage what could be termed a *nutritional acreage*. By this would be meant the additional acreage required to satisfy nutritional minimum needs but still taking into consideration the dietary habits prevailing in each country. Calculations are not based on such unrealistic questions as: What would be required to give the Brazilians a United States diet? Instead, they aim at answering more realistic queries such as: How many more acres of beans or how much additional pasture would be needed to give the undernourished in the country a minimal diet without changing its relative composition?

The extensive malnutrition among the peoples of the islands of the Caribbean area will be discussed in the chapter on Latin America. It was also briefly touched upon in the chapter on the protein crisis. Take Haiti as one concrete example. The estimates show that the additional acreage needed to fill the protein gap and satisfy minimal nutrition requirements would amount to one extra Haiti in terms of tilled land and pastures. Once more it should be pointed out that there is of course the alternate proposition of doubling the yields per acre. This does not appear, however, to be a very realistic likelihood for Haiti within the foreseeable future. Undoubtedly Norwegian dried cod or Peruvian fish meal would constitute a cheaper and more reliable expedient in filling their present protein gap.

Another method which elucidates fairly well the relationship between agricultural production and nutritional standard is to calculate how large an acreage, and alternately how large an increase in yield, would be required, under present production conditions, to attain a raised nutritional level. Such estimates give a rather clear indication of the degree of feasibility for such programs.

Most experts would agree that Indonesia, for instance, is seriously overpopulated. Calculations of the suggested kind bear this out still more clearly. In order to raise the nutritional standard of Indonesia up to Soviet level, an acreage four times as large as the present would be needed if it were to be done chiefly through rice, and a doubling of the acreage if done through peanuts. Brazil would need either a 60 per cent acreage increase or a 60 per cent higher yield per acre of wheat in order to be able, from its own soils, to give the nation an Italian standard. Various combinations are obviously possible, such as 30 per cent greater yield and a 30 per cent increase in acreage; in both cases the result would be a rather modest improvement and

TABLE 13

Thousand Hectares	AGRICULTURE		GHOST ACREAGE		Total Feeding Acreage	Agricultural Self-sufficiency %
	Tilled Land	Pastures	Fisheries	Trade		
Denmark	2,736	381	255.5	491.5	2,881	—
%	95	13.5		27.5	—	108.5
Finland	2,586	283	110	648	3,627	—
%	71.5	8	3	17.5	—	79.5
Norway	829	203	546	525	2,103	—
%	39	10	26	25	—	49
Sweden	3,712	724	434	924	5,794	—
%	64	12.5	7.5	16	—	76.5
Scandinavia	9,863	1,591	1,345.5	1,605.5	14,405	—
%	68.5	11	9.5	11	—	79.5
England (U.K.)	7,126	12,238	2,711	20,629	42,704	—
%	16.5	29	6.5	48	—	45.5
W. Germany	8,727	5,689	2,475	11,607	28,498	—
%	30.5	20	9	40.5	—	50
Netherlands	1,054	1,251	491	1,045	3,841	—
%	27	33	13	27	—	60
Belgium	990	725	331	2,549	4,595	—
%	21.5	15.5	7.5	55.5	—	37

Table 13, continued

Thousand Hectares	AGRICULTURE		GHOST ACREAGE		Total Feeding Acreage	Agricultural Self-sufficiency %
	Tilled Land	Pastures	Fisheries	Trade		
Portugal	4,130		1,208	334	5,672	—
%	73		21	6		73
Israel	378	222	494	523	1,617	—
%	23	14	30	33		37
Switzerland	445	1,727	135	1,427	3,734	—
%	12	46	3.5	38.5		58
Italy	15,809	5,127	982	3,808	25,726	—
%	62	20	4	8		82
China	109,354	177,996	25,667	3,232	309,785	—
%	35	58	8	1		93
India	160,006	12,207	6,685	3,619	182,517	—
%	88	7	3.5	1.5		95
Indonesia	17,681		2,773	518	20,972	—
%	84		13	3		84
Ceylon	1,523		347	458	2,328	—
%	65		15	20		65
Egypt	2,618		1,250	355	4,223	—
%	62		30	8		62

yet would require exceptional measures, besides what normally would be needed to feed the more than one million extra now added to this country every year.

England's Recurrent Crises

It is not surprising that England off and on has payment difficulties and is goaded by its ministers of finance to new and ever increasing export achievements. No one in charge of the British treasury has yet suggested, however, that the nation needs to adjust to reality and its true resources by cutting its coat according to its cloth. The crises now persistently hampering this country seem in the long run chronic, when nearly half of the nation's food and feed has to be paid for from hard-earned foreign exchange. Yet no one would suggest curing the financial ills by reducing the conventional intakes of meat, butter, and eggs, which now constitute more than half of the imported acreage. The remainder is represented by food oils and grain for food and feed.

West Germany allows itself the same extravagance but to a lesser degree. Relatively speaking, less of its imported food consists of animal products, and more of bread, feeding grain, and oils. But even in this case an adjustment to the nutritional realities of our day's world would constitute a policy economically more sound in the long run. In the case of both these countries, maintaining the present dietary habits implies the earmarking of a considerable amount of the export incomes for regular food consumption. The immense global food shortage is a reminder of the world's huge unfilled needs and markets, which far more desperately require this food. Signs of adjustment to these realities are seen in the opening up of China, Japan, and other Asiatic markets to grains and other agricultural commodities from Australia, Canada, and New Zealand.

Western Europe

Western Europe is still plodding along as though nothing had happened. After the war, politicians drowsily identified themselves with the understandable desires of the masses to return to a prewar Utopia, wanting to attain a so-called normalizing after the disruptions of the war. But the population pressure of Europe and of the world has in the meantime become so severe that this is no longer possible. The earlier this reality is acknowledged, the better. Common markets (whether they are named six-state or seven-state ones) cannot in the least change the fundamental fact that Western Europe is overpopulated. This population pressure is felt much more through its persistence in retaining dietary habits which can only be designated as extravagant in the world of today. To live beyond one's means has always been considered condemnable but seems especially dangerous within the realm of food consumption. Beefsteaks and pork chops are, unfortunately, luxuries in the present world, and it can be justly doubted if Europeans can any longer really afford their present lavish food exuberance. The recent crisis of Italy—in the summer of 1964—is but an additional evidence of this dangerous mock-play.

Widespread refusal to see the demographic realities, and myopic endorsement by politicians and economists of the blessings of population growth, is bearing tragic fruits. At the moment the pinch is not felt too strongly in the United States and Europe, because they still retain power to stave off these unpleasantries. But facts are stubborn things, and in less than two decades Europe will be faced with a painful adjustment to a world with other duties and far more formidable tasks than to keep Europeans fat and happy. Africa, Latin America, and Asia will demand their just share. That the goal of human civilization should be to replace human beings in the millions with counting them in the billions seems foolhardy, to say the least. It is deplorable that so many scientists and engineers have endorsed such reck-lessness. In a sense, they bear a great responsibility for the present state of affairs as well as for any future miseries by writing all these checks drawn upon tomorrow but precious few of which have the slightest chance to be honored.

CHAPTER **6**

Asia—

Starvation Center

or Powerhouse?

T HE five years immediately following World War
II, 1945–1950, will undoubtedly become designated as one of
the great dividing lines in human history. In those years, the
European race, and indirectly the entire white race, decisively
lost its world supremacy, which it had held almost since the
sixteenth century. More than one billion people freed themselves
in this critical lustre from political dependence on European
powers. Some ten new sovereign states were created. These
events affected Asia to a considerable degree. It has been said
that the "hub of the Universe" then once more moved back to
Asia, the continent which once saw civilized man emerging and
which probably was the origin of a whole series of races. Above
all, it should be realized as well as recognized that Asia created
impressive civilizations several thousand years before Christ,
at a time when the Europeans were still barbarians. But—this
great emancipation from colonial rule of India, Pakistan, Ceylon,
Indochina, and Indonesia, and the rebirth of China as a world

power—has it really meant such a major switch in the center of gravitation? Hardly, but why?

Net Exportation Ended

Food is the answer. There is not sufficient to eat for the many hundreds of millions living in Asia. Hungry people cannot conduct wars, and they cannot assert themselves culturally or economically. Asia's great tragedy is that the population figures have long ago exceeded available resources by far. Yet, as late as 1939, Asia provided the equally overpopulated Europe with food. Peanuts were shipped in a steady stream from the hungry India, sugar from Java. Soybeans were delivered from Manchuria, copra from Java and the Philippines, for example. To some degree this export still continues or has been resumed, but by and large the postwar years of 1945 to 1950 saw the end of these abnormal conditions. Coinciding with the political emancipation, Asia's brief appearance on the world scene as a food provider for other continents came to an end. Asia switched from being a net exporter of food and feed to the reverse—a net importer. All evidence points to the inevitable situation that this giant continent will remain in this category. The local surpluses which occasionally may accrue will be consumed to an increasing degree by Asia's own people.

Compressed Living Space

Asia, covering one-third of the land surface of the globe, comprises half the world's population, more exactly 55 per cent. But these people have merely one-fourth of the cultivated area at their disposal. Only one-fourth of the world's available food is consumed in this continent.

The huge highlands and mountain ranges of Central Asia and the wide dry belt of steppe and desert traversing the continent, not only split and drastically reduce the available living space; these topographical conditions congest one billion people into river valleys and deltas, or else force them to cultivate the soil under severe climatic handicaps. Asia's teeming millions are largely dependent upon its water- and mud-yielding rivers for their survival. These are India's Ganges, and Brahmaputra, Pakistan's Indus, Burma's Irrawaddi, North Korea's Red River, Cambodia's and Indochina's Mekong, China's Hwang Ho, Yangtze Kiang, and so forth. In the tropical parts of Asia, comprising 8 million square kilometers, more than 800 million people are living. In the remaining tropic of the globe, 30 million square kilometers, merely 250 million live.

Increasing Dependence on Plant Products

How then is survival possible on this area, small in relation to the population? This is accomplished chiefly by resorting to plant products. One acre of rice feeds about four people. Used as pastures, this same area would sustain, at the most, one individual and presumably less. On the average, Asia presently is feeding thirty-six people per ten acres of tilled land. On the whole this would not be feasible if this continent were to feed the harvests of its soils to livestock. This is, in effect, the tragic fate of this very continent which as far as we know has given the world the majority of its domestic animals. But, by and large, this continent can simply no longer afford the luxury of using them as food animals. If this were done, their total output would fall far below the minimum needs for the teeming millions.

A mere 3 per cent of India's diet consists of animal products. Butterfat is a privilege of the rich. A member of a farmer family in the Tonkin delta of North Vietnam gets six and a half pounds of meat and four and a half pounds of fat annually. His protein source is chiefly wild insects. Dogs are eaten in these areas as well as in parts of China. This huge country is not acquainted

with milk, outside of the buffalo regions in the south. Since as
early as the days of Christ it has taken recourse to the soybean,
from which both milk and cheese are produced. China's protein
percentage—the protein part of the total caloric intake—amounts
to 2.3 per cent (in the United States the corresponding figure is

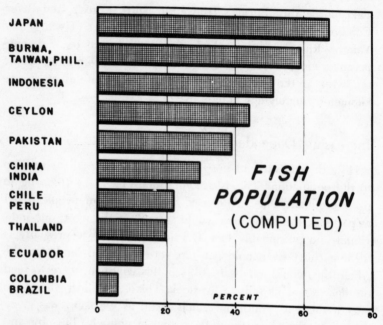

FIG. 24   The percentage of the animal protein intake covered by fish,
expressed in percentage of population that could get their entire
animal protein from aquatic sources.

14 per cent). The Japanese eat a greater amount of algae than
red meat.

Since such major segments of the world population as that of
Asia have been forced to adopt a strict vegetarian diet, mankind
has, for all practical purposes, already gone vegetarian. It has
not yet dawned upon the few hundred million, totally around

500 million, who regularly are drinking milk, eating beefsteaks, pork chops, eggs, and poultry, that they belong to a minority of the world's 3,200 million who can still afford such a luxury diet. These privileged are exceptions, not the rule. We Americans, who belong to this favored minority, could not possibly imagine what it would be like to limit our consumption of meat, as the Chinese do, by using it merely as a condiment in the form of thin strips in the soup and only a few times a week.

Nine-tenths of all rice is grown in Asia. India and China compete as to the largest acreage for rice cultivation. Japan has, thanks to its more favorable and dependable climate, the highest acre yields, almost three times those of India. As to total quantity, China has the lead. This does not prevent it from producing in normal years almost as much wheat as the United States. This means that under normal years China contends with no less than the United States for the second rank in world production of wheat—next to the U.S.S.R., the leader. In northern China and in elevated land in neighboring Central Asiatic countries, millet dominates among the grain. This cereal requires less water. Also in the dry savannah areas to the south in India, Burma, and other regions, various millets are encountered. Even in this case, India and China are the world's largest producers. There is no question that their heavily vegetarian diet is directly reflected in the use of the tilled land as well as in their agricultural production. In the larger part of the Asiatic continent, more than 90 per cent of the daily food intake consists of plant products.

Natural Resources

Through the centuries the forests have been forced to yield space for agricultural lands. The extent to which this has taken place may best be illustrated by the fact that Asia's forest resources, per individual, are now smaller than in any other continent, a mere 0.75 acres. Asia imports in excess of two million cubic meters of lumber annually, and 220 million acres of new forest land would be required to fill the minimum needs of the thirty-five to forty million people now being added to this population of Asia per year—approximately what the United States has at its total disposal now. And yet we do not find it adequate and are buying forest products from Canada, Scandinavia, Mexico, and other countries.

It is true that the enormous forest regions of Siberia ought to suffice for the needs of Asia, but the transportation costs would be exorbitant, not to mention the recognized obstacles of the unavailability of North Siberian rivers for log-carrying purposes, and the modest annual increment in these northern areas with their adverse climate. These forests, presently standing there, are to a major degree overaged and therefore infected by fungi and insects to a considerable extent. According to official Soviet figures 55 per cent of the Siberian forests are overaged.

One could point to the large natural resources of China and India in iron ore and coal. But, however vast these may be, they would not go far toward supplying the needs of two billion people, rapidly becoming four billion. If these Asiatic people were to follow our wasteful pattern and, according to our recommendations, get started on a Western-type industrialization, simple calculations lead to the conclusion that, even when taking into account the possibility of finding major new deposits, almost all these resources would easily be depleted before this century comes to a close. Even giant mining resources dwindle in size and become dwarfish when measured against the enormous needs.

The Asian Giant Choking

Asia is a giant among continents, and although the food shortage remains the chief obstacle with permanent malnutrition and diseases as the grim consequences, conditions vary considerably from country to country. The following chapters therefore will discuss how these circumstances differ in the various key areas of this vast continent. India and China—the two giants which together comprise more than one-third of mankind—are, with their many thousands of years of advanced civilization, basically quite different in structure, not the least with regard to food, in spite of the fact that both live in the shadow of starvation. The critical situation of Japan will also be elucidated. We shall follow how efforts have been made, largely in vain, to ease an intolerable population pressure through migrations and thus achieve relief in the relentless struggle for daily food. Finally, the reserves still remaining will be critically analyzed as to their potentialities. Australia, the "empty" continent which has beckoned to so many, among both Asiatic and European politicians, as the last safety valve of mankind, cannot be listed among these potential possibilities, for good reasons, as we shall see. There is far greater likelihood that Siberia and the vast expanses of Central Asia could qualify as such assets, with their sizeable hidden riches only partly unveiled. The Near East could, too, in a limited sense, be termed an untapped resource. The Indonesian archipelago is rapidly becoming so thronged with people that the situation is almost unbearable. The virgin forests of New Guinea will not last long if the immigration from Java and other brimful islands starts picking up, but the land to be gained here carries soils precarious for cultivation, and the total acreage is not impressive in Asiatic terms. The feeding potentialities of these regions are commonly overrated not the least in the present anti-Malaysian drive by Indonesia expecting to find space for its bulging population.

European Leadership Gone

When discussing the Asiatic question, the white man should not indulge in his traditional complacency, reflected in thoughtless formulations such as designating the Asiatics the rabbit plague of mankind, and similar statements. Nothing could be more misleading. The Europeans have in no way lagged behind in the population race. On the contrary, the European peoples have grown faster, relatively speaking, than the Asiatics during the last few centuries. The United States is presently showing a net growth approaching that of India.

In order to find outlets for its many excess millions, the European race conquered strongholds in four continents: Australia, the two Americas, and major parts of Africa. The Europeans represent the largest emigration in world history, numbering at least seventy million people. Finally, up to World War II, they led the world's takeout from the oceans. Not the least in this latter respect we can already discern the start of a new epoch in history.

It is highly probable that the white race is now facing its crucial test when forced to adjust to the limits of its own resources of land, water, plants, oils, and minerals, and to what they themselves can produce and extract from these assets, now so heavily depleted. At any rate we must definitely end our dependence on hundreds of millions of hectares in other continents. The indigenous populations of these lands sorely need their soil for feeding themselves. On the basis of the strength of their newly acquired political freedom they will claim their self-evident rights. In many cases such economic readjustment is long overdue. If the Western world is not capable of this reorganization of its economic and social life, it will be faced with the risk of being forced to trudge along the same path as Asia today—leading to semistarvation, undernourishment, and apathy.

The Road Back

Asia is, in these terms, ahead of us on the way downhill. Today, we encounter there the sad picture of once eminent civilizations which are now worm-eaten from within and have lost their grandeur and viability principally because they put themselves above nature and sinned against its elementary laws. As long as these fundamental rules were respected, India, China, and Japan all excelled. Their cultures flourished and surpassed ours in their day in many respects. But when hunger and malnutrition get the upper hand, as has happened in large parts of Asia in this very century, then the creative forces peter out. The will to survive and the capacity for work dwindles and with them the basic prerequisites for a spiritual and cultural life. Dictatorship and slavery find fertile soil and become the inevitable alternative to anarchy. Only one road leads away from this kind of misery—the road back to a biological balance. But a massive education is needed to reactivate civil conscience and sense of responsibility. A clear understanding of the facts as well as a realization of the gravity of the present situation is also indispensable. A hopeful sign is the fact that several of the leading Asiatic statesmen—in India as well as in Ceylon, Indonesia, and Japan—have shown the courage to bring population control to the foreground and out into the open, as an urgent measure and integral part of current political programs.

References

BATTISTINI, L. H. *Introducing Asia*. New York, John Day, 1953, 289 pp.

CRESSEY, G. B. *Asia's Lands and Peoples*. New York, McGraw-Hill, 1951, 480 pp.

DOBBY, E. H. G. *Monsoon Asia*. Chicago, Quadrangle Books, Inc., 1961, 380 pp.

Economic Survey of Asia and the Far East 1959. Bangkok, United Nations, 1960, 169 pp.

FORBIN, V. *Les Richesses de L'Asie*. Paris, Payot, 1946, 344 pp.

GINSBURG, N. (ed.). *The Pattern of Asia*. New York, Prentice-Hall, 1958, 929 pp.

GORDON EAST, W., and SPAT, O. H. K. *The Changing Map of Asia*. London, Methuen, 1958, 434 pp.

GOUROU, P. *L'Asie*. Paris, Hachette, 1953, 541 pp.

KING, F. H. *Farmers of Forty Centuries or Permanent Agriculture in China, Korea and Japan*. Madison, Wisconsin, F. H. King, 1911, 441 pp.

LEVY, R. *Regards sur L'Asie*. Paris, Armand Colin, 1952, 230 pp.

MATTHEW, H. G. (ed.). *Asia in the Modern World*. New York, The New American Library, 1963, 268 pp.

NAG, K. *Discovery of Asia*. Calcutta, Inst. Asian-African Rel., 1953, 789 pp.

PAYNE, R. *The Revolt of Asia*. New York, John Day, 1947, 299 pp.

PETERSON, A. D. C. *The Far East, A Social Geography*. London, Duckworth, 1949, 336 pp.

RAWSON, R. R. *The Monsoon Lands of Asia*. London, Hutchinson Educational, 1963, 256 pp.

ROMEIN, J. M. and J. E. (Trans. R. T. CLARK). *The Asian Century*. Berkeley, Calif., University of California Press, 1962, 448 pp.

SPENCER, J. E. *Asia, East by South*. New York, Wiley, 1954, 453 pp.

STAMP, L. D. *Asia, Regional and Economic Geography*. London, Methuen, 1951, 520 pp.

THOMPSON, W. S. *Population and Progress in the Far East*. Chicago, University of Chicago Press, 1959, 443 pp.

WILCOX, E. V. *Acres and People*. New York, Judd, 1947, 297 pp.

ZIMKIN, M. *Asia and the West*. London, Chatto & Windus, 1951, 300 pp.

IMPORTANT MAGAZINES:

Asian Affairs	*Asian Review*	*L'Afrique et l'Asie*
Asian Annual	*Asia and the American*	

CHAPTER 7

The Food Larder
of the Red
Mandarins

MANY have extolled the farsightedness of the Chinese and their skill in crop-raising, but whatever the historians and travelers have had to say, even the Chinese failed in their handling of land resources. For fifty centuries they cultivated their soil and at the same time performed the almost incredible feat of maintaining its fertility more or less unchanged. Meticulously, they returned all waste, both that of animal and of man, to the tilled land, the average annual quantity being from 6 to 7 metric tons per acre. But their chief shortcoming was to become too many. Their river valleys got filled and overfilled with more than ten times as many people to the acre as Holland presently has.

The Chinese civilization flourished 3,000 years ago at the time when the water buffalo was domesticated and the cultivation of rice and wheat began. They knew how to get good yields from the land, and everyone prospered. Opulence was the characteristic feature of those days, but subsequent dynasties encountered

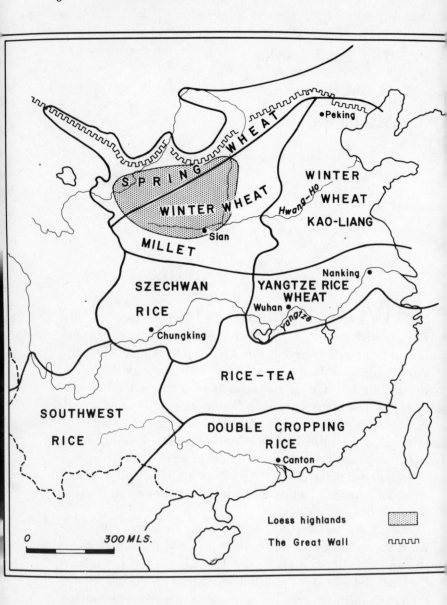

SPRING WHEAT

WINTER WHEAT

MILLET

•Sian

•Peking

WINTER

WHEAT

KAO-LIANG

Hwang-Ho

SZECHWAN

RICE

•Chungking

Nanking •

YANGTZE RICE
WHEAT

Wuhan •

Yangtze

RICE-TEA

SOUTHWEST

RICE

DOUBLE CROPPING
RICE

•Canton

Loess highlands

The Great Wall

0   300 MLS.

growing difficulties in their efforts to make ends meet. The grass-lands of the north and west were ploughed and the big forests were felled one after the other to provide the land required to feed the country's growing millions. Once the grip of the roots of trees and grass had gone, there was nothing to bind the loose earth. Millions of tons of soil were swept down the great rivers, raising their beds. Thus began the grim story of China's floods that until recently have brought death and disaster to millions and caused some of this earth's greatest catastrophes, basically man-made.

Devastation of the Forests

It has been estimated that some 670 million acres of China's forests were cut down in what has been termed one of the greatest acts of ecological stupidity in the history of mankind. Prior to this, nine-tenths of central Shansi Province are said to have been covered with dense forests. Similar figures have been quoted for other provinces. When it comes to the core area of present-day China, trees are hardly to be found, except in temple groves. They are rarely ever mentioned in literary descriptions of more recent date or in fiction like the novels by Pearl Buck, except where the narrative refers to the border states or the southwest regions of this vast country. Major plans have been worked out to restore the original forest cover of China within a period of thirty years, in order to restore the water balance and create protection for the soil. Following the Soviet example, big protective belts of forest are being planted parallel to the Great Wall along the whole of the western frontier. This undertaking is said to have been started, but is it going to prove possible? On one hand, every square yard of cultivatable soil is needed to feed the swiftly growing millions, and on the other hand, cen-turies of sparse and inadequate protection so desiccated the soil that expensive measures have to be taken to give the young trees at least a minimal chance of rooting and of surviving the first few years when they are forced to rely on the scanty water available in the surface layer of the soil. Information on these matters is fragmentary but leaves room for guesses about the great difficulties likely to be encountered in this major undertaking.

The Menace of Internal Parasites

The earth of China has through history been trodden, by eleven to twelve billion people, with an enormous wear and tear of its vegetation cover and land surface; but even worse, there has been a gradual accumulation of parasites. In man's footsteps a massive deployment of bacteria, fungi, worms, and insects has taken place.

Seen in the light of history, the price that China had to pay for her impressive feat in plant husbandry seems unreasonably high. Disease has been spread through the night-soil, and as a result the Chinese scene early became dominated by intestinal worms. Their eggs are spread by the billions everywhere. They are in the dust that swirls in clouds, and from this source alone the people of China are bombarded by billions of helminthian eggs. The weight of liver parasites in the aggregate of Chinese bodies has been estimated to be equivalent to the weight of two million Chinese. These liver parasites are responsible for many a yellow complexion, and more than one-fifth of the population is reported to have its liver seriously damaged by cirrhosis, chiefly caused by protein deficiencies in the daily diet but frequently aggravated by these marauders. This is the grim truth concerning a society that once lost its ecological balance and never was capable of restoring it. The statistics for 1960 recorded ninety million cases of tapeworm. But nine-tenths of the rural population was said to be infected, which means at least four-fifths of the total population. One-third of all deaths are reported to be attributed to these tapeworms—four million a year, twice as many as China's wars of this century are claimed to have cost her annually while they lasted.

Health Campaign

When the gravity of the situation was realized by the new regime, tens of thousands of doctors, nurses, pharmacists, sanitarians, and orderlies were mobilized and sent to serve among the many millions in the rural communities. These are the prime victims of infections and parasites. Springtime used to be a time of epidemics and death on the Chinese countryside. Besides, this coincides with the time when presumably the food storages frequently were empty or poorly filled. The number of new rural hospitals is already counted in the hundred thousand, and a ruthless warfare is being waged against the four dangers: flies, mosquitoes, rats, and bedbugs. Scrupulous cleanliness has become the watchword of this new era. These sanitation armies are in effect far more important in the great battle for food than are the forces represented by the peasants themselves. The order of the day has been to engage everyone in this battle against disease and for more food! This sanitary campaign may be without precedent in human history as to effectiveness and scope. Yet, the shining medal has its somber other side. Partly as a consequence of these successive health measures, China's population figures have surged upward and at an accelerated rate. But, simultaneously, statistics also show that bringing together the millions in congested communes gave increased spread to communicable diseases.

A Greater New York Each Year

According to the latest official Chinese statistics (1958), the population of China amounts to 655 million. This includes Mongolia, Sinkiang, Tibet, and the 12 to 15 million Chinese scattered around Southeast Asia. This figure is no longer contested, as it would have been a few years ago, and it would appear beyond all doubt that the Chinese are the most numerous nation in the world. The number of children in China (approximately 250 million below 15 years of age) by far exceeds the total population of the United States. Almost every fifth person in the world is a Chinese. Since the annual increase is between 15 to 20 million a year, within a couple of decades this figure could easily become every fourth person. No land reform, irrigation, or reclamation project on however gigantic a scale could bring relief in this situation. At the most, it could give a few years breathing space for a few millions in some local area. The bulk of the population could not be affected. Even an economic giant like the United States would find it difficult to deal with an additional population equivalent to a Greater New York every year. This is the uncomfortable reality that those with a demographic blind spot refuse to see. Barring devastating wars, major natural calamities or the adoption of severe birth control measures, the Chinese are heading for one billion in numbers by the 1980's. The leadership has vacillated in its support of birth control programs but seems presently to be making a new all-out effort in this direction, supported by state propaganda.

Today the Chinese has to feed himself on two-fifths of an acre of land or less, an area so small that any reasonable increases in yield add up to only a few pounds and have little significance even on a family level. There is no new land available in the already overcrowded river valleys. To integrate the tiny plots into larger units would improve matters little and would not with certainty allow the degree of efficiency now prevailing nor squeeze out more per acre—on the contrary, such measures might produce even less.

This circumstance should be coupled with the fact that China desperately needs a nationwide network of roads. However, this would involve taking over food-producing land that is already considered too precious to give up. As in Japan, only pathways lead to the fields, thereby leaving as much land as possible to till.

So far China has been able to manage in a limited kind of way by resorting to a strict vegetarian diet: boiled rice, wheat or millet, potatoes, cabbage, soybeans, lettuce, and so forth. In China milk has long been a vegetarian product, being made out of soybeans. On the average, animal products comprise some 2 to 3 per cent, at the most, of the average Chinese diet. On the whole, meat appears only as fish, poultry, or pork strips in the soup. The sumptuous meals offered in the Chinese restaurants of the West are, in the homeland, mostly dishes for festive occasions or what historically was Chinese food when conditions permitted.

Two Billion

Besides a human population now in excess of 700 million, China has to provide for a number of buffaloes, pigs, and poultry. Dogs have been eliminated. The livestock consumes what can be computed to suffice for 2.1 billion people, a figure that is not the least remarkable aspect of China's food balance. The feasibility of such an excessive consumption can be explained by the fact that in China the pig is no competitor to man, as is the case in most Western countries, but rather he fills the role of a scavenger—a converter of waste. Therefore, the hogs of China, representing 720 million population equivalents, do not put pressure on the primary plant production. Another essential feature is the fact that China's livestock, outside of hogs, provide very little food. They are mainly draught animals. In total number, they are, both relatively and absolutely, somewhat less than in India (see Fig. 26). One exception is the water buffalo in the south, providing a limited quantity of milk.

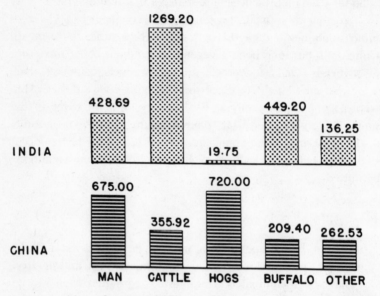

MAN AND LIVESTOCK IN INDIA AND CHINA

1959-60

MILL. POP. EQUIV.

FIG. 25 Note the major differences as to hogs, cattle and water buffaloes. The cattle numbers of India are legendary. The hogs of China fill a vital scavenging function. Water buffaloes can be raised only in south China but are spread to many regions of the Indian subcontinent.

A Modern Version of the Pyramids

It is difficult to conceive the immensity of the measures China has taken to assure food supplies and electric power. This has made her adopt a modern version of the old-time slave system used to build the pyramids. It is reported that eleven million people, if not more, were put to work in some of the biggest canals and waterworks in the world; fifteen million wells have been drilled or dug. These antlike armies are reported to have moved so much earth that they could have built 450 Panama canals or a wall a yard high two thousand times round the equator. Presumably, it is activities of these dimensions that account for the acute lack of labor in agriculture, despite the fact that millions have been mobilized from the cities and towns—office workers, students, teachers, artisans—to help with the harvesting, ploughing, sowing, and the combatting of insects. Here may also lie a basic reason for the creation of the much publicized communes—perhaps the only feasible way of mobilizing the labor reserves of the rural areas, where still today almost 80 per cent of the population is living.

China's agriculture has been modernized more quickly and to a much greater extent than most writers in the West realize. Hundreds of fertilizer factories, both large and small, have been started up in only a few years, and present plans envisaged an annual production of six million metric tons in 1964. Large numbers of factories for the making of tractors and implements have been installed, as well as chemical plants for insecticides. Undoubtedly, the most revolutionary happening is the efforts to mechanize rice cultivation. The number of planting machines used is said already to exceed several hundred thousand.

The Pastures of the Periphery

Two-fifths of the total area of the whole country is grassland, but this is almost exclusively confined to the vast peripheral borderline of states which, though inhabited by peoples of other races, are ruled by the Chinese. For centuries the immense flocks and herds of sheep and cattle here have been tended by peoples such as the Mongolians, Tibetans, Uigurs, Kirghizians, but these lands contributed mighty little to the feeding of the surplus millions in the core of China. One can therefore easily visualize how the Red Mandarins are casting longing glances at these vast expanses, not so much in order to get hold of meat and milk, but rather in order to turn them into new granaries. These pastures are, therefore, endangered when the ploughs are directed by the millions clamoring for food. The figures for tilled land are constantly mounting, yet much of this newly cultivated land is being ravaged by sand and dust storms. Most of these expanses are further short of water and require costly irrigation facilities—often from great distances since water may not be available locally.

Erosion became a serious problem in Manchuria during the Japanese occupation in the thirties because of the ploughing of new land, and it was further aggravated by large-scale cutting of the forests. The damages reached catastrophic proportions, and in 1952 the new regime had to apply the brakes and create extensive protective belts which are now beginning to yield timber and firewood and provide shelter to the fields. They extend from the Khingan Mountain Range in the north to the Liaotung peninsula in the south, and from the Chang Pai Ranges in the east to the steppes of Inner Mongolia and west.

This major Chinese expansion to the west and to the north is taking place outside of the famous Great Wall, which in its day was built to keep the hostile hordes from storming down from the plateaus of Central Asia in search of food. This march of the human lemmings, which are pouring into these peripheral areas from Sinkiang and Inner Mongolia to Manchuria, is a phenomenon of the past decade or two. Manchuria has reportedly accommodated fifty million, in number equivalent to the entire population of the United Kingdom. Cold and drought have to be overcome and borne, by sheer necessity. These lowlands far to the north have to be included in the embrace of the hungry millions.

The Great Northern Granary

There is an element of greatness about the campaign now being directed against this northern world—where severe winter cold holds its grip for eight long months, often with temperatures as low as minus 40°F—the lowlands of Northern Manchuria and the basin of the Amur River. The new China has renamed both the land and the river, which it now calls Heilungkiang, meaning the New Lands.

There one finds immense state farms, several of which comprise 50,000 acres. Large-scale electrification and mechanization is carried out. This territory already has one-quarter of all the tractors in the country. At first, machines and implements originated in the U.S.S.R., but now China is making her own tractors, combine-harvesters, and trucks. Here is still room for a network of roads, and the great plain is already spanned by a new railroad. To these new lands the pioneer-spirited young people of China were sent to transform what for centuries was called "the Great Northern Wilderness" into one of China's new granaries. Already the plains are crisscrossed by long irrigation channels bringing water from the Ussuri, a main tributary of the River of Amur. In those pioneer days one could find here a Peking city, a Tibetan town, and a Canton town, for the big cities south contended with each other in this great adventure, each providing brigades of young workers, and it was a true adventure. Though the soil is virgin and fertile, it is something of a feat to procure a harvest when the vegetation period is often less than a hundred days. What has been created up here is generally given the designation "the Great Northern Granary," though "little" would have been a more adequate name in terms of the huge Chinese continent. Although this newly cultivated area comprises about twelve million acres, this counts little when matched with the millions clamoring for food in China.

There are many new canneries in these regions, too, but their output does not go far. They were built in the first place in order to ensure a supply of vitamins from fruit and vegetables, but the inadequate system of roads and the great shortage of raw materials in relation to the immense needs, has led to feverish, almost desperate, building of greenhouses round the towns of the north. Harbin in Manchuria is said to have 12.5 acres under glass, in which beans and tomatoes are grown all the year round.

Sinkiang, Tibet and Inner Mongolia

Ever since 1955, the young people of China have flocked to these peripheral regions in the north and west. The key province in these new and, what one might call colonization areas, is Sinkiang (Hsing Kiang), or Chinese Turkestan. As late as 1948 this was a Soviet satellite, a kind of buffer state protecting the Central Asian Soviet republics of Kazakhstan, Kirgizia, and Tadzhikistan. In Sinkiang one finds vast grasslands somewhat similar in character to the arid and semiarid sections of the Argentine pampas. Hitherto only from 1 to 2 per cent of the area has been cultivated. Here China has at her disposal 176 million acres of potentially irrigable land, one-third of which could be tilled, more than two and a half times the agricultural area of Argentina. Up to 1950, this vast expanse was inhabited by less than four million people, but since then the Chinese have poured in their millions. Sinkiang has been called China's new prairie. The ploughed acreage has been more than doubled since the Chinese takeover and is reported as 4.5 million acres (1963). A newly built railroad is running through Sinkiang to the U.S.S.R. From its new, modern capital of Urumchi, it is said to be possible to reach by air most major capitals in less time than from any other region in the world. In this respect Urumchi is unique. It is a sort of dream city for those Overlords of the Earth that belong to the new Air Age. Its gigantic airport is also out of all proportion to the areas own needs. China, as we know, has also begun to nibble at the edges of the Indian empire, where its first objective would seem to be Bhutan. The dream seems to be, judging from a map recently published (Spring, 1963) in Peking, to restore the Chinese empire in its medieval grandeur, comprising large portions of Central Asia, Southeast Asia, and the Pacific Far East.

The question of Tibet must also be viewed in the light of this struggle for power in Central Asia. Tibet, which for generations relied on its own pastures, badly depleted though they were, has now been flooded by Chinese. Apparently there are already ten million there—ploughing, irrigating, and squeezing out crops that allow a ration of only one pound and a quarter of grain per person per day. It is characteristic that, despite the alarming reports of catastrophe from the Chinese heartland, record harvests have been reported from Tibet (1960–62). Grain deliveries seem to have been made from here to the needy east. However that may be, no one can alter the fact that it is on the Tibetan plateau that the Yangtze Kiang, China's vital artery, and other rivers have their source.

It is claimed that Inner Mongolia has been developed into China's main livestock center with large sheep flocks and cattle herds. Winter survival is safeguarded by feed grain (oats and corn) produced locally, once again the result of extensive ploughing.

Out of Balance

The industriousness of the Chinese is conjuring forth more food, but at the same time crop-raising is moving into the upper reaches of the river valleys, preceded by major dam constructions and extensive well-drilling. Water is in short supply almost everywhere, and in order to get more they have had to resort to such desperate measures as using airplanes to scatter soot and ash on the glaciers, thereby affecting the melting of the ice and multiplying the runoff to the rivers feeding the dry plains below. Each of these measures is an admirable farming feat, yet they are all quickly forgotten, because scarcely has there been time to reap the full benefits of such accomplishments before fresh millions have been added to the population and new desperate actions are needed. Under these circumstances, land is now cultivated as high up as 10,000 feet under climatically very harsh conditions. Barley and millet are being raised where, in wintertime, the average temperature is minus 40°F and the season of cultivation is restricted to seventy days. Special North Chinese strains are grown. The large-scale ploughing up of what for thousands of years have been grasslands also has its disadvantages: the wintertime winds and torrential rains carry the soil away. The impressive irrigation projects of the new lands are not looked upon with favor by those farther down the river, who are being deprived of the water on which they and their forebears through the centuries depended and which in critical years they need just as badly as those living farther up the river and which they can use to greater benefit under a less rigid climate. It is said that, during a recent drought, for four months there was no water in a very important part of the middle course of the Hwang Ho, something that never happened before, as far as historical records tell.

It is a queer situation, and greater attention is being paid to agriculture in China than, perhaps, ever before in its history. Food has become the all-important problem, and agriculture was to be given priority, however reluctantly, both *in* industrial production as such and *ahead* of industry by absorbing large quantities of steel—and yet the catastrophes and failures are greater than ever. Is there not some contradiction here? The political writers have a variety of explanations: it is the bankruptcy of the commune system; it is the freedom-loving peasants' revolt against authoritarianism. It is the penalty paid for the blindness of doctrinaire Marxism.

Victims of Their Own Ambition?

There is no lack of explanations, yet few seem to have considered the possibility that the Chinese have fallen victim to their own ambition, that they have used fertilizers too intensively, been too quick to introduce new, high-yielding strains without knowing enough about the soil's ability to withstand frost, drought, flooding, and mineral depletion. Sparrows, starlings, and other birds were combatted so effectively that the insects got an unchecked chance to rule. Maybe the limited supplies of water have been taxed too heavily by the hundreds of thousands of wells that were drilled in a desperate effort to save the wilting crops, particularly as these same crops were spurred to maximum productivity by an expanded use of fertilizers. The amount of available water is limited and its shortage became particularly conspicuous after two years of drought. In other words the depletion rate was accelerated to the point of crisis. The uplands of the inland—the huge semicircular periphery of highlands—disposed of ever-growing quantities of water to take care of the "record harvests" in these newly settled areas, thereby depriving the lower ranges of the rivers and their fertile valleys of some of the water on which they traditionally had relied through the centuries. Close-planting and deep-ploughing were said to be responsible for the vaunted successes of 1958. But close-planting also multiplied the amount of water needed for each acre and pushed the amount of required mineral nutrients far beyond what was normal for a given area, while deep-ploughing brought poorer soil to the surface with higher needs for fertilizers and larger consumption of water for dry-matter production, not to speak of the enhanced evaporation resulting from the greater exposure of the tilled soil. The indiscriminate expansion of irrigation also led to extensive salinization and alkalization, spoiling land at a rate which reduced the net gains in irrigated land. The extent of these damages has not been divulged.

Have the Chinese been too efficient and too ruthless in the application of the tricks and dodges of Western techniques, forgetting the precious lessons taught to them by thousands of years of farming? Only future historians may be able to answer this question. The catastrophes in 1959 and 1960 may be only two more in the long row of such calamities with which China has had to cope over the ages. But there are many indications that these were on a larger scale than they normally used to be, owing primarily to the new technical efficiency.

Festina Lente—New Signals

Man is convinced he has outwitted Nature, but it may be the other way around. Nature, forced to balance the books, inexorably takes revenge and this may be a case in point. The new regime had been especially energetic in its campaign in favor of modernization and against prejudice and superstition. A few Chinese scientists, however, did warn their country against being too uncritical in adopting what was new, but they were regarded almost as enemies of the people. But in 1961 the press and bosses of the party were proclaiming this very doctrine and admitting that they did not yet have complete control of Nature. They were calling new signals according to which *festina lente** became China's main guideline. It was further stressed that the "farming experience of your ancestors" should not be forgotten. This new deal was reflected in the fact that veteran farmers reportedly were being brought in to advise the communes, Mao Tse-tung, and Li Fuen, the latter being the chairman of the state planning commission and secretary of agriculture. They were stumping the countryside and warning against despising the experience

* Latin for "hurry slowly."

of past generations as to choice of crop and strains, seed, methods
of cultivation, and so forth. They also recommended caution in
modernization and more careful planning. They further underlined the need for regional field experiments before new strains,
specialized fertilizers, sprays, and other means of combatting
disease in crops were employed on a major scale.

Large-Scale Catastrophe

The Central Committee of the Chinese Communist Party, in
its declaration of January, 1961, attributed the failure of the
1960 harvest to drought, floods, eleven typhoons, and the ravages
of birds and insects. Even in 1959 it was known that one-third
of the acreage sown had been lost, but the 1960 disaster was still
larger. It was then officially admitted that half the crops had
been lost.

Food rationing was introduced in 1955 but became restrictingly
severe in the period of 1959–62, the rations of rice and grain
products being approximately half of so-called normal values.
Collecting wild plants and roots was carried out on a massive
scale in 1961–62. Rabbits were looked upon as a "gift of the
gods." According to foreign journalists and refugees, during the
winter of 1961 the people of large areas of China had little
besides rice—some fish, and in several cases not even vegetables,
except perhaps cabbage. The meat ration was fixed at four
ounces a month, but there was frequently none to be had. This
led to an intensive campaign for the growing of early vegetables
in order to relieve the worst hunger.

How many people, if any, succumbed to these shortages will
presumably never be known. The improved food distribution of
the country and a more equitable socio-economic availability of
food are likely to have radically reduced the traditional large-
scale dying due to starvation which was so characteristic of the
China of earlier days and through the centuries. Fewer die of

starvation, but the more that survive have less to eat. Partial hunger must have been the lot of millions. Food parcels from abroad, which were almost prohibited in 1958, began pouring in from all over Southeast Asia, though principally from Hong Kong, from which so many were sent that the staff of the post office had to be increased several times over, even to the extent that the purchasing power of Hong Kong was affected. Ironically enough, part of the food in these parcels originally came from China, being delivered under the terms of a signed long-term delivery agreement.

Agricultural production reached its nadir in 1960 but despite persistent annual calamities seems to have made some gains every year since then. Yet China is in a serious predicament as to food. It seems as if the 1964 crop may have been as good as that of 1957, but in the meantime population is about 50 million larger—a whole United Kingdom! Advancing paces lose their lustre when a growing number of mouths forces backward paces, equally many in number or maybe more. Even a flourishing economy has great difficulties keeping up with a net rate in population growth of 2–3 per cent, particularly when every available resource in effect is needed to provide for the hundreds of millions already on the bandwagon and in a vigil of great expectation, eager to enter the land of promises and awaiting the dawn of a Golden Era. The "Great Leap Forward" has a seriously delayed timetable.

Purchases on the World Market

The Chinese agricultural crisis has opened up new channels for the movement of cereals in world food trade. A new pattern is actually emerging, from which certain inferences can be drawn as to the future. Gradually, there will presumably be less exchange of foodstuffs *between* the well-fed countries, while increasing amounts will move to the countries of the needy peoples.

China has made substantial purchases in Australia and Canada since 1959, and signed a long-term contract with the latter in 1961. As to total grain purchases, see Table 14. These large volumes, which strained available transport tonnage to the utmost, represented only a small percentage of the consumption of this

TABLE 14

Grain Purchases of China, 1961–64

(MILLION METRIC TONS)

	1961	1962	1963	1964
Canada	2.1	2.0	1.3	2.1
Australia	2.5	1.6	2.8	1.8
France	0.33	0.56	0.75	0.39
Others	0.57	0.74	0.15	1.1*
Total	5.5	4.9	5.0	5.4

* 0.73 from Argentina and 0.41 from Mexico. Source: *Foreign Agriculture.*

enormous recipient country. A normal grain crop amounts to 180 million metric tons. At the most, this imported grain will therefore have added to the rations in the ports and cities to which they were delivered. In spite of almost herculean efforts to expand the road and railroad networks, lack of transportation facilities limits substantially the quantities which can be distributed, particularly to more distant parts of this large country, approximately the size of the United States, including Alaska.

The New Fish Industry

In order to help feed the millions living inland, fishing is being intensified to operate independently of seasons. Around many of the lakes—some of them big—fishing villages, boat-building yards, meteorological stations, canneries, cold-storage plants, and ring roads are being built. The yields from Koko Nor, the big salt lake on the Nan Shan plateau, have been increased manyfold and this single lake is reportedly supplying roughly as much food fish as the fresh waters of the United States totally yield. The fish are sent to the cafeterias in the cities and commune kitchens in the villages to provide the main basis of the animal protein intake.

Marine fisheries are gradually becoming important. For generations the Chinese have developed their inland fisheries and have almost incorporated all kinds of fresh waters—lakes, ponds, rivers—into a large-scale management program. Furthermore the Chinese pioneered fish-farming, but until quite recently they showed reluctance to embark onto the open sea, confining their marine fishing activities to coastal waters. But now their junks are being fitted with motors for long voyages. They are launching into distant high-sea fishing, and it appears that extensive plans, possibly on a lend-lease basis, were worked out with the U.S.S.R., within the framework of the Pacific Fisheries Commission of the Eastern bloc. The Commission work still is being pursued, but, it appears, with lukewarm Chinese participation. Extensive joint biological surveys, however, have been led by the U.S.S.R. in the East China Sea, Yellow Sea, and South China Sea to the benefit of North Vietnam and North Korea. It has recently been reported that the U.S.S.R. in the spring of 1964 launched a large-scale fishing venture of its own in the East China Sea. The rift put an end to direct cooperative efforts. China is now exploring instead the possibilities of developing ties with Japanese fishing. Special agreements have been signed with this country on a private basis. Whether Japan also is building modern trawlers for the revamped fishing fleet of China is not revealed but seems likely. At any rate, the Chinese fishing fleets are presently venturing farther and farther out. Some time ago (1962) the English press printed an account of the departure from Tientsin of a motorized winter fishing fleet. Following the Soviet lead, floating factories for processing accompanied this fleet. Furthermore, a number of depots have been built along the coast, each with an ice factory and a cannery. These fleets are controlled in almost a military fashion from a number of headquarters with telecommunication along the coast from the South China Sea to Pohai Bay in North Korea. These are in constant wireless contact with the fishing boats and record the presence of the various fish shoals on maps. The largest catches are still made in springtime, when innumerable kinds of fish make their way in shoals to the coastal areas and rivers in order to spawn. Another peak period is in the autumn, when many fish retreat from the north and make for the warmer waters of the south.

Spring fishing used to account for more than half of the annual catch, taken in coastal waters, but now the catch is both larger and less seasonal. Owing to the large-scale deforestation mentioned previously and to the serious lack of a natural vegetation cover, the rivers of China carry away ten times as much mud and silt as the majority of the world's other rivers. This results in a large-scale fertilizing of the sea. One is almost justified in speaking in terms of a beginning sea cultivation. In all probability, China could very well assume the top-ranking position among the world's fishing countries and in this respect outdistance Japan. China, with her more than 700 million dependents, has every need and right to the protein supplies of the seas. In terms of the Pacific basin, her takeout unquestionably exceeds that of Japan.

As was pointed out in chapter 3, the present total world catch of fish would not provide the population of the United States with any more protein than it is already getting from red meat alone. Thus, judged by the scale of China's needs, the resources of the sea seem very modest indeed. If China with its seven times larger population were to be satisfied just to raise its present nutritional level to that of Japan, that limited aim would absorb a catch of fish equal to half the present world total; as things are, they have to be content with the starvation diet to which the Chinese of today have adjusted. In fact, it would call for tremendous increases in the catch of China's fisheries just to supply the needs of the added annual population of 15 to 20 million. As its agriculture would not seem to be capable of supplying the extra quantities of protein that are required to reach a satisfactory minimal subsistence diet of this type, China will be forced to resort to an increasing degree to marine fisheries to find a desperately needed protein supplementation. The fresh-water resources are in effect exploited to the limit. Its present fisheries already contribute an amount of protein that would take more than a quarter of the present tilled acreage of China to produce. To China the vast Pacific Ocean is therefore, in effect, already more a fish pond in dimensions and to their general thinking.

Starving for a Glorious Future

In order to fulfill her program of industrialization, China has adopted the same methods as those that were used by the Balkans and other developing states in the twenties and thirties, paying for coveted machinery and equipment with one of the few means at her disposal, namely, agricultural products—fruits of the soils. Its people have to make great sacrifices to attain a glorious future. They go hungry for this lofty goal. Included in China's statistics on her exports are such items as chilled meat sent to the U.S.S.R., dehydrated and frozen eggs to the United Kingdom and West Germany, frozen fish to Western Europe. In various food markets on earth seedless raisins from sunny Sinkiang, canned pears, dry or evaporated cow's milk from Tibet and Lower Mongolia may be encountered.

Furthermore, foods are delivered to a number of places on the globe for political and ideological reasons. Despite her critical situation, China has either given or sold sugar and rice to Egypt, rice to a number of African states, to Ceylon, and to Cuba. In fact, China's diplomatic and economic offensive against Latin America and Africa seems to have been on a larger scale and more effective than that of the Soviet Union. Peking has received a succession of delegations from these two continents. The misery of its own population does not count, when the looming prize is something as attractive as world leadership.

Will China advance further toward the vast expanses of Siberia? Is this the true reason for strained relations between her and the Soviet bloc? In his memoirs, Reynaud, former prime minister of France, gave an account of a conversation he had with Khrushchev. The latter brought up his favorite subject, the reunification of Germany and asked outright why it was that the West was so keen to have a united Germany. Reynaud replied: "Because within twenty-five years you will have a billion Chinese to deal with." For several minutes Khrushchev was speechless, then he changed the subject. "But I am sure that he understood what I meant," Reynaud adds. In a speech that President Charles de Gaulle made in November, 1959, he said: "The Soviet Union, so endowed with land, mines, factories, and other riches, now stands face to face with the yellow hordes of China, innumerable, impoverished, unswerving, and ambitious. They are casting their eyes upon the open expanses of Siberia, where one day they intend to spread."

References

BARNETT, A. D. *Communist China and Asia*. New York, Harper, 1960, 575 pp.

CHANDRASEKHAR, S. *China's Population*. Hong Kong University Press, 1960, 74 pp.

————. *Red China—An Asian View*. New York, Praeger, 1961, 230 pp.

CHANG-TU, H. *China, Its People, Its Society, Its Culture*. New Haven, Conn., Hraf Press, 1960.

CRESSEY, G. B. *Land of the 600 Million—a Geography of China*. New York, McGraw-Hill, 1956, 588 pp.

ESKELUND, K. *The Red Mandarins—Travels in Red China*. London, A. Redman, 1959, 175 pp. (Translated from Danish original, 1959.)

GILLHAUSEN, R., and HELDT, J. *Unheimliches China*. Hamburg, Nannen, 1959, 191 pp.

GLUCKSTEIN, Y. *Mao's China. Economic & Political Survey*. Boston, Beacon, 1957, 438 pp.

GROSSMANN, B. *Die wirtschaftliche Entwicklung der Volksrepublik China*. Stuttgart, Fischer Verlag, 1960, 413 pp.

Ho, P. T. *Studies on the Population of China, 1368–1953*. Cambridge, Mass., Harvard University Press, 1959, 342 pp.

KINMOND, W. *No Dogs in China*. New York, Nelson, 1957, 212 pp.

LI, C. M. *Economic Development of Communist China*. Berkeley, University of California Press, 1959, 284 pp.

MENDE, T. *China and Her Shadow*. New York, Coward-McCann, 1962, 360 pp. (Translated from original French edition, 1960.)

SCOTT, J. C. *Health and Agriculture in China*. London, Faber, 1952, 280 pp.

SHABAD, T. *China's Changing Map*. New York, Praeger, 1956, 294 pp.

SHEN, T. *Agricultural Resources of China*. Ithaca, Cornell University Press, 1951, 350 pp.

SNOW, E. *The Other Side of the River—Red China Today*. New York, Random House, 1962, 810 pp.

WINFIELD, F. *China: The Land and the People*. New York, Sloane, 1950, 432 pp.

WOLLASTON, N. *China in the Morning*. London, Jonathan Cape, 1960, 208 pp.

WU, Y. L. *An Economic Survey of Communist China*. New York, Bookman Associates, 1956, 566 pp.

CHAPTER 8

The Starvation
Fate of
India

To most Westerners, India is the enchanted country of the fakirs and the maharajas, or the homeland of the cobras and the tigers, a distant land, veiled in mystery. To others, it is the Eldorado of philosophers and founders of new religions. To a small minority, the true situation of India stands out quite clearly. This chapter is about this reality.

India is usually counted in the group of countries which earlier were labeled underdeveloped and nowadays are designated the developing or emerging nations. This terminology takes on an almost tragicomic tinge, in view of the fact that India once created some of the world's top-ranking civilizations. Its city cultures around the Indus reached their summit at a time when most of Europe was still in a savage stage and centuries before America was discovered by Columbus. Many an invention and achievement in the development of technology were first conceived on the Indian subcontinent.

India's real difficulty is its biological overdevelopment, a development which has exceeded all reasonable limits and in which the living creatures in the shape of man and livestock have become overwhelming. No doubt this overexpansion is the clue to the decline of India's civilization. The rising tide of humans and livestock has stifled the creative forces and brought in its wake economic impotence.

On a land area only about half that of continental United States (exclusive of Alaska), more than four hundred million people live today. Half of these are pressed together on the huge plain between the mountain walls of Himalaya and the high plateaus of Deccan. The immense river systems of the Indus, the Brahmaputra, and the Ganges with their tributaries have given rise to some of the world's highest population densities. Within a few square miles in this area as many people exist as on the entire Australian continent, which in turn is larger than continental United States. Early civilizations created in this general area displayed excellent systems of crop rotation in which sowing took place in six or seven stages, as the flood water from the rainy monsoon period withdrew toward the river bed, supplemented from the reservoirs in the mountain ranges of Himalaya. The farms were located on the hillocks which the floods never reached. This well-balanced agricultural pattern was completely torn apart by Western technology and under the pressure of the nutritional needs of an ever-increasing human population. Railways on land bridges were constructed to and from the city of Calcutta. The flood water could no longer move unhindered back to the river bed. In addition, malaria-infested marshlands were created by man. Inundation catastrophies became regular happenings the more people settled along the rivers and moved close to their beds in a desperate effort to grow more rice and to accommodate more people.

Monkeys, Finches and Crows Get the Upper Hand

The East Indians have probably cultivated their soil for more than thirty centuries. But it was not until the past century, and to a significant degree not until in this the twentieth century, that conditions became unbearable. This fact cannot be sufficiently underlined to repudiate glib talk about hunger and history as inseparable companions. It is largely in our own days that the population wave has overpowered India. The forests yielded on a massive scale to the plough in this very century. In most of the inhabited areas they now cover a mere 10 per cent of the total land area or even less. This gives the people little choice in the search for fuel but to resort to cattle manure. Drought and soil erosion have followed in the wake of these ravages. The depredations of the roaming cattle have become intolerable, but this too, largely in the latest century, more specifically as a sequel to the ploughing-up campaigns of the two world wars. The remaining pasture lands, already pitifully small in relation to the needs, were taxed still further by being placed under the plough to produce grain crops for the fighting forces. About one-fifth of the cattle lack domicile and are forced to grab a mouthful here and there, along the roadsides, on fallows, and among the remnants of a bush vegetation.

Even the wildlife has lost its feeding basis in the overpopulated country. A monkey problem has been created. A parrot plague has emerged and become persistent. The nilgai, an antelope, ravages the tilled fields and increases steadily in number. Even the wild hogs are forced to seek their sustenance outside of the wild grassland ranges. The elephant himself cannot find enough feed, and in many regions wild elephants now constitute a permanent threat to the crops. Enormous swarms of locusts several square miles in size invade from the west and from the deserts, and pesticides are continuously spread against them from airplanes. Termites and ants are a constant menace to the tilled land. A couple of billion rats—the estimates differ—compete with man for rice and wheat. Certain regions have been forced to request military support in order to protect their rice paddies against weaver birds, which flock to the newly ploughed lands for feed. A persistent and relentless battle is waged against the crows, which take an annual toll in grain, amounting approximately to one-tenth of the United States annual grain crop—including both wheat and corn as well as other cereals.

But even eradication on a massive scale becomes inefficient when the balance of Nature is upset. The death of ten million monkeys out of a total of fifty million is in effect the only war ever sanctioned by the great Indian leader and pacifist Mahatma Gandhi, but it was of little avail in resolving this national dilemma. Such a bloodbath merely created living space and feed for new monkey millions. No measures are adequate enough when the self-regulating mechanisms of Nature no longer function. When the sanitation and police squads of Nature itself no longer are allowed to operate, the situation easily becomes unwieldy. Tigers, leopards, and other animal predators, which normally would have done their part and at a manageable level, have all been heavily decimated in order to create safe abodes to ever-increasing millions of people.

The Indian farmer leads a very troubled life, and the late-born generations now living on this continent are constantly reminded of the fact that wildlife hits back in many ways when its own existence is threatened by the rising population tide.

Against this general background we Westerners would be well advised to show greater modesty in formulating our programs, in particular as many of our recommendations have proved to be inadequate, unrewarding, or even detrimental.

The miserable condition of the pastures is often commented upon. When the monsoon rains set in after a drought period of eight to nine months, the starved animals after a week or so notice the tender new grass coming up in choice spots, and they are attracted in droves to these green islets. They trample down the delicate plants and lay the foundation for an extremely sparse and patchy vegetation cover, consisting mainly of rather coarse, almost inedible plants, in effect the only plants that manage to survive the impact of these hungry grazing animals.

Malnutrition of Enormous Proportions

Other manifestations of the population pressure are widespread undernourishment and diseases which sap the strength of the millions. Malaria, intestinal worms, tuberculosis, etc., all take a more malignant course when the victim is malnourished, and when food is inadequate the cases increase both in number and intensity. Nearly two-thirds of the Indian women show serious anemia, according to the findings of medical and nutritional experts. And the fact is, more than half the population gets so little protein through their daily food that they cannot even provide the blood with adequate amounts for its maintenance. This is one important cause for the high mortality rate among women at childbirth, which in turn has led to a relative shortage of women compared to men. The deficit is close to twenty million! It has been asserted that shortage of protein increases fertility. The opposite would be more correct. Aside from the biologically absurd idea that one could starve oneself into having more children, it is evident from all studies of undernourishment and malnutrition that protein shortage is a major cause of the frightful losses in human lives. Infant nurseries in India report that more than half of their patients are suffering from malnutrition, primarily protein deficiency. The corresponding figure for tropical Africa is round 12 to 15 per cent.

When England first came to this rich subcontinent, about two hundred years ago, there were about sixty million people living within the area of present-day India. Of these about ten million were on a starvation level. Since then, the population has increased about sevenfold and now the situation is reversed, with the number of adequately fed amounting to approximately ten million. The calorie supply, on the average, is not sufficient for sustaining a normal workday. Physical exhaustion and apathy becomes the rule—the more tragic in a nation which, if properly fed, would sparkle with initiative and creativity, as it has done so often in its early history. The troop contingents that were raised in both world wars and which served in international missions around the world clearly prove that food is the major limiting factor to efficiency. These units, when well fed, have all been fully on a par with those from other countries.

The present agricultural output of India would be adequate for about three hundred million people provided it were geared to satisfy minimum nutritional needs, and the present monotonous diet were acceptable to all. More than one hundred million would then be left without anything at all to eat. It is therefore no wonder that practically the whole nation is undernourished. If the nutritional level were raised to that of the United States— which of course forbids itself—the present agricultural output would fill the needs of only about ninety million people, less than one-fifth of the number now living in this country. These figures illustrate in the best possible way the biological overdevelopment of India.

In addition, India has to carry the burden of its livestock. Once upon a time this constituted a productive and flourishing sector of Indian agriculture. But here, too, biological imbalance prevails. Cattle, buffaloes, goats, and poultry, added together, correspond, with regard to protein consumption, to approximately one and a half billion people. The total living mass within the man-controlled sector of the biosphere consequently exceeds two billion. This ranks India first in the world as to the feeding burden it has to carry, and high when it comes to the biological pressure exerted in relation to the soil resources and their agricultural productivity. In this respect India even supersedes the teeming China.

The Livestock Burden

Lamentations are often heard—and read—over the excessive livestock numbers, pointing to the drain these animals exercise

INDIA - CHINA

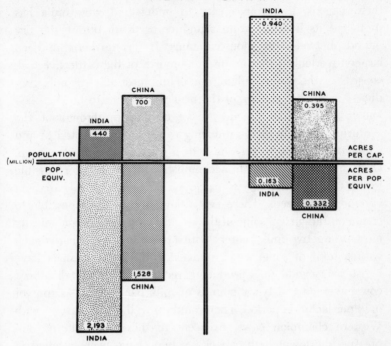

FIG. 26 Comparing agricultural soil resources of China and India in relation to population. Conventionally, China is considered to be in a less favorable position as to tilled land available per inhabitant (see top part of diagram, above horizontal center line). When the feeding burden represented by the living mass of the livestock, in population equivalents, is taken into account their relative status is reversed (see lower section of diagram).

on the feeding capabilities of this country. But it seems to be little known and recognized that this imbalance has become a vexing difficulty only in this very century. The need for grain among the allies, mainly the United Kingdom, during the two world wars largely deprived India of the few pastures which were still left. However, in view of the fact that no less than

70 per cent of all transportation is on the backs of the oxen and their wagons, it becomes easy to understand why India has protected its livestock from slaughter or death during the dry periods between the monsoon rains. It has furthermore been largely overlooked that around one-fourth of the cattle livestock consists of the water buffalo, one of the most efficient milk producers in the hot climate of the tropics. It seems to be even less known that Indian breeders have developed, throughout the centuries, the only meat-producing cattle breed, adapted to and wholly acceptable in regions with a tropical climate—the *zebu*. Only through these Indian accomplishments was it later possible for Brazil to build up its cattle production, chiefly based on various zebu breeds. These zebus have also made it possible to create on Indian soil some of the world's largest and economically most productive milk centers with fifteen to twenty barns each with a total of some 1,000 animals. Professional journals have registered several milk-producing records by such Indian-bred cows, averaging sixty-six pounds of milk per day, or six tons of milk per lactation period. They stand up well in comparison with Western champion cows. Adjacent to these dairy farms, impressive dairies of high capacity volume have been installed in Madras, Bombay, Andraba, and other places. Under the leadership of New Zealand dairy experts, the Indian capital of New Delhi has been provided with an ultra-modern dairy, supplied with United States air-conditioning, Danish ice-cream machinery, Swedish pasteurizers, and Czech control instruments.

Nonetheless, the amazing fact remains that India is carried along, moves ahead, and largely functions thanks to the ball-bearings represented by the backs of these oxen. "Then, in due course, he becomes an ox—the chief pillar of the Indian Empire. And in no merely rhetorical sense, for the stress of agriculture, the more urgent strain of trade, and the movement of a vast and restless people, are on his strong shoulders." These words by Rudyard Kipling's father in his standard work, *Beast and Man in*

India—still a highly readable volume—are quite as valid today as when they were first printed. Gigantic steelworks and cement bastions for irrigation have not changed this basic condition. Both Western and Soviet planners have so far been reluctant or unwilling to recognize this fundamental fact of Indian life. Obvious and even conspicuous facts are all too frequently overlooked. Only efficient aid by massive support in terms of fuel energy could relieve India of the considerable feeding burden represented by their oxen and thereby open up productional resources within the food sector by releasing feed-producing acres now earmarked for this purpose. It is understandable that both the United States and the U.S.S.R. shudder at the mere thought of such a perspective. Even if India would be content with a fraction of the per capita energy consumption of the wasteful Western world, the rate of depletion of the world's fuel resources would mount considerably, not to speak of the disruptions that would take place in the present market pattern. If India were to use oil to the extent that we do in the West, the present oil consumption would expand in volume that would considerably affect our share. Traditional calculations for how long our oil and coal resources may last are almost always based on the false assumption that we—about four hundred million privileged people in Western Europe and North America—are going to continue our energy gamble undisturbed, disposing of the lion's share of the world's takeout.

Are We Serious?

It appears as if we are not too anxious to recognize the real magnitude of the needs of India. We like to blur the picture. The following questions can be posed in all earnestness: Are we really serious in our talk about aid to the developing nations? Do we seriously want to help? What would happen if the bluff were called and India really took all our words at their face value? Our actions so far, even when on a large scale, stand out as Lilliputian achievements. They become enormously dwarfed when placed in the context of the Indian equation. A more realistic approach is urgently needed in the debate of these problems. This seems particularly desirable among the economists, from whom a greater respect for figures could be expected. In economic terms, it is admittedly an impressive feat to clear away, with mammoth bulldozers, a stifling weed, the so-called Kan's grass (closely related to the sugar cane), from no less than fifteen million acres of potential agricultural land. This large acreage was thereby added to the tilled land of India, and this within the lapse of two years. This acreage amounts to a third of the wheatlands of America, or twice the cropland of Michigan. Imagine creating so much land in less than two years! But this acreage does not suffice to produce food in quantities to satisfy adequately the needs of those humans added *each single year* to the population of India, presently from ten to twelve million, according to most recent estimates.

One of the largest plants for manufacturing fertilizers is located at Sindri in India. Its annual production is approximately 350,000 metric tons, but this quantity is hardly enough to give food to more than this annual population increment. In other words, India would need an additional factory of this same impressive capacity every year if it were, through fertilizers, merely to keep pace with the population increase, not to speak of urgently needed improvements. Furthermore, this does not take into account the fact that normally it would require at least three to five years to build such a plant and to get it into final operation. The total consumption of fertilizer in India today is approximately half that of the Netherlands, which has a tilled acreage one hundred sixty times smaller, or only 50 per cent above that of the small island of Taiwan!

We are not going to analyze here what it would mean if India were to copy the West in other respects also. Its commercial navy would surpass those of the United States and Western Europe combined. Its book production would amount to more than 180,000 titles a year. Paper shortage is already a main obstacle in the campaign against illiteracy. It has been rumored that difficulties are encountered even in procuring paper for election ballots. The total circulation of all newspapers is a pitiful three million. English is the mother tongue of about one per cent of the populace. The remaining 99 per cent are split among nearly eight hundred languages and dialects. Among five of the fourteen main tongues the struggle has started for the distinction of becoming the official language of the country. English, which up till now has been the chief cohesive element, is obviously spread very thin.

The Annexation of the Indian Ocean

Within a brief period India has advanced to the sixth place among the world's fishing nations. Its open coastline combined with the productional vagaries of tropical waters, has so far delayed a full development of its ocean fisheries. It is highly praiseworthy that UNESCO has concentrated its oceanographic activities to the Indian Ocean. But the budget for this program was criticized by the experts—and justly so—as grossly inadequate. This is most indicative of our perverted priorities. In chapter 21 of this book, "Food or Moon Rockets," the vast discrepancy is pointed out between the billions allocated to space research and the comparatively insignificant appropriations made to urgent projects in mankind's fight against hunger and disease.

Laudable Norwegian contributions have been made to the development of the Indian fisheries. But the current glib talk about the inexhaustible resources of the sea also takes on a false ring when confronted with the Indian reality. If the total world catch could be used for India alone, it would not provide the inhabitants with more protein than corresponds to one average-sized herring a day. The present Indian catch of 1.5 million metric tons, when converted into such an arbitrary herring unit, yields only one such herring per person a month. If half the need of animal protein were to be satisfied through milk, a ten times larger catch would still be required; that is, an additional world catch amounting to approximately half the present one would be required merely to give India a protein standard equal to the modest level of that of Japan. It is indicative of how conventional thinking still dominates our actions in this respect, that a substantial part of the shrimp catch of India is not used to feed its own hungry, but is frozen by private enterprises for exportation to the United States. As mentioned in the chapter on Asia, shiploads of peanuts as late as in the year 1939 moved in a steady stream of merchant vessels from the undernourished India to the English mother country. This traffic has now been reduced to a trifle, and efforts on a broad front are made to channel the oilseed press cakes into human food also. Dried fish is exported to Ceylon and other countries. More rational thinking about economics as well as nutrition is urgently needed in the future when it comes to world trade, currency policies, and the appraisal of prosperity.

The Overwhelming Demographic Problem

During the first five-year-plan, 1951–1955, the population increase amounted to about five million annually; during the second five-year-plan, 1956–1960, this rose to six and a half million per year. Politicians and economists presently acknowledge that the yearly growth amounts to from eleven to twelve million. This immense sea of human beings will exceed half a billion as early as in 1970. These shocking facts should force everyone to have sobering second thoughts. During the sixties alone, India is adding to its teeming millions a number of people amounting to almost half that of the present-day United States!

Even if India were to limit its immediate goals to keeping up the present miserable nutritional standard, rice and other grain production would have to augment its yields during the sixties at a rate three times greater than during the previous decade when extraordinary measures were taken. Increases have been recorded, but they are far from adequate and were partly due to favorable weather conditions during the end of the fifties.

In accordance with the four-year agreement within the framework of United States Public Law 480, signed in 1959, the United States has provided India with a quantity of wheat corresponding to a total annual United States crop (eighteen million metric tons). In addition, one million metric tons of rice was signed up for delivery. This is an impressive grain delivery—in volume perhaps the largest single one in the entire history of world food trade. Yet, taking into account India's extreme grain diet (high cereal consumption per capita, and further recognizing that this total quantity is to be divided up over a four-year period, this amount does not fill more than 8 per cent of the annual intake of cereal foods in India (inclusive of rice). Besides, the intention was to store buffer quantities at various locations in the country as a kind of reserve to meet acute hunger catastrophes, not to improve the present dietary standards. As pointed out above, India's total grain crop must augment three times as fast as presently, if the country is to keep pace with the population growth. If this cannot be achieved, the country will by 1966 be faced with an importation need seven times as large as the present one. This is much more than United States agriculture would be able to provide if it were to use up all its stored wheat surpluses and still count on a continued excess production for regular trade. Furthermore, India's port facilities and presumably the world's commercial fleets would run into considerable difficulties in coping with such a gigantic regular transport volume of twenty-five to twenty-seven million metric tons of grain annually.

In July, 1961, the world press reported that India had a bumper grain crop of 78.5 million metric tons, far above what its agriculture had ever yielded before. Both rice and wheat reached top figures, 33.7 million tons and 10.5 million tons, respectively. But the plans which had been made by the government authorities and endorsed by the lending World Bank were based upon a still higher total crop of 80.5 million metric tons. Nonetheless, an additional three million metric tons would have to be imported to keep the nutritional standard at its normal level and would certainly not do anything to improve the plight or relieve the scarcity facing millions of undernourished and malnourished people of this subcontinent.

Food Riots in 1964

In the fall of 1964, the situation grew critical due to crop failures. Riots were reported from many parts of the country— not surprising when the overwhelming majority of the population barely subsist or are normally underfed. Urgent countermeasures were taken. Several ships en route to other countries were re-routed to India. United States regular deliveries of wheat (400,000 tons) were increased by another 200,000 tons. Spiralling prices, inadequate transportation and storage facilities, and hoarding accompany this food crisis and show its complex and grave nature.

Basically its nature is simple. Food production has been more or less stagnant in the latest two years while population is growing in excess of 11 million a year. Lofty assurances that India will be able to feed herself by the end of the fourth five-year plan in 1971 sound ominously hollow when confronted with reality. It seems highly unlikely that India in the next decade will perform the miracle of growing faster than any other major agriculture so far in history, namely with 5 per cent per year.

Possible Gains

There is only one sphere in which India could make substantial gains, and paradoxically enough that is not by growing more but by taking better care of what now is being produced. Reliable figures are still lacking on this vital matter. But indirect evidence as well as expert observations support the conclusion that losses of grain and beans very well exceed one-third and frequently attain one-half of the harvested crops. It would seem more beneficial to the future of India to watch this crucial segment of the food front than to support abstract and costly atomic research. It is to the credit of the United States to have initiated the construction of a network of grain silos for storage—as part of the delivery and support program outlined above (p. 133). But far more of this kind is needed. Nothing will be effective in the long run if the rampaging population cannot be brought under control.

Population Control

Nehru was probably the first statesman who had the courage to bring the demographic hypocrisy officially into the open. He asserted in his famous radio talk on these matters in 1953 that India would be a much happier country with half as large a population. He gave unconditional support to family-planning activities and furthermore pinned down the fact that none of the revered religious documents of India contained anything opposed to birth control. Even if the many efforts in this respect are crowned with success—and this is to be earnestly hoped for—the population will still grow on a big scale for quite a number of years. Barring any major catastrophe, India will be faced with the prospect of having a population in excess of eight hundred million before the end of this century. Nearly half of India's present population is below fifteen years of age, which partly explains why the increase will be so large. We express dismay at child marriages and child labor. In view of the above figure these undesirable phenomena are less surprising.

Indian Efforts to Achieve Progress

The scope and fervor of Indian work for progress could be discussed here at great length. A series of modern agricultural colleges and institutes have devoted themselves for decades to purposeful and progressive research in plant and animal breeding as well as to disease control. The sugar industry has 130 modern factories and is the number two industry of the country. Some of the world's best strains of sugar cane were developed under the leadership of the well-known Coimbatore Institute. New strains of rice and wheat have been developed, others are under way. Several hundred insemination centers have been built and new ones are being added with impressive speed. The elephant has been trained for agricultural work and surpasses in several regions the tractor in economic efficiency. Milk production contests were organized for years over the whole country.

City sewage and refuse is returned to the soil through huge irrigation systems after purification and conversion into special humus products. India might even be the world's leading nation in this respect. All major cities and several of the smaller ones have solved these problems and have thus eliminated, or in any case considerably reduced, water pollution. Fish cultivation—an age-old Indian art—is being practised on an increasing number of farms. Several research institutes for salt-water and fresh-water fishery have been organized and carry on first-rate research and development programs.

The Food Research Institute at Mysore has received world-wide recognition for its well-organized research work and magnificent contributions to the fields of nutrition and that of food technology. In both cases the work has been directed to areas of major concern to the Indian population. But as always, the needs are overwhelming, and even the excellency of these scientific endeavors fades away in the twilight of hunger and basic shortages. Tremendous efforts are made to alleviate needs and implement findings but the magnitude of the task is overwhelming.

Industrialization—Fallacy or Remedy?

However, there prevails a deplorably erroneous notion that industrialization as such would increase the food supply. It is often said that India's unemployed number as many as the whole work force in the United States. This refers to the approximately seventy-five million seasonally unemployed in the monsoon-governed agriculture. Large-scale industrialization may seem an appropriate measure, but it does not change the basic condition that the people must have food when they work in the mines, power plants, iron works, or canning factories. Obviously this industrialization increases the productivity of the country and takes care of the human surplus that could not possibly stay on the land and continue dividing it up into smaller and smaller plots. Very little new land can be exploited. Industrialization further improves the individual's purchasing power and thereby increases demand, but this actually means that more food is needed, not less. Food therefore remains the key problem. It is against this background that the recent agreements with the United States about large wheat deliveries have to be viewed.

Industrialization, however, can be seriously questioned as a long-term solution to overpopulation, particularly when the population figures zoom into hundreds of millions. Such numbers become almost unwieldy. The average size of the present Indian farm is slightly above ten acres. Even if industrialization were fully successful and reached the proportions of Western Europe and the United States in terms of reduced rural population, the average size of the farms would still remain very small—thirty acres—hardly profitable in any modern sense. The excessive population growth in the meantime, during which this mass exodus to the factories and cities would take place, will reduce this size figure further.

If fakir tricks are not to become the permanent miserable lot of India, only one road remains for this country to travel, namely the road back to an adjusted biological balance. Even applying all the patented miracle remedies prescribed by the West, there are no record crops and fish harvests big enough when it comes to feeding any number of people in a reasonably satisfactory way. Indian overpopulation is a terrifying reality. India is probably the world's richest country in iron ore resources, maybe also with respect to other valuable metals. But when these assets are confronted with the actual needs of this country, it is obvious that they would be exhausted even before the end of this century if they were to be exploited on a level anywhere near what we in the United States and Europe have come to consider normal.

References

ARAKERI, H. R., CHALAM, G. V., SATYANARAYANA, P., and DONAHUE, R. L. *Soil Management in India.* London, Asia Publishing House, 1958, 584 pp.

BANSIL, P. C. *India's Food Resources and Population.* Bombay, Vora, 1958, 252 pp.

CHANDRASEKHAR, S. *Population and Planned Parenthood in India.* London, Allen & Unwin, 1955, 108 pp.

DATTA, B. *The Economics of Industrialization.* Calcutta, World Press, 1960, 331 pp.

DAVIS, K. *The Population of India and Pakistan.* Princeton, Princeton University Press, 1951, 263 pp.

Food and Population and Development of Food Industries in India. Mysore, Central Food Technological Research Institute, 1952, 357 pp.

GHOSH, K. C. *Economic Resources of India and Pakistan.* Calcutta, V. P. Basn, 1956, 270 pp.

GRIFFITHS, P. J. *Modern India.* New York, Praeger, 1957, 255 pp.

India's Food Crisis & Steps to Meet It. Report by the Agricultural Production Team sponsored by the Ford Foundation (April 1959). Issued by the Government of India, 260 pp.

JACKSON, B. *India and the West.* New York, Norton, 1961, 256 pp.

KIPLING, L. *Beast and Man in India.* London and New York, Macmillan and Co., 1891, 402 pp.

MAYADAS, C. *Between Us and Hunger.* London, Oxford University Press, 1954, 157 pp.

RANDHAWA, M. S. *Agriculture and Animal Husbandry in India.* New Delhi, Indian Council of Agricultural Research, 1958, 364 pp.

RANDHAWA, M. S. and NATH, P. *Farmers of India,* Vol. I. New Delhi, Indian Council of Agricultural Research, 1959, 302 pp.

RANDHAWA, M. S., SIVARAMAN, M. S., NAIDU, I. J., and VAIDYA, S. *Farmers of India,* Vol. II. New Delhi, Indian Council of Agricultural Research, 1961, 428 pp.

RUBEN, W. *Die Ökonomische und Soziale Entwicklung Indiens.* Berlin, Akad.-Verlag, 1959, 208 pp. (Translated from Russian)

SPATE, O. H. K. *India and Pakistan.* London, Methuen, 1954, 827 pp.

THIRUMALAI, S. *Post-War Agricultural Problems and Policies in India.* New York, Institute of Pacific Relations, 1954, 280 pp.

WOYTINSKY, W. S. *India—the Awakening Giant.* New York, Harper, 1957, 201 pp.

CHAPTER 9

Japan—
The Time Bomb

THE Japanese islands have a population half that of the United States living on an area 10 per cent less than that of California. The tilled acreage is little more than fifteen million acres—not even twice that of California and less than a twentieth of the U.S. cropland. In pastures the ratio is still more unfavorable, Japan having hardly any pasture land at all. She simply cannot afford to use more than one million acres this way.

On this limited space Japan must feed around 97 million people, and the number increases at a rate of one million per year.

For a great number of years in its early history Japan succeeded in being self-supporting in food. Rice was supplemented with fish, in which form high quality protein was procured from the sea. Besides, one-tenth of the daily food intake consisted of seaweeds. But the situation gradually became untenable, particularly after the great upsurge in population which started in the latter part of the nineteenth century. The great explosive

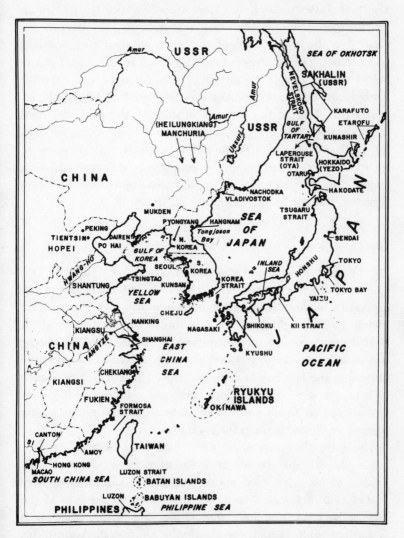

FIG. 27 Map of Japan and adjacent parts of the U.S.S.R. and China. Korea, Taiwan and the northern tip of the Philippines may also be seen.

expansion of the thirties took place and the old colonies (since 1895) of Taiwan and Korea were forcefully pressed into more intense food deliveries; but their resources soon became inadequate for also taking care of the needs of their own teeming populations. The increased food deliveries to the island rulers led to sufferings and malnutrition. In addition, Manchuria with its soybean and forest resources was conquered, and finally Japan started nibbling at the main continent. At the peak she held approximately half the Chinese mainland. These extensive conquests, however, did little to alleviate effectively this pressure for food. Besides, this empire by conquest hastily created was a fragile one. The increases in yield which unquestionably were achieved did not go far enough to fill the gaps.

Japan—a Huge Market Garden

"The Japanese have no agriculture, only horticulture." This statement has been attributed to several United States experts, especially among those returning home when the occupation ended. It sheds light upon the parceling of the rural areas which cannot even afford to relinquish land for roads. Even the raising of rice is by and large pursued almost as a kind of horticulture. However, the fact is generally overlooked that it is only thanks to such an intense cultivation, combined with the ample precipitation, that Japan has been able to attain and retain Asiatic records in yields per acre for several crops.

There are altogether about six million farm units on the four main islands. That is almost twice as many farms as in the United States. The tilled acreage of Japan constitutes a mere 14 per cent of the land area. But more than 60 per cent of the land is so steep and hilly that either it is inaccessible, or it is inconceivable that it ever could be cultivated. Against this background it is almost self-evident why the average farm size is only two and a half acres. More than two-thirds of the farms are even smaller, and two-fifths of the peasants have to be satisfied with less than one acre. On two-fifths of the present tilled land double-cropping is practised, meaning that two or more crops are grown per year.

TABLE 15

Rice Yields (100 kg/hectare) in Selected Countries

Country	1958–59	1959–60	1960–61	1961–62
Australia	66.2	64.7	61.6	66.3
Spain	57.8	57.7	61.7	63.6
Italy	54.8	55.6	48.3	54.6
Egypt	49.6	50.2	50.0	50.5
Morocco	38.3	46.8	43.9	59.1
Japan	46.2	47.5	48.6	47.0
Algeria	38.8	42.6	44.2	45.2
United States	35.5	37.9	38.4	38.2
Uruguay	27.7	36.8	34.5	34.5
Argentina	31.2	33.9	32.4	34.4
Taiwan	30.3	29.7	31.0	32.1
China	26.9	26.9	27.0	—
Indonesia	17.1	17.4	18.0	18.4
Brazil	15.3	16.2	17.0	17.5
Burma	16.5	17.0	16.2	16.8
Pakistan	13.2	14.8	16.0	16.6
India	14.0	14.1	15.3	15.1
Thailand	13.8	13.3	13.7	13.9

More than half (54 per cent) of the tilled land (8.0 million acres of the total of 15 million acres) is used for rice, this being the chief crop. The yield per acre is about three-fourths (74 per cent) higher than that of the Chinese and approximately three times higher than in India and 2.5 times that of Indonesia. This feat is explained chiefly by the degree of intensity of Japanese "agriculture," chiefly in the use of fertilizers. Partly as a consequence of the land reform and postwar efforts to produce a maximum of food, Japan belongs to one of the very few countries which has increased the absolute number of farmers (up to 1957). Only then did urbanization, industrialization and mechanization start affecting the agricultural labor force, but with detrimental effects on production, particularly in coastal fisheries. Okinawans are now brought in to fill the gaps!

For decades the growing of rice has been stimulated in various ways by substantial subsidies but also by means of nationwide contests. Although rice basically is a tropical plant, the Japanese have managed the almost impossible by successfully transforming rice into a temperate crop. Rice fields are found as far north as on the northernmost tip of Hokkaido, the main island of the northern part of the country. Although this is the latitude of Milan, Italy, the winter climate is far more rigorous and more like that of Michigan, both located on the same latitude. So is Nova Scotia, but it is cooled by the Labrador Current, while Hokkaido has the benefit of the warming Japan Current (Kuroshio), although in this region it is battling the cold Kuril Current (Oyashio).

The yields per acre have been pushed upward incessantly, chiefly by extending the degree of double-cropping. The sad lack of any comprehensive understanding of the Japanese scene is reflected in recent reports (circular article from the Information Service of the United Nations—*New York Times*, July 25, 1961, p. 33, 40) of how Japan now is threatened by rice surpluses in the immediate future. A unilateral emphasis on producing rice no doubt may lead very easily to surpluses (although minor), but this would do little toward solving Japan's immense and chronic total food deficit, relieved only by a constant ferrying of food and feed to these islands, chiefly from North America and Australia. More food is imported today than the country's own agricultural lands yield. There is no single postwar year in which Japan has not been forced to import rice and in many cases in quite substantial quantities.

Japanese agriculture is in the top rank in the world as to yields per acre. Several leading United States experts have also pointed out on several occasions that during the occupation they discovered that we Westerners have a great deal to learn from Japanese cultivating skills, and precious little to teach them. On the contrary, our advice and recommendations often turned out to be of dubious value when judged by their consequences. This applies particularly to the efforts of gaining new agricultural land by pulling down forests.

Japan is best characterized as the country of the sweet potato and the radish. The latter is by far the dominating vegetable crop—70 per cent of the horticultural crop acreage. The sweet potato has for generations been the most important adjunct to their rice-dominated diet. It is called the Chinese potato by the Japanese, as that country is credited with having passed this crop on to Japan via Korea and Okinawa. About one-tenth of the tilled land is devoted to sweet potato. It has always saved the country from overt hunger in years when the autumn typhoons devastated the rice fields. Our common potato is called by the Japanese the Dutch (not the Irish) potato, but is mostly grown in the northern islands and in small quantities—one-third of the U.S. crop and a fortieth of that of Europe. In contrast, Japan leads the world in sweet potato production.

Breaking of New Land and the Land Reform

Even the hard-working and skillful Japanese farmer finds it difficult to till the many mountainous regions and to make the soil there yield more than possibly a meager sustenance for himself and his family. After the end of World War II, almost a quarter of a million farmers were put to work in colonizing such lands on the northern island—Hokkaido, roughly the size of Maine, the only new land that Japan still had to offer. About one-third of these "colonizers" have so far been forced to give this up—it was simply not feasible to eke out an existence. The remainder feed themselves, but make small contributions to the food stores of Japan.

The vagaries of Hokkaido are clearly documented by the total destruction of its crops twice within the latest decade—namely 1956 and 1964. There is good reason why only 5 per cent of Japan's population lives in what most Japanese call their "Siberia." Despite generous inducements the government has not overcome the reluctance of the farmers to move here.

The land reform, which the United States occupation pushed through, was a gigantic operation. It affected one-third of the total population, two-thirds of the rural dwellers, and one-third of the tilled land. It brought about a social upheaval when hundreds of thousands of earlier tenants and share-croppers became landowners. Evidently, though, it could achieve nothing toward augmenting the size of the farms. On the contrary, it contributed to a further reduction in size as so many more people were provided with land. There was hardly any new land available to include in this great reapportionment.

Desperate efforts to cut down forests in order to clear land for cultivation soon backfired. This method has been tried previously in Japanese history, always with the same detrimental effect: flood damages and dangerous losses of soil through water erosion. In this respect the limit for land clearance is presumably reached. The present forest coverage is needed in order to maintain the overall water balance of the country. Furthermore, the forests are to a great extent located in regions which are topographically less accessible and therefore also of limited value as a forest resource.

Since 1920 the cultivated acreage of Japan has not expanded significantly, in spite of the unquestionable breaking of new land which has taken place. Industries, cities, roads, and other consequences of the industrial drive have gobbled up almost as much land as this new cultivation has added.

Rain from the South and the North

The Japanese islands are located between a northern and southern latitude corresponding to that of Milan, Italy, and Cairo, Egypt, respectively, but the climate is much more severe than in the Mediterranean regions. The four main islands of this insular empire are placed as a kind of shield beside the Asiatic land giant, straight across the dominating direction of the monsoon winds. The summer brings rain from the Pacific and the winter brings snow from Siberia. Japan is therefore richly blessed with rain, sometimes in excess. Typhoons and floods are quite regular phenomena, taking a substantial toll of the growing crops almost every year. The rivers swell and put the fields under water.

Cold air currents from the Sea of Okhotsk bring cold and fog into the north. As a consequence, Japan normally does not suffer from water shortage. Water is therefore no limiting factor to Japanese crops as it is in so many other agricultural regions of the world. The Japanese have had to resort to other means than irrigation to push their high yields per acre further upwards.

Soil Fertilizers

In the cut openings of the forest, the so-called "genya," the grass grew. However, one could not afford to leave this grass there nor allow the cattle to use it for grazing. A laborious collection was organized from no less than 1.25 million acres of such genya. The clippings from them are carried down to adjacent rice fields to be used, after composting, as green manure on the paddies.

Per acre, Japan uses four times more commercial fertilizers than the Western European average. This is the key to their high soil productivity. But it makes agriculture dependent upon industry, constantly hampered in a country like Japan, which lacks almost *all* essential raw materials, including those required for a fertilizer production. All potash and phosphate have to be shipped in from distant places: Morocco, Egypt, the United States, and New Zealand. On top of the huge food importation comes this massive and costly influx of bulky raw materials, moving into the fertilizer industry.

Japan is second to no country in the West when it comes to the use of agricultural spray compounds. This heavy use of chemicals in agriculture obviously reduces correspondingly the quantities of chemicals available for export, for construction work, and for consumer goods. Some of Asia's largest nitrogen and mineral factories have been built in Japan since the war. Their production is almost wholly reserved for agricultural purposes. It is estimated that about 60 per cent of Japan's gigantic chemical industry is already earmarked for the food sector and thus in effect is mobilized to protect this vital battlefront of their daily existence.

Carp Cultivation and Drainage

The Japanese are said to have learned from the Chinese the cultivation of carp. This activity was once the pride of the nation but has now dropped to less than one-third of the total production of prewar years, in spite of energetic efforts to preserve and enlarge this kind of protein production. The intensification of agriculture has in this respect an unexpected long-distance effect. The widespread use of pesticides has led to toxic reactions in lakes and rivers. The raising of fish was immediately affected.

The tremendous pressure to create more land had in addition the peculiar consequence that lakes and other waters were drained. Thirty such drainage projects are reportedly in progress or have recently been terminated. Together, these undertakings are estimated to contribute a little less than 30,000 acres. In addition to this figure is one major project which is under way and approaches its termination. This will be further discussed below. In latter years, the Japanese have been following in the footsteps of the Dutch in trying to recover land from the sea. Since the war, fifty or so such operations, large and small, have been completed or are in progress. Together, however, they will not yield more than 47,000 acres of tilled land, an area which cannot provide rice even for one single year's increment of the population, much less satisfy the total food requirements of this addition to the mouths to be fed. Supplemented with soybeans from other acreages, the rice crop from this new acreage might possibly take care of the needs of 100,000 people, or about one-ninth of the annual net growth of the population!

Hachirogata

In 1957 the drainage of Hachirogata was completed, once the second largest lake of Japan and situated in the northern part of Honshu, the main island. This operation started forty years ago. Forty thousand acres of land were gained, and a highly diminished lake of 22,000 acres is all that remains. Fifty miles of canals were built. Two gigantic pumps, each with a capacity of five hundred gallons, are operating continuously. And the net result of all this is 50,000 metric tons of rice a year, about enough to cover the needs of almost half a million people! Popular articles reported the exorbitant happiness of the many farmers in this region who each received a few additional square feet. The gain is not likely to be significant in such an overcrowded country.

One might ask if it would not be more profitable to keep these lakes and use them as fish ponds. There is no doubt that this would be vastly preferable, and from a nutritive point of view more resourceful. But when the problems of overpopulation must be met, desperation dictates the measures, not economy or rational thinking. Long ago Japan was forced to make a choice between calories and protein. Bulk "filling" of stomachs got the priority in agriculture and became almost exclusively the provider of calories, and the task of satisfying the need for proteins, vitamins, or minerals became a subordinate or secondary concern. The vital task of providing essential protein was to a major degree transferred to the fisheries. This had a certain logic for an insular nation like Japan, surrounded as it is on all sides by abundant fishing waters in the oceans, particularly in the waters facing the Asiatic mainland. But this is not necessarily good economy, particularly since the fish resources of the coastal regions no longer suffice and it has become necessary to make lengthy fishing trips thousands of miles away—even to distant other ocean basins—in order to haul this essential protein to home-land shores.

Rice, the Staple Food

It is indicative that the gains from all these drainage operations and other undertakings to open up new land are largely earmarked for rice cultivation. The production of rice has become the chief goal of Japanese agriculture. Everything else is of secondary importance. It is therefore highly justified to appraise every food measure in terms of rice, but the findings need to be balanced by a clear understanding of the indisputable fact that man cannot subsist on rice alone. Besides the Hachirogata project, which furnishes rice for half a million people (half of *one year's* population increment) an additional 120,000 acres would be required to provide the additional protein needed to satisfy the minimal nutritional needs of this number of people despite the high yields per acre.

From the vantage point of the United States, the Japanese dietary level is frugal (see Fig. 28). Fish, which accounts for no less than 67 per cent of the animal protein is nonetheless consumed per capita in a quantity which is only four times that of the United States. The amount of protein we Americans get daily

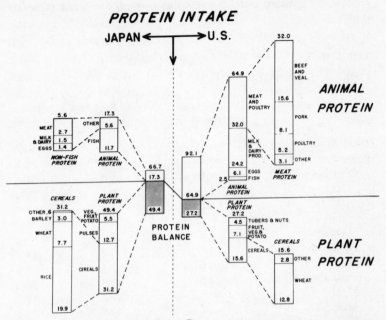

FIG. 28 Comparison of daily diet of the United States and Japan as reflected in protein intake. Note the over-all higher protein consumption by United States citizens. Animal proteins take the lead in the United States, plant proteins in Japan. Aquatic foods dominate the animal protein consumption of Japan, rice and soybeans that of plant proteins.

in milk and dairy products is in Japan extended over sixteen days, and what we get per day in meat, over ten days. Three-fourths of their total protein intake comes from plant sources, led by rice and with soybeans as second (see Table 16). The United States figure for plant protein is one-third of the total protein intake for the United States but in absolute terms it is about half that of Japan. In other words, we as individuals get 50 per cent more total proteins and eleven times more animal protein from terrestrial sources; with fish 3.7 times more animal protein. Still more drastic examples can be extracted from the table.

TABLE 16

Daily Protein Diet Per Capita

	United States (grams)	United Kingdom (grams)	Japan (grams)
Total Protein	92.1	85.1	66.7
Plant Protein	27.2	36.1	49.4
Cereals	15.6	25.2	31.2
Rice	0.5	0.2	19.9
Wheat	12.8	23.7	7.7
Barley	0.1	0.6	3.0
Others	2.2	0.7	0.6
Pulses and Nuts	4.6	3.4	12.7*
Others	4.6	7.5	5.5
Animal Protein	64.9	49.0	17.3
Meat	26.8	20.1	2.7
Milk	24.2	19.2	1.5
Eggs and Poultry	12.3	5.2	1.4
Fish	2.5	4.4	11.7

* Soybeans 8.4.
Source: FAO Food Supply Data—1960–61

Meat and Milk Luxury Items

The news media of the West have repeatedly carried articles on the profound transformation of the Japanese diet. The Japanese are learning to eat bread instead of rice; the meat and dairy production of Japan is rapidly mounting—these are two of the most common statements. But the picture has mostly been one-sided. In spite of indisputable increases, meat and milk make only minor contributions to the national household (see Table 16 above). A more widespread consumption of these animal foods would have catastrophic consequences for the overall feeding of the nation. Tens of millions would have to go without food altogether if such a major shift really took place. Japan manages to feed itself only by taking from the soil horticultural produce and calorie-supplying foods, chiefly rice.

The switch to wheat is based entirely on importation, and is thus a dubious economic basis for any permanent change in the dietary habits (see below, Table 17). Besides, the average per capita consumption of rice has risen in recent years, reflecting a minor improvement in the purchasing power of the millions. They are now in a position to satisfy their needs with slightly more filling servings of this cherished food, which retains its position as a backbone of the daily diet of the Japanese. Fat is desperately short in the Japanese diet and would need at least a fivefold increase to reach recommended minimum requirement standards.

TABLE 17

Production, Imports, and Consumption of Wheat In Japan

	Production Million Megatons	Imports Million Megatons	Per Capita* Consumption (Grams) per Day
1952	1.5	1.6	68.2
1953	1.4	1.9	67.4
1954	1.5	2.1	72.8
1955	1.5	2.2	68.7
1956	1.4	2.2	65.4
1957	1.3	2.4	68.0
1958	1.3	2.3	67.9
1959	1.4	2.8	70.4
1960	1.5	2.7	70.6
1961	1.8	2.7	70.7

* Part of available wheat used as feed and for chemical production, some is lost in storage.

Animal protein is hauled largely from the sea. Even with the intense cultivation methods used by Japanese agriculture an additional tilled acreage approximately one and a half times that of the present cultivated land would be required, if, for example, milk should be substituted for fish (see Fig. 29, p. 159).

Emigration

The truth is that nearly thirty million people are depending upon importation of food and feed from abroad. Another forty-five million can be said to survive thanks to the oceans. To an industrial giant like Japan, it would perhaps be feasible to continue to buy this amount of agricultural products, but what makes the country a time-delayed bomb is the annual increase of almost one million people. If these additional multitudes each year were to be removed from the islands, an emigration would have to be staged almost one and a half times as large as the average emigration to North America early in this century. At its peak this human influx to the United States reached 560,000 people in one single year. These are, however, purely theoretical speculations. Everyone knows that there is no country on this earth which today could swallow such numbers—around 2,300 people daily—to say nothing of the insurmountable transportation and resettlement problem involving huge capital expenditures (minimum $5,000 per person).

Japan has further been receiving a growing number of nationals that have returned from the earlier colonial regions of Taiwan, Korea, and the now United States-occupied Ryukyu Islands (Okinawa)—see Table 18, p. 155. The emigration has been only slightly in excess of this influx—on the average 26,967 per year in the six-year period 1956–1961: total emigration 779,200 as against an influx of 635,400.

Yet, emigration agreements have been made with various countries. Brazil promised in 1959 to receive 100,000 Japanese prior to 1962. This treaty was renewed in 1963, but no details have been publicized so far. But this constitutes merely a fraction of the numbers added to the Japanese population in that very same period (4.5 million). Furthermore, the emigration to Brazil has, in reality, only amounted to a couple of thousand per year in spite of all special measures, such as emigration loans, and free overseas transportation. Since the Japanese law concerning "mass" emigration went into effect in 1952, a total of 21,914 were registered as having left Japan up to the year 1960. Yet, the Japanese beachhead in Brazil is larger than in any other country and amounts today to almost half a million people. I had the opportunity of visiting some of the Japanese-speaking cities in inland Brazil. It is almost depressing to realize that a whole century of Japanese colonization amounts, in terms of received emigrants, to little more than half of one year's population growth of present-day Japan. The truth is, of course, that basically there are no longer any havens of refuge left on this earth that are large enough to accommodate the hundreds of millions of excess people added to the world population every decade—reaching in Japan about twelve million per decade and presumably still more in the immediate future.

TABLE 18

Migrations in and out of Japan—1956–1961

	1956	1957	1958	1959	1960	1961
Emigrants	82,311	104,252	102,048	114,868	187,770	186,897
Immigrants	74,411	91,717	92,208	98,815	126,496	154,892
Net emigration	7,900	12,535	9,840	16,053	61,274	32,005

Source: U.N. Demographic Yearbook

The Crowdedness

In all spheres of life, Japan is reminded forcefully of the complications created by the overcrowdedness. The trains are filled above capacity; there is not room enough for automobiles in the cities. Public transportation carries twice or three times more people than current stipulations regarding maximum load permit. Traffic congestions causing delays of several hours are the rule in a great many cities. Commuting between home and work and between work sites may take four to six hours daily. The high degree of moonlighting involves additional commuting between working places.

In the general area stretching from Tokyo in the northeast to Osaka in the southwest of the main island of Honshu live more than fifty million people. Space is becoming seriously short. On the narrow coastal shelves and valleys where agriculture and people are in direct competition for land, space is hardly any longer to be found. The Japanese press (May, 1964) reported that in the city of Kobe the decision has been made to grind down parts of the surrounding adjacent mountains in order to create filling material for new development areas to be created along the coastline—a kind of man-made extension of the coastal shelf.

This population wave is indeed ominous, the more so since Japan has based its economy on the practice of the doctrine: "Export or perish." England already experienced the untenability of this method in a world where available food surpluses are shrinking. With a worldwide industrialization, fewer and fewer nations will submit to starving themselves in order to be able to buy industrial goods. Basically, however, the British Isles are in a far more favorable position than Japan. It is still possible for them to adjust their diet to a heavier reliance on plant products, under the assumption that their soil can take the strain which increased production of vegetables would require—among other things, more open, exposed soils, less pastures.

India now manufactures the cotton fabrics it earlier bought from Japan and has less food to spare than Japan, but presumably India could deliver some industrial articles and raw materials. China, the heir to Manchuria, can supply Japan with lumber, coal, and iron ore but no food, with the possible exception of minor quantities of soybeans if they are able to limit their own bulging population through strict birth control. The situation in Japan is aggravated further by its lack of almost all essential raw materials, as mentioned earlier.

The critical shortage of energy constitutes the bottleneck of the industrialization process. Available water power is almost completely harnessed. The coal resources are approaching depletion. All liquid fuel has to be brought in.

From an economic viewpoint, "the Japanese miracle" is to some extent like the West German one—subject to long-distance control. According to latest reports, the United States loans to Japan exceed three billion dollars. Much European capital has also poured into Japan. Since the war, United States foreign aid has in addition funneled more than two billion dollars into Japan. The winning of wars is expensive! Somebody has said that Japan walks on stilts, but in order to be able to walk steadily, she must come down on her feet. This is presumably behind the Japanese declarations of 1961 that they would like to improve relations with the Communist bloc. A permanent Japanese trade delegation is frequently wined and dined in Peking by the energetic prime minister of China, Chou En-Lai. Japanese industry delegations make frequent visits to China. Major industrial exhibitions have been held by the Japanese in China and vice versa. Mutual trade is expanding as a result and is presumably paving the way for a more long-range cooperation in the economic field. After all, it is in Asia where Japan has a real chance of broadening its *Lebensraum*.

It is a sage guess the Tokyo visit by the then Soviet trade minister Anastas Mikoyan in August 1961 signaled that the Russian archenemy was wooing the industrial potential of Japan, primarily to accelerate the development of the Siberian resources. This was confirmed as the basis for the present (1964) trade negotiations between the U.S.S.R. and Japan, at renewed visits by Mikoyan to Tokyo in the spring of 1964. This alternative constitutes an enticing perspective for a Japan hungry for raw materials and looking for markets for their export articles. But it will, in the long run, not provide food for the excess millions of Japan. Full employment is a great economic asset but only if hunger can be kept in abeyance.

The Food Import—a Veritable Ferrying Operation

Several Japanese scientists have on various occasions assured me that it is only a question of time when Japan will reach self-sufficiency in food. All kinds of abstract reasonings are brought forth in support of these statements. To anyone oriented about demographic facts, such speculations seem rather unrealistic.

In an almost uninterrupted stream, vessels loaded with food leave the ports of North America (United States and Canada) to keep the Japanese nation alive. Two food-laden 5,000-ton ships anchor in Japanese ports every day all year round. Wheat, soybeans, and corn are the dominant import items. For all practical purposes this amounts to nothing less than a regular ferry operation. Also, Australia makes significant contributions in the form of meat, cheese, rice, and other grains and is now seriously making an effort to create new permanent markets for its agricultural products (see chapter 10, p. 198). Burma, Taiwan, and Thailand supply rice and corn.

A considerable part of the Japanese national income is set aside for the purchase of food. The large soybean importation constitutes an indispensable protein supplementation. Large acreages—enormous in relation to Japan's total tilled land—would be required if this protein were produced within the country itself, in spite of the extremely efficient and intensive farming. The total net importation of food and feed at the end of the fifties would require, even under the high producing conditions of Japanese agriculture, a tilled acreage almost as large as that which this island is now cultivating. Since that time the importation has been growing at an alarming rate. As in Italy, this method of eating up the cash gains earned through hard work is keeping the country in the red.

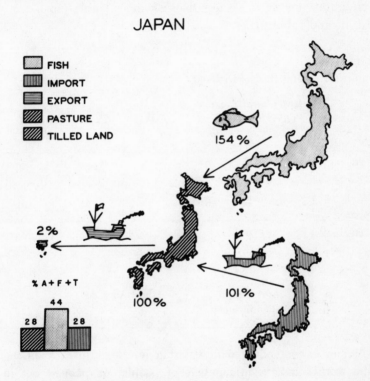

FIG. 29 The feeding basis of Japan (1958–59). Fisheries provide an amount of animal protein that would take Japanese agriculture 154 per cent of its tilled land (F) to produce. Correspondingly, the imported agricultural products (T) would require 101 per cent. In terms of acreage (lower left corner) agriculture (A) constitutes 28 per cent of the feeding basis, fisheries (F) 44 per cent, and net importation (T) 28 per cent.

Ghost Acreage and Population Equivalents

The annual net importation of food and feed (average 1958–60) represents a tilled acreage corresponding to a whole arable Japan. If we add to this the fish acreage of 154 per cent which the fish consumption equates (see pp. 82–83), the result is a ghost acreage amounting to no less than 2.5 times arable Japan (see Fig. 30 and Table 19).

TABLE 19
Japan's Feeding Basis (1958–59)

| | Agricultural Acreage | | Fish Acreage | Trade Acreage | Total Acreage |
	Tilled Land	Pastures			
Hectare (1000)	5,048	1,356	9,366	6,093	21,863
%	23	6	43	28	100
Hectare (1000)	6,404		15,459		21,863
%	29		71		100
	Agricultural Self-sufficiency		Ghost Acreage		

Japan is contending with Pakistan for the fifth rank among the world's nations in numbers of people. As pointed out in chapter 3, the animal production is so insignificant that when it is expressed in population equivalents, with the livestock inclusive of poultry evaluated as consumers, Japan plunges down to the twenty-third place in biological terms. The pressure exerted by the biomass (man and livestock) on the soil resources is thus not nearly so ominous as the simple population figures would

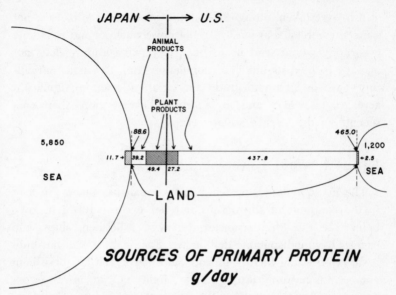

SOURCES OF PRIMARY PROTEIN
g/day

FIG. 30 The feeding basis of Japan as compared to that of the United States, in terms of the protein involved in the primary production on land and in the sea to feed an average Japanese and American respectively. Two surprising features are the "narrow" dependence on land in Japan and the considerable reliance on the seas in the United States. All figures are calculated on the food intake reported for each country (1961). The animal products have been converted into the primary plant protein required for their making, using an average conversion factor of 7. The primary protein in the sea accounts not only for the consumption of aquatic products but also for the quantities fed as fish meal to livestock. This explains why the final ratio between Japan (5,850) and the United States (1,200) is 4.6. These calculations are based on the assumption that the main utilization level from which seafood is extracted is that of secondary carnivores with a total conversion factor of 500 (5 in the first step and 10 in the two consecutive steps).

indicate. Even Denmark surpasses Japan when population pressure is measured in these terms. If the ghost acreage represented by imported agricultural products and including the consumption of fish were taken into consideration, the sustenance basis is not quite as impressive as most textbooks of economics and economic geography would lead us to believe. Japan certainly does not manage to feed its immense population from its small "agricultural gardens." Through trade, the Japanese resort to significant acreages elsewhere and, in addition, harvest more than one-seventh of the world's aquatic crops.

Japan, a World Power of the Oceans

The overpopulated, protein-hungry Japan has taken the lead in the conquest of the oceans but not exclusively on its own behalf. In the Mediterranean, Japanese fishermen, ships, and experts have indisputable dominance. For Egypt, Japan has built a shrimp-freezing factory in Port Said. An Israeli-Japanese joint company is not only fishing in the Mediterranean but also goes on extended catching expeditions to both the Indian Ocean and the Atlantic—with Japanese-built ships.

Yugoslavia has ordered six to ten tuna-fishing boats from Japan, fully equipped. The U.S.S.R. has on order a number of big floating factories, large trawlers, and tuna vessels in Japanese shipyards—tuna-fishing boats with freezing installations as well as floating factories for the canning of herring. Similar orders, and others for freezing trawlers, have been placed in Japan by Greece and Rumania. Japan also delivers complete canning factories to be mounted on land. Along the Tripolis coast Japan seems to catch on its own behalf. Italian as well as Moroccan fishermen are being trained in tuna fisheries by the Japanese. On top of this, there are Italian-Japanese enterprises which are fishing commercially, extending their operations to the Middle and South Atlantic.

Primarily, however, Japan provides technical assistance to fisheries within the Asiatic sphere: to Ceylon, Thailand, Indonesia, Hong Kong, Macao, Malaya, and Singapore, as well as to

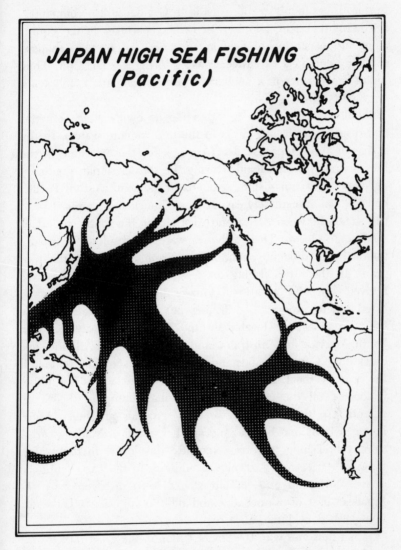

FIG. 31 Japanese fishing activities in the Pacific—dark areas.

Burma. Investments are also made in Ceylonese fish companies. Furthermore Japan, jointly with Poland, partakes in the equipment and expansion of Ceylon's fisheries. An Iranian-Japanese company conducts extensive fisheries in the Persian Gulf. Thus Japan is a partner in a network of fishing companies embracing large parts of the globe.

Simultaneously, Japan is expanding its own fishing activities and dispatching fishing fleets to the most remote waters. In the spring of 1961, Japanese fleets partook for the first time in the fisheries off Newfoundland. During the thirties, Japan gradually developed five tuna-fishing grounds in the southwestern Pacific, one of them immediately east of New Guinea and another two in the waters between Africa and Australia in the southern part of the Indian Ocean. These fisheries were the result of a broadly planned and diligently conducted oceanographic research program. In the fifties fishing on these earlier tuna grounds was revived, but nine additional tuna-fishing grounds can now be listed where programmed fishing has started. Three of these fishing regions are located in the Pacific, half-way between South America and Australia, and two in the mid-Atlantic—one outside the Canary Islands and one in a corresponding region off the coast of the Lesser Antilles on the Caribbean side. Another is located off the coast of the Brazilian hump in the South Atlantic. In the Indian Ocean new grounds are being fished between India and Burma, and another, north of Madagascar. A third tuna-fishing area was recently developed in the waters between Africa and Australia in addition to the two mentioned above. New cod and halibut stocks were discovered by the Japanese east of Kamchatka and off the Aleutians. These are being fished by Japan on a regular basis.

Japan thus vies with the Soviet Union in the great race for the world's oceans and their remaining fish resources. Since the 1930's Japan has further been contending with Norway for the world leadership in whaling. But in spite of its dominant posi-

JAPAN HIGH SEA FISHING
(Atlantic & Indo Pacific)

FIG. 32 Japanese fishing activities in the Atlantic and Indo-Pacific—dark areas.

tion, Japan now seems to accede to Soviet expansion in this very same sphere—in contrast to the thirties when Japanese whaling operations were undertaken under the cover and protection of their naval forces, at that time wielding undisputed supremacy in the Pacific. Now all this has changed, particularly in the North Pacific where the U.S.S.R. now has the lead. The Japanese have been almost entirely forced out of the Sea of Okhotsk. They have also been compelled to limit considerably their fishing operations in the Bering Sea and generally in all areas where the Soviets operate on a major scale. In recompense, Japan has come back with renewed force in other parts of the Bering Sea. To sum up: the situation in the North Pacific is that Japanese fishing fleets can now be seen in large numbers all over the Pacific, not the least in the waters north of New Zealand and in a circular belt around Australia.

Japan has also taken the lead in the developments of the Argentinian and Brazilian fisheries. Special joint companies have been created for the exploitation of the fish resources of these nations. Part of their catch is brought back to Japan. But Japanese fishermen are almost permanently stationed in both these countries. This is true also in Venezuela. Joint Japanese companies have installed a series of modern fish markets in major Brazilian cities. A Japanese tuna cannery has started in São Paulo. In the same pattern, the Indian Ocean is now being exploited in close cooperation with joint companies of India, Pakistan, Iran, Egypt, Kenya, Tanganyika, Madagascar, and Mozambique.

Since 1961 Japanese fleets have also emerged in the North Atlantic and have been seen in the fishing waters of Iceland and Greenland. A joint company is creating a base with processing facilities on Nova Scotia. Japanese fishermen bring in catches to the French islands of St. Pierre and Miquelon, off Newfoundland, from where fish is marketed in the United States on a growing scale.

Japan, which for two or three decades was the world's number-one fishing nation, has regained this position. There is still some doubt as to the real catches of China. She started to move onto the high seas in 1959, sending big fleets northward from Tientsin. The rift with the U.S.S.R. seems to have halted further growth, which was based on Soviet lend-lease arrangements and ship deliveries, which appear not to have materialized. These strivings on the part of China are not so astonishing when we recognize the fact that in absolute numbers the population grows from fifteen to twenty times more per year than that of Japan. China in one way can therefore be said to have both a stronger motivation and greater justification in resorting to the seas for support.

Demographic Magic

Many theorists count upon a further decline in the birth rate of Japan as a way out of the present dilemma. History hardly knows any more drastic instance than the spectacular postwar drop in Japanese birthrates as it fell from 34.3 per thousand (1947) to 18.0 per thousand (1958). But the net growth still remains at a rather unchanged level of around one million annually. Referring to Figure 33, one can see the danger of drawing too sweeping conclusions or making less justified generalizations on the basis of such recent figures. Discounting the disruptions of the war years, Japan has returned to almost the same general level of growth it maintained for almost one century. Consequently, there is actually no effective halt in the rate of population growth. The decline in the curve for the net growth has tapered off after the baby boom and peak of the immediate postwar period. This drop is unquestionably due to a decline in the birth rates. The level of stabilization and stagnation is almost identical to the one prevailing in prewar years and as far back as 1875. At best, one can say that so far Japan has managed to

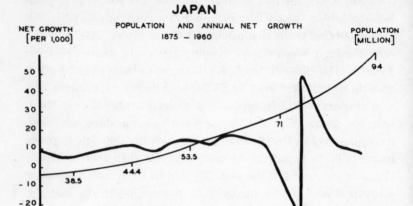

FIG. 33 Net growth of Japan's population, stabilized at long-time level of one per cent. The abnormally high postwar peak is no good reference point in judging Japanese in population growth. This postwar baby boom has resulted in close to half of the population being below twenty years of age, inevitably pushing net growth figures upward unless still more drastic reductions occur in birth rates.

steer clear of the population explosions that are hampering India, China, and several other parts of Asia. But there is, nevertheless, reason to be concerned about the future, as 40 per cent of the population now is below the age of fifteen—owing to this war-baby boom of 1945–47. These individuals will in the years immediately ahead reach procreative ages and form families. Furthermore, a very somber sidelight is thrown upon these figures when one takes into account the abortions. Unofficially, their number is estimated at two to three million a year (more than one million are statistically registered each year). Consequently, the basic fertility is in reality much higher than the birth figures indicate. A comforting aspect, however, is that the government—like Nehru earlier and the leaders of Ceylon and

Indonesia—has grasped the true significance of this disturbing situation and is giving positive support to family-planning activities through a network of information centers. But even if these efforts were entirely successful, it would take at least another twenty to thirty years before any such restraint would be evident in a stabilized, or still better, reduced population.

As is the case with most nations, the population increase is due less to the birth figures—they have a downward trend in most countries at present—than to the great decline in infant and child mortality. The fifty-year-old Japanese enjoys no chances of a significantly lengthened life span for his remaining days—it is a matter of two or possibly three years. This figure deviates considerably from the change in average life span, as the following comparison shows:

TABLE 20

Average Life Span in Japan

	Men	Women
1935	47	50 years
1958	64	68 years

Little could Commodore Perry anticipate, when he broke by force the national isolation of Japan in 1853 by pointing his ships guns from Yosuka Bay in threat toward the capital of Edo, that two generations later—within 85 years—this people would have zoomed from around 26 million to 75 million. Not only had it trebled its population but in order to provide for its people Japan now ruled over one of the largest empires of the world from the Aleutians in the north, several thousand miles to the South Pacific islands of the Carolines and the Marshalls and from these islands via that of Taiwan, out in the Pacific, also several thousand miles west into the heart of the Asian mainland.

As late as 1940, the population of the Japanese islands

amounted to seventy millions. Since the Second World War, the number has increased more than twenty-five million—a whole Perry-Japan. This represents one of the most spectacular population explosions in history—comparable only to the Chinese upsurge in the eighteenth century. Japanese scientific and technical circles in general now console themselves with the magic demographic formulas assuring them that in another thirty years the

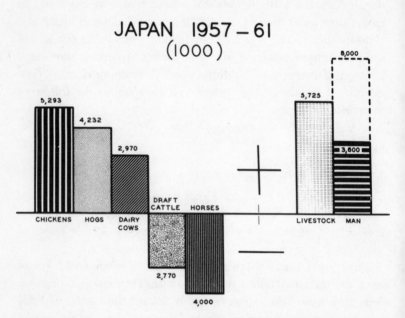

FIG. 34 Changes in population equivalents—the Japanese move toward animal production in recent years, as reflected in the acquisition of additional chicken, hogs, and dairy cows; all figures are in 1,000 population equivalents. In terms of protein this livestock increment corresponds to almost 12.5 million people. This expansion has been feasible primarily through mechanization, reducing the number of oxen and horses (6.77 million). The net increase in living mass is 5.73 million. To this comes a growth of the human population of 3.6 million. The dotted line indicates, as an estimate, the number of abortions in this period.

danger will be over. The country will then have made the almost infamous so-called demographic transition. The population will have reached "stability." Death rate and birth rate will balance each other, resulting in only a "small" population growth of half a million annually! Far too many seem to believe in these theoretical conjectures as some kind of unchangeable laws of Nature. This is a dangerous fallacy.

Tokyo's Marshall Plan

There is some justification in using the designation, an "Asiatic Marshall Plan" under Japanese guidance, a kind of Tokyo Plan. Within its framework, generous development loans are given as well as corresponding technical aid to the Philippines, India, Laos, Singapore, and Thailand. Within such contexts Japan delivers mining equipment and textile factories to Mexico and weaving mills to Argentina, and constructs steelworks in Brazil. In India, giant companies have been formed for the setting up of fisheries in the Red Sea and the Indian Ocean. A training center for fishing has been started in 1962. Japan has invested in around fifty enterprises involving fisheries in Asia and in other parts of the world.

There has also been a very ingenious interweaving of war reparation payments with such industrial and economic penetration in several of the countries affected by the Japanese war conquests in the thirties and forties.

A Seething but Poor Country

Japan sometimes has been called the dynamo of Asia. It is a world leader in shipbuilding, and is number four in electric power. In spite of this, it occupies the ninth place in gross national income.

The popular picture painted today of Japan by the West is

that of a seething country where the fruits of industrialization are a flourishing economy and a mounting export. Even a superficial study of economic statistics reveal, however, a glaring poverty. There are far too many people to share the cake. Tokyo with its fourteen million people is now the largest city on earth—but annually adds to its population another three or four hundred thousand, which pour into this desperately congested city from an equally overcrowded countryside. The farms simply cannot be split any further. In many coastal areas the houseboat has become the only refuge, and constitutes the basis for a small-scale freight traffic. In Tokyo, housing construction is going on at a very impressive rate, but still the needs of the invading hordes of people are far from being met. Many people live in primitive shacks built of corrugated tin, odd bits of woodboard, and discarded boxes. Sheet-metal containers are used to collect rainwater. Suburban cities for sleeping are superimposed upon the old city structure and its surroundings, thereby creating insurmountable commuting difficulties and unsolved traffic needs. The land cannot even be found to build the required roads.

It is true that Japan has performed miracles in the postwar period, but the dimensions of even miracles are soon scaled down when faced with the demands of the millions. There is an ominous gap between the facade of impressive figures published by the economists about this Japan—one of the world's industrial giants—and the figures which show up not only in the backyards and at the farm plots but also at the breakfast and dinner tables of the average Japanese. The new middle class which largely is reaping the benefits of this new economical upsurge embraces only some five to six million people, still a minor portion of a population rapidly moving towards a hundred million.

It does not help that the abortionists, whether licensed or not, are having a boom. The "mass emigration," implemented by the government and given its full support, economically and otherwise, is, as has been said earlier, offset by returning colonizers, and to place hope in this device is only one of innumerable illustrations of the shadow-boxing in which the Japanese politicians are engaged; but they are certainly not alone on this globe in performing such a show.

References

BORGSTROM, GEO. *Japan's Success in World Fishing.* London, Heighway Pub.; Fishing News, 1964, 320 pp.

BORTON, H., COHEN, J. B., *et al. Japan Between East and West.* New York, Harper, 1957, 327 pp.

DORE, R. P. *Land Reform in Japan.* London, Oxford University Press, 1959, 530 pp.

GRAD, A. J. *Land and Peasant in Japan.* An Introductory Survey. New York, Institute of Pacific Relations, 1952, 262 pp.

HEWES, L. I., JR. *Japan—Land and Men.* An account of the Japanese Land Reform Program 1945–51. Ames, Iowa State College Press, 1955, 154 pp.

LING, S. C. *Japan and Communist China.* New York, Institute of Pacific Relations, 1959, 380 pp.

LOCKWOOD, W. W. *The Economic Development of Japan.* Princeton, N.J., Princeton University Press, 1954, 295 pp.

NAGNI, I. *Japonica Rice—Its Breeding and Culture.* Tokyo, Yokendo Ltd., 1959, 844 pp.

TAEUBNER, I. B. *The Population of Japan.* Princeton, N.J., Princeton University Press, 1958.

TOBATA, S. *Japan's Agriculture.* Tokyo, Ministry of Foreign Affairs, 1956.

―――. *An Introduction to Agriculture of Japan.* Tokyo, Agriculture, Forestry and Fisheries Productivity Conference, 1958, 74 pp.

TSUNETA YANO MEMORIAL SOCIETY. *Nippon—a Charted Survey of Japan.* Tokyo, Kokusei-Sha, 1963, 265 pp.

IMPORTANT MAGAZINES:

Contemporary Japan
Japan Quarterly
New Japan

CHAPTER **10**

Australia—
The Safety Valve
of Asia?

IT is only natural for the politicians of Asia—this over-populated continent—to cast greedy eyes upon Australia, the "last continent," and of which it has been said that it is destined to become the United States of this century. In area, Australia is larger than the United States but it has only eleven million inhabitants, a little less than Greater New York and three million less than Greater Tokyo. If Australia were inhabited by less demanding and more contented people than the Europeans, the Western estimates about the continent as the possible home for half a billion might be doubled or tripled. These are the almost unanimous pronouncements to be picked up from Asiatic news-papers, books, and pamphlets or regularly to be heard from speaker's rostrums around that vast continent. No doubt, the Japanese plans during the latest world war included the conquest of this coveted prize—a whole continent for its expanding, vig-orous people.

So far, so good! But here the Asiatics are guilty of the same

FIG. 35 Map of Australia with immediately surrounding countries.

incongruous misjudgment of the Australian feeding potential that for a long time persisted among the spokesmen for the teeming millions of Europe. Less than two hundred thousand immigrants, primarily Europeans, presently arrive per year on the Australian shores. But it is evident to almost everyone that the limit soon will be reached. Non-Europeans are barred from entrance. Currently Australia has immigration agreements with a number of European countries such as Italy, the Netherlands, and West Germany, in each case with a quota of twenty thousand per year. Although this means that one-tenth of the present inhabitants have entered the country since the war ended, the total influx is certainly not very encouraging. It is in the range of about two million for the whole postwar period. For the above-mentioned European countries, this emigration may be significant; but for how long can Australia remain a white man's reserve in view of the enormous population pressure from its immediate surroundings in Asia?

Already an influx of this fairly modest size has indirectly affected the total amount of food and feed available for export. In addition, it has brought about a 10 per cent reduction in the protein standard of the population. The more people that arrive at this already low population level, the less seems to be available for the world household. Australia is truly a false Eldorado, but in spite of this fact, it will more and more feel the pinch of its location at the crossroads of European and Asiatic interests. Until now, the huge Asiatic tidal wave of people have sought other outlets: the Japanese in the thirties went to Manchuria, Korea, Taiwan, but also to Brazil and the United States. The Chinese swarmed north, west, and south into Mongolia, Tibet, Sinkiang and the whole of Southeast Asia, where the Chinese now in several countries hold key positions in trade and industry. They number some fifteen million today. Half of the Malaysian population is Chinese. Singapore is largely a Chinese city. Indochina has half a million Chinese. Even the island of Java in Indonesia has more than half a million.

TABLE 21

Long-term Immigration

	1954	1955	1956	1957
United States	230,096	280,678	351,753	269,504
Australia	104,014	130,795	123,822	118,695
Canada	159,825	115,039	170,792	288,762
Brazil	72,248	55,166	44,806	53,613

	1958	1959	1960	1961
United States	249,175	270,591	272,338	274,561
Australia	109,857	124,022	139,371	129,586
Canada	131,551	106,928	104,111	71,689
Brazil	49,839	44,520	40,507	43,589

Source: U.N. Demographic Yearbook

The Indians have gone east as well as west. More than one million are in Burma. They also created a beachhead on the African continent, where their presence has aroused strong feelings, although this receives less publicity in the South African race conflict. These East Indians are also found in British East Africa, Zanzibar, Kenya, and Tanganyika. Some two million have pushed into Ceylon. French and British Guiana in South America have a couple of hundred thousand East Indians in each.

Alternate Possibilities

Where are the acreages to be found that are desperately needed by these many millions who already lack both food and soil? Some of the Middle East countries can probably mobilize a few million acres, but huge investments are needed, in the first place for irrigation. Potentially available acreages have been estimated at forty-two million acres in Iran, twelve million acres in Iraq, and around twenty-five million acres in Turkey. But is it likely that these acreages really will become the new granaries for mankind? Will not those nations which now live in these regions give priority to their own rapidly increasing numbers? Furthermore, serious shortages already prevail in most of these countries and among their immediate neighbors, such as Egypt, Israel, Jordan, and Lebanon. Crops are less dependable in these regions, as yields vary considerably from year to year. If surpluses really did build up, there is great risk and likelihood that they would last merely for short periods of time and would soon be exhausted. The dependence on water is also great. Saudi Arabia experienced a short-lived postwar prosperity thanks to irrigation. This soon ended when it turned out that the water reserves, which it had taken centuries to build up, were emptied —in less than one decade!*

Siberia, along with adjacent regions of Soviet Asia, is often pictured as the last remaining major resource of the globe. Since the days of the Czars this vast land has been a closed country and geographically less accessible owing to its great land mass with great distances. The full exploitation of this huge timberland was always hindered by the shortage of water. As a consequence of the Second World War, the Soviet Union was forced to move the gravity point of its vast empire to the eastern side of the Ural Mountain range. Simultaneously, the unrelenting pressure of the Japanese forced the Chinese to move westward in the direction of the Siberian expanses. These happenings no doubt accelerated the development of this Asiatic heartland. Its potential, which is discussed in chapter 12, is without any doubt much

* D. D. Crary, 1951. Recent agricultural developments in Saudi Arabia, *Geographical Review 41*, 366–383.

greater than that of Australia. This statement may be surprising. An effort will therefore be made here to analyze and appraise this latter continent, irrevocably the last remaining bastion of the white race, but at the same time the chief neighbor of Asia.

U.S. - U.S.S.R.

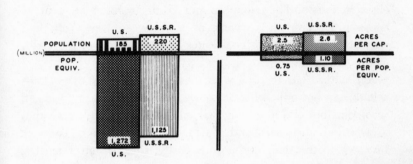

FIG. 36 The basic resources of the U.S. and the U.S.S.R. are amazingly similar, but those of the Soviet Union are under far greater climatic liabilities. Above the center line, conventional figures for population density; below the line, taking into account the living mass of livestock.

Characteristic Features

Australia still remains the large empty continent. The "white" men that went ashore here at various places in the beginning of the seventeenth century have still not taken actual possession of more than a few strips of land along the coasts. Man has really not taken possession of this continent. The first white colony was created in 1788 in an area which eighteen years earlier had been given the name New South Wales by a Swede named Selander. As already mentioned, a mere eleven million people nowadays live on this whole huge continent. In the river basins of India and China more people live on a few square miles than there are in the whole of Australia. Another characteristic feature of this continent is the fact that four-fifths of its inhabitants live in cities. In this respect Australia is uniquely developed. Two-fifths of the population are found in two southeastern cities: Sydney and Melbourne. An obvious result of this population distribution is that it is far and long between the cities, and emptiness prevails. The distance between the two chief metropolises in the south, Melbourne and Perth, is about as great as between London and Athens, or as between New York and Denver (Colo.); yet this constitutes only two-thirds of the width of the continent.

Agriculture has to cope with these enormous distances, too—a handicap not only when it comes to deliveries of grain, meat, wool, etc., but also in getting needed supplies of fertilizers, other agricultural chemicals, and machinery to the farms. To walk livestock to the slaughterhouse is costly, since in effect meat is thus used as fuel. In Australia this would be ruinous. Therefore, a vast air-transport system has been organized to bring together cattle for slaughtering (Air-Beef Centers); in the north, coastal transportation, also. Airplanes are used in fighting locusts, flying foxes, and kangaroos, as well as for fertilizing the vast expanses. Cattle and sheep must roam over large areas in their search for food, owing to the shortage of water which merely allows a sparse basic vegetation.

Pastoral Agriculture—an Anomaly

It may be labeled as an irony of history that it fell upon the British to colonize this continent. They transferred their own kind of pastoral agriculture, practiced on the home islands, to a region which for climatic as well as geographical reasons lacked the necessary prerequisites for this type of exploitation. The consequences have been disastrous. The intense drilling for water to compensate for the extreme parsimony of nature not only brought about a steep decline in the groundwater levels, but it also indirectly affected the vegetation cover. During the dry season sheep clustered around the water holes to survive, trampling down the vegetation. Then came the rains and they swarmed out over the vast green expanses. But around the water holes, the recovery of the vegetation was poor. Now, half a century later, the number of such holes is about ten times larger. They consequently lie much closer to each other. Considerably larger areas are being trampled down, and fall prey to the wind and soil erosion. The penetrating book *Flying Foxes and Drifting Sand* is a summary of the findings of an investigation through many years, made by soil scientists on behalf of the Australian government. The principal author of this book concludes that a sick person who is aware of his condition and who does not take steps in time to counteract it, or who omits to take the prescribed therapeuticals for remedy, is regarded as foolish. But, he adds, when, as in this case, the most important natural resource of a country, the soil, is at stake, one acts in this absurd way. One refuses to take the medicine.

One step in the right direction was taken, however, by the Australian government some years ago, when stipulations were enacted as to the maximum number of animals allowed per acre. Plans were also made to double the acreage of each farm in the critical dry regions. Many a farmer seized upon this opportunity in order—as he believed—to increase his income by keeping more animals rather than double the amount of land available to each. Journalists, especially in Western countries, interpreted these measures as a considerable enlargement of Australia's food-producing potential. In reality it was the first sign of a dawning awareness of the limitations set by nature itself on what is feasible in this continent. This acreage expansion constituted a desperate long-range measure to maintain the present level of production, and was by no means a step toward an increased production in other ways than the indirect gain that would accrue from the livestock already in these areas (chiefly sheep) being provided more adequate food with less risk of malnutrition.

The Potential

Economists, agricultural scientists, geographers, and not the least the science writers in Sunday edition magazine sections of newspapers, overbid each other in glowing descriptions of the many millions Australia might be able to support. Around the turn of the century and shortly thereafter, these figures were in the range of two hundred and fifty to five hundred millions. Stark reality, however, has gradually adjusted them downward, and present estimates are usually within the range of fifty to a hundred million. Recently this author had the opportunity to listen to an analysis of Australia's feeding potential by the dean of one of the country's leading agricultural colleges. He came to the conclusion that it ought to be possible to support twenty to twenty-five million people without undue lowering of the present nutritional level. This means that Australia can safely be counted on to support a population about twice as large as the present one. In the light of world increases of sixty-five million persons per year this potential does not mean much.

It is further sobering to view Australia in its natural geographical environment of the Pacific scene. One then finds that the neighboring Asiatic countries provide an *annual* net contribution to the world population growth of at least thirty million people; add to this some three to five million in the Pacific parts of Latin America. In order to develop Australia's assumed potential of providing for another ten million, some ten to twenty years would undoubtedly be needed, even if this program were well planned and efficiently executed. In other words, this would mean that even with the mobilization of more of the available agricultural resources and the full use of all modern techniques, what this so-called "empty" continent would have to offer at a reasonable economic outlay would not be totally adequate to take care of more than one-third of the growth of *one single year* in its Pacific sphere. Furthermore, this could only be accomplished over a period extending over one or two decades, within which time this very same region would fill up with from four hundred to nine hundred million people. This should be sobering and thought-provoking to all those who like to speculate about the enormous feeding potential of the earth. This case alone should convince anyone of the critical fact that man as a biological phenomenon has already surpassed all reasonable limits.

If all Australians were forced to become vegetarians, Australia would still be able to care for only about ten to twelve years of population increment around this Pacific basin. This calculation is based on the fact that the livestock—sheep and cattle—consume an amount of protein which nutritionally ought to suffice for 332 million people. This is, however, a purely theoretical speculation, since ploughing up of the Australian soil already has gone beyond what the climatic conditions safely permit. The dry pastures adjacent to the large, central desert areas can be profitably exploited only if a well-balanced number of grazing animals are kept there. Turning the sod by the plough would expose the soil to further desiccation and wind erosion, which has already had devastating effects in many areas. The shortage of water overextends the required acreage and makes this land more suited for nomadic exploitation.

The Meat Country

Australia is often pointed out as being one of the world's great meat producers. Until recently, England was the most important purchaser. However, this country, with a total land area of only one-thirtieth that of Australia, produces within its isles almost one-third more meat than the whole Australian continent. Australia contributes, in fact, less meat to the world market than

Denmark. New Zealand, though tiny in relation to Australia, provides the world market with more meat than the entire continent of Australia. It should be noted that Australia is in a sense an agricultural colony of New Zealand. An acreage corresponding to half the tilled area of New Zealand is in Australia devoted to wheat deliveries to this neighboring country. This amounts to not less than a quarter of a million metric tons annually. At present, meat from Australia and New Zealand is imported by the United States in increasing quantities. The United States pays a higher price than England and received in 1963 more meat than the United Kingdom and thus reached the top-ranking position as meat importer in our hungry world. There is a social stratification also among the well-nourished nations! Third-grade beef, sold to the United States, brings in a higher price than first-choice beef exported to England on a long-range contract. In recent years, in addition to beef, kangaroo and wild buffalo meat has been delivered to the United States. Kangaroo meat is nowadays used both in the United States and in West Germany. In the latter country it goes into what is called "game stew."

It is understandable that political leaders of the hundreds of millions in hunger-ridden Asia, just outside the gates of this paradise of plenty, look with resentment and no little envy upon the butter, beef, lamb, and preserved meat bypassing their own doors. These half-starved nations are astounded when they realize also that there are on this earth favored people who can afford to raise the cost of their daily food with such long-distance transportation, having the food carried almost around the globe before it is eaten.

The Aborigines Starve

Alarming reports have been made public about the increasing starvation among the Australian aborigines because their traditional feeding base is becoming upset. They need the expanse of land to get enough food but they have been excluded from large areas which are reserved for the British atomic tests and rocket firings. In some regions mining has been started. The loss of hunting grounds is of lesser importance than the fact that all these projects demand a great deal of water, which is in great shortage, not only for this primitive people but directly and indirectly for the game which constitutes their feeding basis.

In the area of nutrition they are swindled. They are given cheap sugar and flour in exchange for the loss of protein-rich game—when they are not enticed with simple alcohol. Their living space has thus been severely reduced, and their whole way of living is endangered by the advance of the whites. At the time the whites arrived in Australia, the number of aborigines was estimated at 300,000. It has now shrunk to 52,000.

Production Hazards

The hazardous conditions under which Australia produces foods may best be illustrated by the catastrophes in the years 1951 and 1952 when severe droughts hit the country and killed off millions of animals. Butter became a rare item in the cities and had to be rationed, as did sugar, egg, potatoes, and lamb. Potatoes had to be brought in from New Zealand and onions from Egypt. Practically always, in years of critical drought, this continent is forced to supplement its fare with imported food and feed. The primary agricultural production of the continent during the fifties grew only one per cent annually, while the population, inclusive of immigration, increased 3 per cent a year. This has changed in the sixties with the opening up of the vast Asiatic markets, but the vagaries of the climate persist.

A common topic is the shortage of labor in Australian industry and the need for alleviating this by bringing in more people. But the effect of this is generally overlooked. It is readily forgotten that a human being has not only a pair of working hands but also an eating mouth. More people would raise the demands for food and thus the demands upon agricultural output of the kind that the high nutritive standard prescribes.

A great deal has been written about the large so-called ninety-mile desert which has been transformed into abounding alfalfa fields and luscious pastures by fertilizing with trace elements, such as zinc, copper, manganese, molybdenum, and sulphate. In this way, the pastures in this region were increased threefold in area and now comprise about twenty million acres. The number of sheep has increased, as well as the output of meat and wool. This is no doubt an impressive conquest for plant growing, but as usual the limiting factors have been overlooked. Here, as in most other regions, water sets the limitations for production. In this special case large deficiencies of phosphate constitute an additional handicap. Therefore the high yields of the first few years have not been sustained. Irrigation as well as large-scale fertilizing of a conventional type is now imperative.

The Pastures and the Future

The pastoral acreage is eighteen times that of the tilled land. In most regions, it has not been possible to increase the yields of the pasture lands further, water being the limiting factor. The urgent task has therefore been to prevent further mineral depletion of the pastures in order to avert a decline in numbers as well as a quality deterioration of animal production. By and large, increased yields have so far been attained by claiming new lands for pastures. A survey made in the fifties reports that at the most 150 million more acres can be added to the Australian pastureland. At the rate presently prevailing for the opening up of new land for agricultural use, this final reserve would be completely taken before the end of the sixties. This mirrors in a rather grave way both the present pressure for additional pastureland as well as the current rate of expansion. After this stage is reached, the yields per acre will have to be increased, which will require massive irrigation and large-scale fertilizing.

Besides, Australia's animal husbandry faces new problems which seem extremely difficult to solve. The dung from sheep and cattle is estimated as amounting to about thirty-three million metric tons annually. A very small proportion of this is now being returned to the production of milk, meat, and wool. The soil and climate are such that it was never possible to implant the essential dung insects which in regions with our type of climate ordinarily move these nutrients back into the soil. These insects are nearly absent in the Australian fauna. This means considerable additional expenditures for fertilizers, if they are at all possible to utilize efficiently with the present water shortage. Many efforts have been made to introduce these beneficial helpers, but so far with no success. The microclimate presumably is too dry for these industrious creatures. It is therefore dubious if the Australian climate as such would permit the formation of a type of soil which would make a full utilization of this dung feasible. At present the major part of this nitrogen, which otherwise should return into its productive cycle in the soil, is lost to the air, mostly in the form of nitrogen but also as ammonia. This could be termed a kind of short-circuiting, seriously eclipsing the nitrogen efficiency.

Rabbits, Kangaroos, Flying Foxes, and Dingos

The campaign against the rabbit plague, by spreading a contagious disease, myxomatosis, was initially very successful and brought about a considerable increase in production, especially of wool and lamb. Nine rabbits devour an amount of grass corresponding to what two sheep require. It has been estimated that these marauding creatures deprived Australia of a pasture production corresponding to the needs of fifteen to twenty million sheep—one-fourth of the total number in 1956. On the other hand, the processing (freezing, canning, etc.) of rabbits for overseas markets and domestic needs (5.5 lbs. per person a year in Australia) became quite a flourishing industry. Consequently, their ravages did not entirely represent net losses. In the long run this may be the only recourse in order to cope with this upset balance, particularly since most evidence now points to the conclusion that the rabbits seem to have acquired immunity against myxomatosis and now are capable of living with this disease.

The hordes of kangaroos which earlier were regularly decimated by the aborigines have become a serious menace to plant production as well as to the vegetation cover. As mentioned earlier, the aborigines now receive cheap food, primarily sugar and grain flour, from the white intruders. Therefore these aborigines hunt less and do not keep after the kangaroo stock as they used to do. In some critical areas, so-called kangaroo fences have been erected, but they have proved to be rather inefficient against the high-jumping animals.

In the state of New South Wales alone, the kangaroo stock is estimated at five million animals, and this is considerably in excess of what the wild vegetation is estimated to be able to sustain. To shoot the quick-footed beasts is too expensive and neither simple nor efficient. To poison them is too risky, since sheep as well as cattle also fall victims. The kangaroos are also adroit at finding the water holes, already too few for the sheep and cattle. In this way they take their toll of the inadequate flow. Most damaging, however, is their direct attack upon the crops, which are either eaten or trampled down.

The dingos—the so-called wild dogs—constitute a still more grave threat. They seriously thin out the sheep herds, especially during drought periods when the sheep are debilitated owing to the lack of water. In many regions it has become necessary to erect special fences around the sheep-grazing grounds to avoid excessive losses. One is twice the length of the British Isles—about 1,500 miles—and runs straight across South Australia from the Great Bight to the border of New South Wales. The object is to keep the dingo out of the sheep lands to the south of this fence. Veritable air attacks have been organized to spread poison against them but the effect has been temporary.

A large species of bat—the above mentioned *flying foxes*—do great harm to fruit plantations in several areas. They have also been sprayed from the air. But some build up again in large flocks and are considered more fierce marauders than the locusts ever were.

During 1958 and 1959, mice and rats once again appeared in massive hordes. Although conditions cannot be compared with the devastating rodent invasions of 1917, the signs have pointed unmistakably toward the risk of something similar occurring again. In both instances these attacks were the consequences of inadequate space for grain storage. The regular silos were filled up and the farmers resorted to various temporary devices for holding the grain supplies. They were simply piled up in the open air, protected at best by a tarpaulin or something equally deficient.

Wool and Skim Milk

Wool accounts for around half of the income from exportation. When one day wool gets into open competition with food, the outcome is not clear. It will depend upon who at that point holds the decisive word in world economy. Wool is to a considerable degree composed of protein, the most coveted nutrient in the present global household.

Wool is used chiefly by the people living in the northern temperate regions of the world, primarily the luxury nations. It is a market created by them and for them. Australia's wool contains about 320,000 metric tons of protein, conservatively esti-

TABLE 22

World Trade in Wool (in 1,000 metric tons). Average 1958–59

Export		*Import*	
Australia	550	Western Europe	824
New Zealand	170	Japan	125
South America	177	U.S.A.	120
South Africa	95		
	992		1,069
World Total	1,150		

mated. This corresponds to about one-tenth of the protein yield of world fisheries. Keratine (wool protein) is not directly suitable as food, but research and breeding ought to be able to produce an animal which is adapted to the Australian pastures and which can produce at least as much protein in some other and edible form. As a matter of fact, more protein ought to be obtained, because in order to make wool protein, the sheep today needs particularly high amounts of sulphur—at any rate, quantities far in excess of those required in producing food for humans.

As stated above, wool is largely a commodity of the privileged few of the world's peoples. Concern is even voiced (1964) over the stability of those markets, in face of the prospect that China may become a regular buyer of this commodity. Wool constitutes nowadays a mere one-tenth of the world consumption of textile fibers. Nonetheless, when millions and even billions crave for food, it becomes an absurdity and an anachronism. Protein is far too expensive and too precious to the world household to be utilized as clothing material. Calculated on the basis of the total world trade in wool, 880,000 metric tons of protein is at stake. This would be sufficient for 80 million people on an Italian dietary standard, or 160 million on a Japanese level. Of the 1.2 million metric tons of wool now moving in world trade channels, one-tenth goes to Japan, one-tenth to the United States, and the remaining eight-tenths to Western Europe. The rest of the world receives a mere pittance.

For the foreseeable future however, the Merino sheep is destined to remain in Australia because of its remarkable ability to tolerate highly saline water. This explains its dominance in the Australian wool production. This points to another hindrance to life on this continent, in that large areas are provided only with water carrying so much salt that neither people nor animals can stand it without detriment. The Merino sheep is in this respect a kind of unique physiological miracle.

Australia, like Scandinavia and some parts of the Soviet Union, is one of the few countries in the world that can afford the luxury of feeding animal products to their livestock (primarily hogs). This means that man depends on a *tertiary* production with no less than two conversion links. One pound of protein in this case requires almost fifty pounds of primary protein.

But such extravagance is not restricted to the feeding of hogs. It is also a question of a poor, extremely wasteful utilization of invaluable milk protein. By making butter and discarding the whey it has been estimated that as much protein is lost for direct human consumption in Australia as what this whole nation eats in the form of meat. At the most, one-fifth of the skim milk, the by-product of butter manufacture, is saved by processing into other dairy products. Some of the remainder is passed on to hogs and calves but—still worse—most is allowed to drain off into sewers or is otherwise discarded, particularly when excessive distances prevent its return delivery to the farms. And all this goes on at the threshold of protein-hungry Asia! The amount of skim milk that Australia's calves and pigs consume would be sufficient to double the present intake of animal protein in Japan. In the light of such facts, it becomes more understandable why Japan, with such rugged determination, grasped after the Australian continent in the large-scale conquests of the

Second World War. Totally, Australia produces in round figures
the following quantities of animal protein:

TABLE 23

Production and Consumption of Animal Protein in Australia
(in 1,000 metric tons) (1958–59)

	Annual commodity production	Percent protein	Animal protein produced		Animal protein consumed
Meat	1,600	15	240		145
Milk	6,000	3.5	210		69
Egg	115	12	14		12.5
				Sum	
Poultry	45	18	8	472	8
Wool	410	80	328	328	234.5
			Total	800	

It would be desirable to supplement this table with export
figures in order to arrive at approximate figures for waste. But
this is difficult to do, since exports have been made partly from
surplus supplies accumulated over more than one year. This requires a study in depth. At any rate, considerable quantities of
about 50,000 tons are unaccounted for and seem to be wasted.

Fisheries

Australian fisheries are seriously underdeveloped and—however
strange this may sound—even in this case water shortage is a
limiting factor. The run-off from this huge continent is minimal,
and the additions of minerals to the sea waters around the
coasts are limited to a few regions and to brief periods during
the year. No less than 60 per cent of the fish which is consumed
within the country is imported, which naturally increases its

cost considerably. Few of the immediately surrounding waters are abundant in fish. Whenever commercial fisheries were started, the point was very soon reached when supplies dwindled as a consequence of overfishing.

The pelagic fish resources are, of course, larger, but they necessitate sizeable investments and should be considered an important part of the picture of Australia's feeding potential for the millions of the future. Japan has in effect already moved in on the surrounding high-seas in forces and encircled this continent with a ring of major tuna fishing grounds, now part of the regular fishing ventures of that country.

Snowy Mountains

The so-called Snowy Mountains constitute one of the few regions in Australia which can offer water resources not yet wholly tapped. Huge hydroelectric plants and big irrigation systems are under construction. Seven large dams are being built. The total length of the water pipelines in this major project is 62 miles; the irrigation canals together will measure 375 miles. Sixteen hydroelectric plants are already installed. This entire and huge project is now on the verge of being completed at a total cost of about one hundred billion U.S. dollars. This is indeed an enormous investment as well as an impressive undertaking. The total acreage which is calculated to receive irrigation from these huge installations will amount to a modest 600,000 acres. Thus not many of the world's excess million human beings could really be fed from this rather limited area. The increase in the annual plant and animal production which will accrue from these measures have been estimated as having a value of fifty-two million U.S. dollars, no impressive figure when judged in a global perspective, but, of course, important for the particular state in which this technical feat has been accomplished—New South Wales. Other irrigation projects recently completed or presently under construction in this vast continent all together will not contribute more than 370,000 additional acres. By and large, these water-conserving projects will not do more than possibly halt the persistent drop in the water tables, which inevitably would lead to a decline in the agricultural production. In other words, the net gain to the Australian food balance is likely to be less than simple acreage figures would imply.

The Rice Bastion—Humpty Doo

A number of large U.S.-Australian companies have been formed to develop the rice cultivation in the northern part of the continent. The plan is to bring under cultivation 625,000 to 750,000 acres over a fifteen-year period. This would unquestionably constitute a significant contribution to the farm-producing potential of Australia. But this acreage shrinks to a pittance when measured against the task it was intended to fulfill and the promises that advanced publicity made about this project—that it was to feed the hungry of Asia.

In this particular area of Australia, dry conditions prevail during half the year; during the other half of the year it rains rather heavily. Often there are downpours of from five to fifteen inches in one single instance. Irrigation is therefore clearly indicated and it is highly prudent to economize with these water resources. The ultimate goal of this project originally was to place 1.5, possibly 1.8, million acres of marshland under rice cultivation. According to plans, this was to be done over a thirty-year period. Yet, even when fully exploited, this would constitute merely 0.5 per cent of the world's present rice acreage. The name of the chief cultivation area is Humpty Doo. A great deal has been written about the development of these coastal areas in northern Australia as a feeding bastion for Asia. Unfortunately, no reasonable relationship exists between the indisputable facts as to the size and the magnitude of this undertaking and the promises and prospects held forth in all the publicity about this venture and the contributions it might possibly make towards the solution of Asia's hunger problem.

This rice-cultivation project has been written up as the "largest agricultural project in world history." This, of course, is sheer nonsense. It has further been presented as a "salvation to Asia"— once again a statement without any foundation in reality. The rice-eaters grow by at least thirty millions a year. This means that—even with a minimal diet—an additional three million metric tons of rice are needed annually. Thirty years from now the project might possibly yield this quantity. It was further calculated that owing to the favorable growing conditions for rice, this key crop would be raised at a price one-third of the world market quotations. None of these promises have been fulfilled. Prices became excessive. The demands for capital as investment by far surpassed any anticipations. Innumerable complications were encountered in the simple control of the irrigation flow. Poorly investigated level differences made it necessary to resort to any amount of machine pumping for the moving of water from one sector of the irrigated area to another. The rice became costly in spite of the fact that this supposedly was an ideal location—the promised land of the wild rice. But this grass obviously seeks to recover its natural territory. It is a much more embarrassing weed than the wild oats ever were in Western Europe and the United States. So far, the wild geese have caused the greatest trouble. It is estimated that they strip the fields of almost half the grain crop.

In the face of all these debacles under tropical or substropical conditions, many voices have been raised for the opening up of these regions to people who have more experience cultivating on these latitudes and who also are more patient and less demanding.

The Great North

The inner region of the northern province has been called the Wild West of our time or the Great North of Australia. It is about twice the size of Texas. There are some cattle ranches comprising six million acres (2.5 million hectares). But the vegetation is so feeble and sparse that no less than forty acres per cattle head are required for feeding. Crocodiles are lurking at the watering places to snatch the calves; they inflict considerable losses. In this region large donkey herds run wild and compete with the livestock for the pastures. A couple of years ago, thirty thousand such donkeys were shot, but with little long-range benefit. Even camels have run wild here and have caused great damage. It is said that in fifteen minutes camels are capable of dismantling the most solid fence merely by pushing their own bodies against it with full force.

Termites also rule uncontrolled and have been known to finish off a wooden house in a couple of weeks, and a piece of wooden furniture, a piano, or a table, in a few days. Their mounds may reach more than three yards in height. Efforts to exterminate this pest have had surprisingly little effect in both time and space.

In other regions—the northwestern part called Katherine—the soil is so poor in nitrogen and phosphate that only after several years of cultivating peanuts and alfalfa is it possible to expect a reasonable animal productivity. Conventional husbandry with grazing only results in half-starved and very lean animals.

In the heartland of the continent, at a place called Alice Springs, an agricultural research station is located which carries on a tenacious battle to perform magic with the drops of water that nature on rare occasions provides. Dew is almost the only external source of water. Some progress has been registered in maintaining pastures covered with a very sparse vegetation. But the big difference persists between a nomadic way of life for a few—where the livestock roam over vast areas to collect sufficient for survival—and the cropping of surpluses for the millions.

A New Pattern?

In recent years a new warp in the pattern of foreign trade has become discernible. The undernourished world has appeared as purchaser, not the least in Australia. This became still more accentuated when this change coincided with a record crop in the years 1960–61. During that season two million metric tons of wheat were sold to China. This was far above the total wheat export during 1958 (1.44 million metric tons) and more than the country had in surplus storage at the end of the period 1957–60 (1.65 million metric tons). These large purchases by China have continued. In 1962 and in 1963 this country was the largest buyer of Australian grain. In 1964 China acquired on the world market more than 5 million metric tons of grain; the largest quantity was from Canada, followed by Australia with 1.8 million (p. 115) tons. This new Chinese market has affected the wheat growing of Australia. Both the acreage and yield have mounted but not without repercussions on the raising of other crops and the feed grain production. Besides China, the buyers have been Egypt, Ceylon, Indonesia, Japan, and Italy—undernourished and over-populated countries. Considerable quantities of barley, 320,000 metric tons, have also been sold to China, which has almost emptied the Australian storage bins of this grain. China has also started to buy wool in no insignificant quantities. International concern has even been voiced (1964) that this might upset the world wool market.

If all these grain deliveries are added together, however, they do not amount to more than from 2 to 3 per cent of China's average consumption of rice and other grain. There is good reason to assume that this major shift on the scene of the international wheat market will become permanent. This does not imply that there was anything wrong with the Western European market, but it is gradually becoming politically prudent and expedient for white Australia to reduce tension within its Asiatic sphere and, if possible, to place a damper on the yearnings toward this huge "empty" continent.

The have-not nations finally make themselves heard with their enormous unsatisfied demands for food. Regardless of this development, a new factor has entered the scene of world economy. Many traditional concepts of currencies, credits, purchasing power, and so forth, will probably have to be revised considerably when the "have" nations, in their own long-range interest, are gradually forced to unrig their monopolies. In particular, the so-called Rural Party in Australia now regards China and other Asiatic countries as huge untouched markets for Australia's agricultural products. This discovery obviously has been facilitated by the strivings of the Common Market of Europe to incorporate the United Kingdom.

One clear evidence of the fact that this country now is making a serious effort to adjust to reality is the appearance of an Australian journalist's book about Japan, with the title *The Country Upstairs*. This book rapidly became a best-seller. In the era of jets and rockets and missiles, Australia is gradually realizing what it means to have almost a hundred million people with the tough energy of the Japanese and a flourishing industrial potential within hours from Sydney and other Australian metropolises.

Water the Dictator

Particularly in Australia great expectations are attached to the developments of cheap and effective methods for the desalinization of seawater. Descriptions of how to take this coveted commodity from the tremendous reservoir of the Pacific Ocean is comforting reading to those who previously have been concerned or even worried about the future of our water-wasting civilization. This has been true in particular of the Australians, to whom water shortage is the major issue of the day.

Engineers of all categories have generously spread the gospel and painted sparkling visions of Australia's future, predicting the rebirth of this southern continent like a new Venus from the sea. If ever desalinization of seawater is to become a great success story as is commonly anticipated, and on a major scale, this should be on the Australian scene. For the coastal regions and the marginal human settlements of this continent it will no doubt be the only way out for the future. As mentioned earlier in this chapter, desalting would also have its place in making usable locally the water available from drilled wells and ground-water resources, which in large parts of the continent is becoming increasingly saline.

But it is a serious fallacy to believe that food regularly could be produced with artificially recovered water. Mankind could not afford the gigantic pipelines and enormous tunnels, not to speak of the many large plants for treatment that would be required. Open canals are excluded in advance owing to the high evaporation losses. Also prohibitive are the fabulous costs in energy required to pump all this water around (up and across the continents). As a matter of fact, they would amount to more than the aggregate industry utilizes in the most developed countries. Science writers and specialists who write and talk in these terms have little knowledge of the enormous quantities of water that are needed in plant production.

On the latitudes of Australia, furthermore, it is a question of quantities, which are appreciably higher than those required in Iowa, for example, for corresponding crops. Wheat needs in Australia about 2.5 times as much water per ton of fullgrown grain as it needs in the Middle West grain basket.

The magnitude of the desalting establishments needed would surpass many times in production volume that of the largest chemical industries on earth today. Giant factories would be needed to take care of the actual needs. Modern engineering and technology would be wise to concentrate efforts and resources (including brain power) on more realistic projects with some degree of economic feasibility.

Water will remain the Great Dictator of Australia and will continue fairly unhampered a rough-handed sway over the country for a very long time to come, if not forever.

References

ABBOTT, C. L. A. *Australia's Frontier Province*. London, Angus and Robertson, 1950, 218 pp.

BEVAN, I. *The Sunburnt Country, Profile of Australia*. London, Collins, 1953, 256 pp.

CALLAGHAN, A. R. and MILLINGTON, A. J. *The Wheat Industry in Australia*. London, Angus and Robertson, 1956, 486 pp.

GROOM, A. *I Saw a Strange Land*. London, Angus and Robertson, 1950, 216 pp.

KEAST, A., CROCKER, R. L., and CHRISTIAN, C. S. *Biogeography and Ecology in Australia*. Den Haag, Dr. W. Junk, 1959, 640 pp.

LEVI, W. *Australia's Outlook on Asia*. E. Lansing, Michigan State University Press, 1958, 246 pp.

LODEWYCKZ, A. *People for Australia*. London, Angus and Robertson, 1958, 230 pp.

RATCLIFFE, F. *Flying Fox and Drifting Sand*. London, Angus and Robertson, 1948, 332 pp.

REES, H. *Australasia (Australia, New Zealand, and the Pacific Islands)*. London, MacDonald and Evans Ltd., 1962, 264 pp.

SIMPSON, COLIN, 1962. *The Country Upstairs* (2nd. ed.) Angus and Robertson, Sydney, 287 pp. (1st. ed., 1956)

TAYLOR, G. *Australia, A Study of Warm Environments and Their Effect on British Settlement*. 7th edition. London, Methuen, 1959, 490 pp.

WADHAM, S., WILSON, R. K., and WOOD, J. *Land Utilization in Australia*. Melbourne, Melbourne University Press, 1957, 344 pp.

WATT, R. D. *The Romance of the Australian Land Industries*. London, Angus and Robertson, 1955, 271 pp.

YEARBOOKS of:

Australia	Queensland
W. Australia	Victoria
S. Australia	New South Wales
Tasmania	

CHAPTER 11

The Soviet
Food Front

THE land area of the Soviet Union is three times that of the United States. Nearly one-third of the country is under permafrost, that is, permanently covered by tundra with ice. The entire Soviet union of republics is placed to the north of the United States mainland. The city of Odessa is located on the same latitude as Duluth in northern Minnesota, and the Crimean peninsula corresponds in geographical latitude to that of the border region between Canada and the United States at the Great Lakes. The Soviet subtropical areas are limited to certain parts of Crimea and the irrigated acreages of southern Central Asia. Thus, the agricultural production of the U.S.S.R. is pursued under climatic conditions that are far more rigorous than those of the United States.

Another distinctive feature is the risk of severe drought, a risk twice as great as in the United States. If the climatic data of the last hundred years are indicative, this means that the risk for crop failures in the U.S.S.R. is twice as large. It can further be noted that on the average the *degree* of water shortage at a time of drought is in general more severe than in corresponding instances in the United States.

The severity has as a general rule been rated as twice that of major United States droughts, either in duration or in degree of water scarcity. As a consequence the damages to crops and livestock are correspondingly greater. These circumstantial facts lend support to the general conclusion that a Russian prime minister, whether a capitalist or a communist, is running an

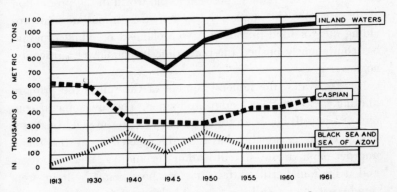

SOVIET INLAND FISH CATCH

FIG. 37   Note the stagnation of Soviet inland fisheries despite extensive countermeasures.

almost four times greater risk of being caught in a food calamity caused by water shortage than a U.S. president.

The overall water regime of the U.S.S.R. is part of the pattern prevailing for the entire Eurasian land mass. The average rainfall figure drops considerably each five hundred miles as one moves from the coast of France via Central Europe into Eastern Europe; it continues to drop in European Russia and further along in Western and Eastern Siberia, finally ending up where the disruptions of the coastal ranges of the Far East render some extra rain from regional sources. This explains why even in the Asiatic parts of the country more than half of the precipitation originates in the Atlantic Ocean. The further one moves into the continent the greater are therefore the drought hazards. This is essential to know and understand when judging the difficulties which arise here in the newly broken lands of Kazakhstan and adjacent regions in Western Siberia, as we shall see.

It is not the plan to discuss here in detail what Soviet soils yield, but merely to point out that grain remains the dominating crop; wheat is first, with rye second. Among special crops, preference is given to sugarbeets and sunflowers; the U.S.S.R. nowadays has the top-ranking position in the world in the production of these crops. The sunflower has gained in importance in providing oils for food purposes. A well-planned breeding program has continuously pushed the borderline for sunflower cultivation northward.

Next to water, the mineral content of the soil is the primary limiting factor in Soviet crop production. The low mineral content of key soils has been the main obstacle to the yield increases which could reasonably have been expected from the major improvements made in cultivation techniques, mechanization, and irrigation. Fertilizer factories are now being built in great numbers it seems. Still the mineral balance of the soil apparently is negative. Nevertheless, the yields per acre increased during the fifties and did not lag behind in comparison with areas in the United States with a similar climate.

If one looks for an agricultural region in the United States which—in climatic conditions such as a frost-free vegetation period, volume and distribution of precipitation, as well as temperature—is most comparable to the climate within the well-known fertile "triangle" within which most of the Soviet agricultural production takes place, one finds it in North Dakota. The only difference is the day-length. The North Dakota yields of spring wheat differ only slightly from those of the U.S.S.R.

It is highly misleading, as frequently happens when editorializing on these matters, to compare United States winter wheat yields with those of Soviet spring wheat. They are in effect two distinct kinds of wheats, and winter varieties persistently show higher figures. This brings to the fore the hazard involved in comparing large cultivation areas such as the United States and the Soviet Union. The latter comprises one-sixth of the earth's total land area and extends over large parts of two continents. The United States spans in a broad belt a continent and embraces, like the Soviet Union, a wide belt of geographical latitudes and longitudes. Therefore, highly differing climates, topographical conditions, and soil types are found in different parts of both countries.

The political debate, unfortunately, has overlooked the evident complications in making comparisons. In terms of crop production, it is simply not reasonable or scientifically justified to speak about a specific American, and much less a specific Russian, agriculture. Enormous disparities prevail between the fertile pastures of the Amur basin, Yakut's frost-bitten patches of tilled land, Kazakhstan's enormous expanses bordering on the steppe, the desert areas of Central Asia, the black soils of the Ukraine, the lush subtropical vegetation of Crimea, the rich lands of Moldavia's horticultural and dairy regions, merely to pick a few examples among numerous others, such as the rolling pasture lands of the Baltic republics and the drained marshlands of White Russia.

Certain general comments are nonetheless appropriate, and some broad conclusions are valid. Only in the Kuban region in the lower Caucasus are climatic conditions such as to be somewhat comparable to those of the most fertile parts of the United States prairies, for example, the wheat state of Kansas with a frost-free period of 190 days. In comparison, the new grain regions of Kazakhstan enjoy only 120 to 122 frost-free days, and around Moscow 130 frost-free days may be counted upon. These figures are averages, however, and frost spells are not uncommon even during the vegetation period.

The Goal is American Standard

In 1959 Russia's total milk production seems to have achieved parity with that of the United States. As a large portion of the milk is still being utilized for local butter production or goes into preserved products such as those for the north (see p. 235), the access to fresh milk is far below that of the U.S. level. Dairy establishments are, however, being constructed at a rapid pace, and factories for the production of dried milk and condensed milk are being erected in increasing numbers. The Soviet Union struggles with the tremendous distances between the producing areas and the population centers. Since refrigerators are not yet common in the homes and the majority of the food stores lack refrigeration, the keeping quality of the milk obviously has to be extended by other means. Resorting to acidifying bacteria is one means of coping with this problem. The traditional fermented milks, *kefir* and *kumys*, of old-time Russia are yet important items in the dairy assortment. Even pure cultures are offered for sale for those who prefer to prepare this cherished milk at home. Cottage cheese is another popular article, frequently sweetened and with raisins added. Regular hard cheeses of conventional kinds are rapidly becoming available.

Frozen milk was first made in Siberia's cold expanses several hundred years ago by various indigenous peoples, such as Yakuts and others. It is still said to be available in distant parts of this vast region, but its place has to a substantial degree been taken by sweetened condensed milk, which has such a low freezing point that even during severe winters it can be distributed without risk. Several tens of millions of the U.S.S.R.'s industrialized population live far away from milk-producing centers. They receive their milk either as condensed milk or in a dehydrated form, which is reconstituted locally in dairies.

Ice cream is another form in which milk protein is being distributed. It is rapidly becoming everyday food. In Moscow, the per capita consumption exceeds that of the United States and amounts to about fifteen pounds per person annually. But the country as a whole has still a considerable way to go before the U.S. level is reached. Anastas Mikoyan, the secretary of commerce, newly elected president of the U.S.S.R., never concealed that he learned the blessings of ice cream in the United States, far back in the thirties. It is one of the many points where the Soviet Union admittedly and successfully copies the United States. In the huge agricultural and industrial exhibits in Moscow, as well as in the professional Soviet journals, one is struck by the frequent underlining of United States accomplishments and by the United States being held up to the people as the model for progress. To reach and preferably to surpass U.S. levels are material goals set for a number of their strivings, not the least in food. A number of books have been published on this general theme: "to equal and surpass the U.S.A."

When visiting one of Moscow's seven ice-cream factories, it was surprising to discover that they did not limit their manufacture to a few standard products. Their output comprised a rich assortment of no less than forty-five different items. Among these were artistically decorated ice-cream cakes. This symbolizes a new luxury way of life and evidently a broad-scale effort to upgrade the standards of everyday living.

The availability of meat per capita is still about one-third that of the U.S. But in this respect also the latter part of the fifties gave evidence of considerable progress, almost a doubling. In spite of this, meat lags behind, not in quality but in quantity. Efforts are now being made to augment by all possible means the production of pork and beef, primarily through considerable expansion of grazing pastures and an increased growing of corn. A number of modern slaughterhouses are being constructed. No less than seventeen large complete slaughterhouses were placed on order in Sweden in 1963. These establishments are combined with factories for sausages and meat preserves. About 65 per cent of the meat goes into this kind of production.

Also in this area of food production one encounters the adverse distribution problem—how to overcome the vast distances of the giant country and offer equal improvements to all parts. In addition, two other factors play a role. Not only distribution difficulties but probably also military considerations explain why such a large part of the meat goes into the manufacture of meat products with a long shelf life. Furthermore, the Soviet woman is—to an extent which we in the West only are beginning to realize—gainfully employed outside the home. This has raised the need for ready-made foods, and therefore the assortment of preserved and prepared meat products has been considerably broadened and made available to the public. The quality of these products is often surprisingly high, sometimes above what has been considered economically defensible in the meat industries of the West.

The Green Belts

A characteristic feature of the Soviet food front is the green belts of fruit and vegetable cultivation which surround most large cities. They are huge, specially equipped establishments. One of those which supplies Moscow comprises 750 acres. The whole area is irrigated—often attached to sewage plants for disposal purposes. In most cases, cultivation is on a year-round basis. This same Moscow farm has 45 acres of hot and cold greenhouses. Totally, there are 75 acres of hothouses around Moscow. Comparable figures can be given for Sverdlovsk, Novosibirsk, and several other cities.

The enormous distances and excessive transportation costs have brought about this type of local production, which effectively competes with canned or otherwise preserved fruits and vegetables. Providing vitamin C in adequate quantities to the entire population is still an acute problem for the U.S.S.R., which is almost completely devoid of citrus fruits, simply owing to the lack of adequate subtropical regions for large-scale citrus-growing. The irrigated lands of Central Asia are badly needed for cotton production. Potatoes, white cabbage, and tomatoes have become the most important vitamin sources. Wild-rose hips are collected on a major scale as a source of ascorbic acid whether used directly as food or as extracted by the pharmaceutical industry.

Food Research

Special research institutes are devoted to milk and meat. Their chief divisions are located in Moscow. Besides these two, there is a special research institute for canning and drying of foods but with somewhat greater emphasis on fruits and vegetables. It works closely with the specialized food institutes. The development in Kazakhstan and in the newly cultivated areas are discussed in chapter 12. Other institutes are devoted to refrigeration with special divisions for food fish utilization. There are a number of additional institutes for research on bread, fats and oils, mechanization and automation of the food industry, grain milling, and so forth.

The Miracle

There is no doubt that large strides have been registered on the Soviet food front during the fifties and particularly in the latter part. How then was this miracle, as it has been called both in the East and the West, produced? Did they resort to grain stores accumulated over a long period of time in order to produce within a brief period of time increased amounts of animal products such as meat and butter? Or was additional feed imported on a major scale?

It is difficult to obtain reliable figures from the statistics and still more precarious to evaluate their true significance. But by comparing United States and Soviet official figures it has been possible to arrive at a plausible idea of the magnitude of the Chinese deliveries. They were dominated by soybeans (639,000 metric tons in 1959, an important part of the Chinese harvest— maybe one-eighth). In addition, the Chinese—by starving themselves—did supply peanuts, vegetable oils, and frozen meat (!) in order to pay for Soviet industrial goods. All this came to an abrupt end (1960–61) primarily because of the big catastrophes that swept over China (see pp. 113–14). This coincided however with the unofficial start of the rift. Many rate this as the termination of major deliveries of industrial goods from the U.S.S.R. It is now known that the Soviet Union at this point withdrew technical aid, and recalled about a thousand engineers. A number of large construction works were halted in China by these Soviet actions. Termination dates of other undertakings were considerably delayed.

It is interesting to note, however, that the foods delivered were primarily protein carriers. Obviously this is also the Soviet Union's weak point, as it demanded from its chief partner exactly what he himself needed most. Yet, the fact remains that the Chinese deliveries in no major way contributed to the miracle. The Soviet Union was basically able by other means to advance its positions on the food front. The miracle is largely explained by other factors more closely at work within the country. In the first place, the opening up of new lands in Western Siberia and northern Kazakhstan provides the main clue. A land of promise was created here. The steppe and the forest were converted into a grain prairie. Between 1954 and 1958 approximately ninety million acres were cleared and ploughed. This is no less than one-half above the wheat acreage in the United States. The tilled land of the U.S.S.R. has thereby been augmented by no less than 16 per cent. More than half the country's spring wheat acreage is located in this new region. In other words, a whole Argentina has been conjured forth within the Soviet borders, and this feat was achieved in the incredibly brief period of four to five years.

The mechanization of agriculture made the second most important contribution to this miracle, with a gain of at least thirty-five—probably fifty—million acres. The drainage of extensive marshlands further provided much new tillable land, the drainage of the Masurian marshes in White Russia providing the largest acreage—estimated at fifteen million acres when completed. These steps added together provided a solid base for an increased agricultural production and explain the so-called miracle—the great thrust forward in the food sector. It is interesting to note that only through gaining new tillable land in the various ways indicated above is it possible to make such sizeable gains within such a brief period of time. Improved techniques, more fertilizers, new breeds and varieties require longer time for full effect. Khrushchev and his millions understood this fundamental relationship and acted accordingly.

Outside the Soviet Union, the scope of Khrushchev's new "food deal" has hardly been fully realized. Many thousand farms, homes and schools were built and thousands of miles of roads and railways were constructed in the new grain basket (see pp. 227–28).

The total increase in the number of livestock achieved through this operation corresponds to an expanded feed consumption approximately equivalent to what in terms of protein would suffice to feed 110 million people, about half of the Soviet Union's present population. One-third of these "new" animals have, however, been placed in agricultural regions safer from a climatic point of view than the Siberian expanses—in the Baltic states and in the earlier Bessarabia, nowadays called the Moldavian Soviet Republic. These two regions have multiplied their animal production several times over. The remainder is found in the central region of this new granary (see chapter 12).

But new granaries and new acreages are not so easily conjured forth a second time. If additional new lands were cleared both in Eastern Siberia and in the Far East, these undertakings would not be of the same magnitude, as such large untapped areas no longer remain. In the new seven-year-plan main emphasis is therefore placed on seed control, cleaning of seed, irrigation, and commercial fertilizers. Expanded irrigation may, however, in some cases mean additional acreages. The Kara Kum Canal excluded, which is discussed in chapter 12, the largest project now under construction is probably the 250-mile-long canal across the northern part of the Crimea. This will run from the Kachovka reservoir on the river Dnieper, via the Perekop isthmus on to the Kerch Strait. This giant canal is expected to be finished in 1965. It will provide water to a million and a half acres earmarked for the cultivation of rice, corn, cotton, and grapes.

The Latest Crisis

A major disappointment to Soviet planners is the fact that set production goals did not materialize in the sixties. Increases were obtained in grain, milk and meat but not of the magnitude anticipated. These difficulties need not necessarily be given a political interpretation. Early winter, with snow covering the fields prior to harvest, is to be expected in these newly tilled Siberian lands where the continental climate brings an abrupt transition from summer to winter. It could be anticipated that the feed situation would become critical for such an ambitious plan as the projected general increase in the animal production, where such sizable quantities of additional feed grain and other food were needed. It is therefore really not surprising to find that certain agricultural regions bought more feed from government stocks than they themselves produced in their striving to reach these set goals. This does not necessarily mean poorly handled plant production. The vagaries of the climate very clearly aggravated the situation—this is a regular feature throughout Russian history.

Against this background it is quite conceivable that the desired goals of the planners were set far too high, not taking into account that Soviet soils may not be a sufficiently reliable foundation for such an enormously enlarged fodder base. Soviet soil scientists have in effect issued repeated warnings against the intense ploughing of the Siberian regions in question, aware of the obvious water shortage, the great risks for wind erosion damages on the wide plains, and of the low basic fertility of the soils, particularly in phosphates. It is quite possible that the consequences of these liabilities have been so seriously felt that this might explain why such importance is now being attached to the second stage of this development plan for Western Siberia and the Kazakhstan area, namely livestock production, thereby reducing hazardous ploughing over too large expanses. Mixed farming would obviously diminish the risks of soil erosion and affect the rate of soil depletion.

In addition, it should be pointed out that the Russians are not the only ones who have had to eat horsemeat while the mechanization process was pursued. This was the case with both Europeans and Americans—although the latter were mostly unaware of this fact. Soviet agricultural troubles often are allowed to dim unquestionable achievements. Among these mention should be made of how the U.S.S.R. has become the largest sugar producer in the world (via sugarbeet), next to India, but it further heads the world in sunflower-seed production (two-thirds of the world's output), in potato production, and has created vast cotton acreages (second only to those of the United States), rendering, besides fibers, invaluable oil and protein.

TABLE 24
U.S.S.R. Approximate Portion of World Crops

(SELECTED CROPS)
1959–62

Wheat	>1/3	Sugar beets	1/3
Rye	1/2	Sunflower seeds	2/3
Potatoes	1/3		

The U.S.S.R. is top-ranking in wheat, producing per year twice the amount reported for 1948–52, 150 per cent more than in the thirties and twice the crop of the United States. It also leads world production in rye (one-half of the world crop), the yields per acre of which have grown by 30 per cent during the fifties; barley shows a comparable yield increase of 50 per cent. Use of fertilizers has doubled in this same decade and now has in total amount reached a level one-fifth that of intensely producing Europe.

The Daily Diet

In spite of the great progress made in animal production, bread and potatoes still constitute the bulk in the everyday diet of the Russians, as has been the case throughout history. Comparing everyday diets in the U.S.S.R. and the United States on the basis of statistical averages, the evidence—in spite of the considerable progress made—is that two-thirds of the protein content in the Russian food intake consists of vegetable protein, while in the United States the opposite is true. Thus the U.S.S.R. still can be characterized as a bread-and-potato-eating nation but with an important breakthrough for milk. This will soon be followed by fish (see chapter 13), while meat in various forms presumably will lag behind for a very long time, if not always. Soviet soils are less likely, even with the most modern and efficient procedures, ever to reach the productivity levels of Western Europe or the major agricultural regions of the United States. Geographical location and climate clearly indicate this.

If the Soviet Union today would like to provide its people with the United States diet, present food resources—what is being produced on the average—would be enough for only 147 million of the country's present 240 million inhabitants, approximately. On top of this, the U.S.S.R. has to take care of a yearly growth of more than three million people.

Remarkably enough, the Soviet Union must, however, be classified among the well-nourished nations—the "have" nations. The U.S.S.R. is clearly on the favorable side of the great hunger curtain. It is therefore a safe conjecture that the encounter with the enormous needs and shortages of Indonesia, China, and India has evoked concern even among the most orthodox Russian communists. In spite of everything, the regime is committed to an improved standard of living for its own people. This implies a common interest with the West, which in the long run may prove stronger than doctrines.

References

BALZAK, S. S., VASYUTIN, V. F., and FEIGIN, Y. G. *Economic Geography of the USSR*. New York, Macmillan, 1949, 620 pp.

BERG, L. S. *Natural Regions of the USSR*. New York, Macmillan, 1950, 436 pp.

GEORGE, P. *L'U.R.S.S.* Paris, Presses Universitaires de France, 1962, 497 pp.

GUNTHER, J. *Inside Russia Today*. New York, Harper, 1958, 550 pp.

LYDOLPH, P. E. *Geography of USSR*. Madison, University of Wisconsin Press, 1963, 452 pp.

MANDEL, W. M. *A Guide to the Soviet Union*. New York, Dial, 1946, 511 pp.

SHABAD, T. *Geography of the USSR*. New York, Columbia University Press, 1951, 390 pp.

TREADGOLD, D. W. *Twentieth Century Russia*. Chicago, Rand McNally, 1959, 550 pp.

USSR Today and Tomorrow—Facts, Figures, Pictures. Moscow, Foreign Language Publishing House, 1959, 325 pp.

Several Soviet books printed in the Russian language are available on these topics. Owing to the language barrier, it was not considered worthwhile to list these above.

CHAPTER **12**

The Heartland of Asia—
About the Future of Siberia
and Central Asia

"SIBERIA—truly a New America, as it is often called —has immense possibilities. It is the cradle of Russia's future greatness, the gauge of our progress toward democracy and political and economic health. Still more pregnant with future possibilities is our great Far Eastern neighbor—Outer Mongolia. What do you know about it? You yawn and blink shamelessly, and yet Mongolia has nearly a million square miles and untold mineral wealth; it is a virgin land that tempts the greed of China, of Japan, and of the United States. They are all ready to snatch at it to the detriment of our Russian interests—interests that have been recognized by all our rivals, whenever there has been a division of that remote quarter of the globe into spheres of influence."

These are the words of the attorney Komarovskij in *Doctor Zhivago*, the famous novel by Boris Pasternak. This eloquent hopefulness about the future of Siberia does not represent a

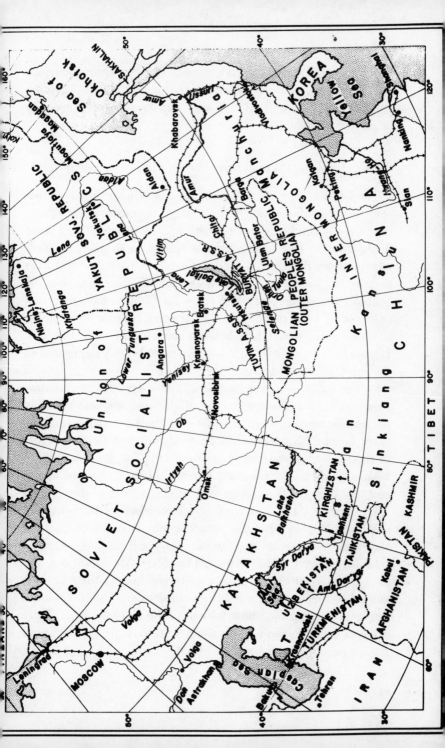

new theme in Russian literature and history. Throughout the centuries czars, military leaders, scientists, and authors have expressed similar dreams, but not until our days and time are they beginning to come true.

China Looking Westward, the Soviets Eastward

The heart of the Asiatic continent is no longer an out-of-the-way corner of the world. It is the stage of intense activity, and it is already the homeland for fifty million people. There is no doubt that this heartland is already subject to an intense tug-of-war between the U.S.S.R. and China. The Second World War contributed substantially to this shifting of interest toward the central parts of the continent. The giant Chinese state was compelled—under the pressure of the Japanese invasion—to look for support inland, having largely lost touch with the coastal regions. Hordes of refugees as well as development brigades appeared in the most unexpected places. Agriculture was started in regions which in many cases were not at all suited for cultivation. However, the most important feature of this invasion was probably the comprehensive inventory taken of the natural resources of these areas. This Chinese stream westward had its counterpart in the Soviet Russian movement eastward. The Russian millions looked for food, coal, iron, and a great deal more, to speed up the recovery from the devastating and ruthless attacks of the German Nazi armies. At the cost of great sacrifice and tremendous suffering, a great liberation attack could be launched against the invaders and victory attained. Stalin will probably at some time be assessed by historians not merely as the tyrant but also as a ruler equal to this great catastrophe and as the man who started to make true the centuries-old dream of several Russian czars: to develop the idle resources of the Siberian giant. There seem to be few people in the West who have a clear picture of the magnitude of this undertaking.

The Old and the New Siberia

The Russian classics have described Siberia as the home of human suffering: the endless transports of prisoners; the seven million farmers who around the turn of the century fled from the serfdom under which for all material purposes they still existed in czarist Russia—these enormous expanses were filled with hardships, starvation, and suffering; the ecstasy of the screaming sects, probably a consequence of combined malnutrition and exposure to the rigors of the climate. In Siberia we also meet with a cavalcade of peoples, such as the Samoyeds, the Tungus, the Evens, the Orochis, the Udegegs, the Goldi, the Gilyaks, the Koryaks, the Chukchis, the Aleuts, the Yukagirs, the Yakuts, and then of course the Eskimos, largely along the Arctic coast.

A severe and harsh Nature has drawn narrow limits for food production. In the north the pine forests stretch out for miles, still teeming with fur-bearing animals, bordered to the north by the endless taiga. These soils are heavily podsolic, leached and depleted through centuries. This taiga gradually changes into the icebound stretches of the tundras and the Arctic. In the south we meet steppes, deserts, high plateaus, and insurmountable mountains. Not until far to the east in the Pacific region is this endless Siberian plain broken up by mountain ranges. Nature offers little that is attractive in this almost desolate massive belt across the continent. Outside of a small and narrow cultivated zone, man can widen his living space only through relentless labor.

Nowadays, this same Siberia has taken on a new countenance, seething with life. Almost everywhere new lands are opened up; ploughing, drilling, lumbering, planting, and building construction are all going on in order to create a new Utopia with the aid of science and technology. Already a number of large new universities are in operation with several thousand students, and in many cases with internationally famous scientists on their faculties. In all cases, science has been mobilized to shape this world of the future.

Urbanization

Doubtless it is no sheer coincidence that Khrushchev in recent years made several of his most important political proclamations in speeches given in Alma-Ata, the capital of the Kazakhstan Cossacks; in Novosibirsk, the capital of Western Siberia; in Bratsk in Eastern Siberia, the seat of a giant power station; and in Vladivostok, which remains the key base for the Soviet marine posture in the Pacific. As late as 1900, in the entire Asiatic part of Russia there was only one city of more than a hundred thousand inhabitants—Tashkent. As late as in 1925, there were still no more than ten places that could be called cities in this vast region. Nowadays the number of cities east of the Volga exceeds fifty, of these six more have passed the half-million mark, and three have almost one million inhabitants. Magnitogorsk, located on the slopes of the Urals, was a small rural village in 1928, but is now a flourishing city of half a million. The gold city Kolyma, in the Soviet Far East, has in less than five years reached the size of 180,000. The mining city Norilsk on the Arctic Sea—the largest Soviet city north of the Arctic circle—was a trading post in 1948, and now claims a population of 190,000. If people continue to move in at an unabated rate, this will be a city of a quarter million by 1965. One-fifth of the U.S.S.R.'s entire population now lives in this continental heartland.

TABLE 25

Approximate Populations in Millions (1960)

Caucasus	9.5	Eastern Siberia	2.8
Middle Asia	23.0	Far East	4.3
Western Siberia	12.3		

What Does Siberia Mean?

Siberia is a term which has been given highly diverse interpre-
tations. Sometimes it is used to signify all Soviet-dominated land
on the other side of the Urals or the Volga. In other contexts it
has become the comprehensive name for the northern parts of
Asiatic Russia. Now and then Siberia is given an administrative
connotation and is defined as the land to the west of the Far
Eastern Maritime Region. In this case it is usually divided into
two units, Eastern and Western Siberia, about equal in size.
The Far Eastern Provinces of the Soviet Union—to the east of
the Yakut Republic—comprise about one-third of Soviet Asia,
sometimes called the Soviet Far East.

The whole of the Yakut area is part of the largest Soviet
republic, namely the Russian Federated Soviet Republic. To the
south of these tremendous northern expanses we find a whole
series of buffer states—Soviet Republics, but mostly inhabited by
non-Russian peoples: Turkmen, Altaics, Kalmucks, Uzbeks,
Kirghizians, Tadzhiks, Buryats, and several others. Since World
War II a considerable immigration of Russians has taken place
to these territories. All these buffer states together form what is
called Soviet Central Asia. This border region constitutes a
tension-filled area between mainland China and the Soviet
Union.

Mongolia

One of the Soviet border states is formally independent of
the U.S.S.R.—Outer Mongolia (Mongolian People's Republic).
When Mikoyan visited the United States in 1958 and spoke to
the students of the University of California, the question was
raised why such a prominent Soviet leader as Molotov had been
relegated to the status of ambassador to Ulan Bator, the capital

of Outer Mongolia. In reply Mikoyan suggested that his audience study the map. They would then find that this is a most important post in the Soviet Foreign Service. Six years later, our own powerful country was negotiating the appointment of an ambassador to Outer Mongolia!

Doubtless an intense tug-of-war is going on along the whole Chinese-Russian border, from Sinkiang in the east to Manchuria in the west. This constitutes an enormous, politically seismic area where the tensions will lead to many quakes and tremors in our own lifetime. Outer Mongolia may be formally independent, but in technical and economic respects, as well as in many other ways, it is a Soviet satellite. Its relations with mainland China were never too close, owing to the immense obstacle of the Gobi desert. In contrast, it is readily accessible from the north, which is why the Soviet penetration has been comparatively easy. The Outer Mongolia state structure is completely patterned after Soviet models. For a couple of centuries this area was conquered by the Chinese in their drive against the repeated Mongolian invasions of their homeland. Nowadays, Soviet scientists, technicians, and agricultural experts head the development program in the mines, the canning factories, and the goat-skin industry. Traditionally a pastoral country, Outer Mongolia is gradually being converted into a grain producer, and the ploughing of new land is being pushed. Livestock-raising is rapidly changing from a nomadic occupation to one of permanent settlements based on grain-feeding. But China has not disappeared from the arena. It may be that China, by providing hundreds of thousands of workers in agriculture, road-building, and house construction—as well as sizeable development loans—established a firmer and more lasting hold over the country than Soviet Russia ever had. Reports from later years seem to indicate that efforts are made to have these Chinese workers return.

Soviet Mongolia has its counterpart in the Chinese Mongolia, in geographical terms named Inner Mongolia. Once again, as several times earlier in history, the Chinese have roamed into this land as settlers. Their typical huts of clay sods are now seen everywhere in the territory. Even in the strategically located Ordos desert, for centuries crossed by caravan trails, assiduous Chinese farmers try to eke out an existence from the soil under desperate conditions. In historical retrospect, this area has been the scene of sharp encounters between the nomadic Mongolian people and Chinese intruders.

The ploughing of the soil, enforced by the new Chinese rulers, already shows catastrophic consequences. Dust storms have followed such permanent soil cultivation. It was from these Mongolian border territories that the waves of intruders threw themselves upon China in olden times, and the famous Great Chinese Wall was erected for protection against these very invasions.

Uzbekistan and Sinkiang

A similar competing twin-state arrangement is found in Turkestan. Soviet Turkestan is called Uzbekistan. By means of huge irrigation systems, built under Soviet leadership, this state has become the Soviet Union's largest supplier of cotton. But on the other side of the magic border we find Chinese Turkestan. There has been a great deal of speculation about the real reason the U.S.S.R. ceded this key state to China. As late as in 1948, the Soviet Russians were the masters and exploited feverishly its natural resources, among them oil. After the victory of Mao Tse-tung, the country was nonetheless handed over to the new Chinese government. The name was changed to Sinkiang (Hsien Kiang) which means "New Frontier." There is no doubt that it plays this very role in present Chinese development plans. Although it has been the new frontier for China ever since the Han Empire two hundred years before Christ, there was no planned development until in our latter days. Sinkiang is largely a high plateau region and contains one of the largest deserts on earth, Takla Makan. The huge Tien Shan mountain range, however, collects a great deal of water, which when released down to the valleys in innumerable small rivers makes agriculture possible and creates the base for vast expanses of pastures (see also p. 106 in the chapter on China). Through new irrigation systems on the fringes of that dreaded desert, efforts are now made to gain new agricultural lands, although under very parsimonious and precarious conditions. It remains to be seen whether the Takla Makan to any major degree can be thus conquered.

The Hunger Steppe

The well-known Hunger Steppe—75,000 km², or 28,850 square miles—spans over Kazakhstan and parts of Uzbekistan and the Turkmen Soviet Republic. It is gradually being subdued with the aid of some of the world's largest irrigation undertakings, covering millions of acres. The Kara Kum Canal, 335 miles long, was inaugurated in 1960. Above all, the shortage of water provides the clue to the scarcity of people in these Central Asiatic territories. They now total, in all these republics together, some 25 million inhabitants, but show the highest relative growth of all areas east of the Urals, namely 38 per cent (in the 20-year period 1939–59). This figure is surpassed only by the Far East but merely by 4.5 million people. Kazakhstan (9.5 million in 1959) is the largest and belongs in geographical terms more closely to Siberia than the others. Immigration on a large scale is not likely, however. Evidently, the Soviet federal government plans to reserve these agricultural areas as suppliers of important raw materials, including food, and therefore wants to save water for these essential production tasks. Comprehensive development has also resulted in a great increase in the role and significance of the Central Asian area for the entire country. These republics now produce over 90 per cent of the nation's cotton, two-thirds of all the raw silk, dried fruit and karakul, 15–16 per cent of wool and grapes, and over 20 per cent of the vegetable oil.

Newly discovered rich deposits of several metals in this general region may, however, force a change in this basic policy by putting a serious strain on available water resources so critically short in this entire area.

TABLE 26

Population Increase 1939–1959 in Percentage

U.S.S.R. (total)	9.5	Western Siberia	24
Ural Region	32	Eastern Siberia	34
Middle Asia	38	Soviet Far East	70

The Amur Region

The tension between the Soviet Union and mainland China is, perhaps, most acute far out in the east. Through the gyrations of history, the Amur River has become the boundary line between the two. It is an old and tragic misconception that rivers constitute good natural boundaries. This assumption is particularly erroneous in the case of the Amur River, which is the water-gathering and life-giving artery to a huge natural basin. In spite of the northern latitude, Amur is ice-free during major parts of the year, thanks to being a receptacle for water from hot springs, some of which are in the river bed itself. This makes the river even more important as a coordinating element.

On the map northeastern China, called Tungpei by the Chinese, looks like a spearhead piercing the Soviet giant. This is Manchuria, to which China has already sent many million people and into which more can be expected to stream. Many of the new widely propagandized Chinese cultivation projects are underway in this very area, including a new important granary in Heilungkiang. Several of the Soviet's new power stations are located on the Amur and its tributary, the Ussuri. In a recently published Soviet book about the twenty-first century a vision is presented of this region developed into a key area within the Soviet empire. The city of Khabarovsk, located where the two rivers meet, is already one of the world's largest inland ports. This book visualizes this city as the center of a huge inland system of waterways connecting three major waters: (1) the Yellow Sea, (2) the Sea of Okhotsk—more specifically, the Gulf of Peter the Great near Vladivostok—and (3) the Tartar Gulf, with its new big port Sovietskaya Gavan, meaning simply the Soviet Port. In this vision all ice is kept away by artificial heating.

The city of Komsomolsk in the same region is rapidly being developed into a Soviet showcase. A new canning, fishing, and shipbuilding city, Nachodka, has been created not far from Vladivostok to the east.

In the early days of the Mao regime a great deal was made of the fact that the name of Amur was a Chinese word meaning peace. It is indicative that this designation nowadays never is used by the Chinese. They prefer to call Amur by a brand new name: the River of the Electric Dragon. This is a modification of the ancient Chinese name for this river, namely Chei-Lung-Sian, meaning the River of the Black Dragon. Its tributary, the Sungari, on Chinese territory is a key source of irrigation water (see chapter 7).

The New America—the Land of the Future

When in 1800 a census was taken which revealed that the population of Siberia was merely one-third that of the United States at that time, the Russian-Siberia fans of those days prophesied that before the end of that century there would be as many people in Siberia as in the United States. By 1880 the U.S. population was ten times as numerous as that of Siberia.

The ten million figure was not reached until 1910. By now there are fifty million on the other side of the Urals. In spite of the northern location, the severe climate, and recalcitrant Nature, Siberia can probably feed at least ten times as many. Will it some day, perhaps, become the New America, as it was named by Dostoyevski, this land which is twice as large as the European part of Russia and considerably larger than the United States?

After having discussed the rich resources of Siberia in terms of gold, coal, iron, diamonds, its endless forests, the oil of the Sakhalin island, and the rivers abounding in fish, Fridtjof Nansen wrote in his book *Through Siberia—the Land of the Future*, a thick volume published half a century ago, which has become almost a classic in its field: "In spite of all this, the true riches of Siberia are her enormous expanses of cultivatable soil—partly also fertile—of which the major portion is still virgin land. Siberia's true gold is her black soil."

The Tselinny Region

The Nansen forecast did not come true until the nineteen fifties. Not until then did Siberian agriculture become an economic reality of worldwide significance, and all indications point toward this becoming a permanent feature. I refer to the large newly tilled lands of southwest Siberia and adjacent parts of northern Kazakhstan, the huge new breadbasket of the U.S.S.R. The Tselinny region with its capital, Akmolinsk, renamed Tselinograd, is the core of this new grain bastion. The farmers breaking soil here were called *tselinniks*. All these new names allude to the virginity of the area—the word "tselinny" meaning virgin soil. Not until 1954 was ploughing started on a big scale for the great breaking of new soil on both sides of the Karaganda mountain range. A total of eighty-five to ninety million acres were opened up here—this is a tilled area only slightly less than one-third that of the United States and more than ten times that of California or four times that of Iowa.

On this new acreage spring wheat is the main crop. Grain cultivation is the first phase in this huge undertaking of colonization. The next step calls for the creation of a large center for animal production on the slopes of the Karaganda mountains. In Semipalatinsk, large slaughterhouses and meat canneries, as well as a branch of the central meat research institute in Moscow, have been started up. The total increase in number of livestock for the entire U.S.S.R. during the fifties, including cattle, sheep, hogs, and poultry, corresponds in terms of human consumers to seventy million population equivalents. In other words, these "new" animals eat as much feed protein as if the U.S.S.R. population had grown by seventy million people. Against this background the present crisis, following serious crop failures that were due primarily to drought conditions, becomes readily understood and need not in any way be related to political shortcomings.

This huge ploughing-up project has sometimes been called Khrushchev's great gamble. In scope and magnitude this venture probably lacks any historical counterpart. In this region 200,000 tractors, 75,000 harvesting tractors, and more than 100,000 trucks are said to operate. It is without doubt an awe-inspiring feat and to no little degree an organizational triumph to have created in such a brief period a wheat acreage larger than the total wheatlands of the United States. Hundreds of miles of railroads have been constructed for hauling away the grain and for bringing in fertilizers. Homes, schools, and hospitals have been built in great numbers. Tents which served as habitations during the first years of this project have disappeared and have been supplanted by permanent homes. Soil erosion, however, is troublesome on these vast expanses where the wind picks up speed as it sweeps along. Also, the soil is short of mineral nutrients in most parts of this region. Already after two or three years of cropping, substantial mineral supplements are needed if yields are not to drop critically. Fertilizer factories are therefore being built at a rapid rate. Drought is a more constant menace. The average annual precipitation is only twelve inches and replaces only one-third of the evaporation; in other words, there is a permanent water shortage. The water of the river Ishim has already been directed to these areas through a closed channel 700 miles long. A still longer subterranean water channel, 975 miles long, is under construction from the Balayu River.

On the other side of the ledger a fortunate chance discovery of substantial underground water resources can be reported. In several cases these waters are fed from hot springs. These subterranean lakes are now gradually being exploited. It is conceivable that these discoveries might possibly make major water projects superfluous, such as the bringing in of water to this region from the river Irtysh, an important tributary to the giant river of Ob. To sum up, the determination with which this opening up of new land to the plough has been carried out clearly indicates that the goal is to transform this entire region into a permanent feeding base for the Soviet Union, and these endeavors are definitely no temporary, although impressive, firework on the world scene.

Admittedly, this ambitious undertaking is in many respects a gamble, but one that makes a great deal of sense. The vagaries of Nature are great, but those of politics still greater, and this heartland lies less than six hundred miles from China's Sinkiang! Recent Chinese accomplishments in opening up new lands in a similar way fade considerably in significance when compared with the magnitude of this major Soviet venture. The Tselinny region would constitute a far more valuable pawn for China than the overpopulated rice bowls of Southeast Asia about which fighting now is raging.

Communications

The Trans-Siberian railroad—the large transverse artery across this vast mainland mass—was built in the second half of the nineteenth century, and is now gradually being supplemented by a whole network of new railroads. New lines run toward China and farther on into the Chinese territories of Sinkiang, Mongolia, and Manchuria. The present seven-year plan of the U.S.S.R. includes 5,500 miles of new railroads inside the Soviet Union. However, this has not prevented the construction of a whole series of modern highways running toward the Arctic region, toward key boundary areas, as well as along these borders. They constitute a system of central highways, planned and under construction by the U.S.S.R.

New Soviet models of jet planes (TU-104) which carry from 170 to 220 passengers fly the distance between Moscow and Khabarovsk on the Amur river (3,500 miles) in seven hours. In another hour they land in the new fishing metropolis Magadan on the Sea of Okhotsk. Small planes, carrying forty-four passengers but with a flying speed of 550 to 600 miles an hour, are of great benefit to Siberia's internal communications.

Baykal

In western Siberia a new Ruhr has been created called Kuzbas, which was forced into being by the Second World War. Together with the Ural region this formed the chief base for the war efforts and is now one of the cornerstones of the industrial might of the postwar Soviet Union. Another important, still more recent heavy industry center is located around the great inland lake of Siberia, Lake Baykal. Almost a mile and a quarter deep, this lake contains more water than the whole Baltic Sea.

From Lake Baykal the huge Angara River thrusts itself down onto the Siberian plain and gradually joins the gigantic Yenisey.

Angara serves the world's largest power station, which was inaugurated by Khrushchev in 1961. This is located at Bratsk. The river is there harnessed in a dam 143 yards high in order to produce when finished four and a half million kilowatts. Its artificial dam reservoir will be half the size of Lake Michigan. A large number of huge electric plants are under construction in this general area of Siberia. They will be further discussed below.

Irkutsk, at the southern end of Lake Baykal, is a new center of learning for Siberia, located exactly halfway between the Urals and the Pacific. It is also the location of the East Siberian branch of the Soviet Academy of Science. The regions to the east of Lake Baykal are sometimes called by the common name Transbaykalia. Another new metropolis of significance is found in that part, namely the university city of Chita. The largest diamond fields of the U.S.S.R. and possibly the world are located along the Khatanga River. They are expected to outproduce those of South Africa before long. This is not far from the border of the Yakut Republic.

The Yakut Autonomous Republic

It is an interesting fact that the U.S.S.R., in spite of important reserves and tremendous capital needs in more centrally located areas of the vast country, is placing particular emphasis on creating and developing the two new industrial bastions of support in this eastern region: the Yakut Republic, and the Far East Maritime Province with Sakhalin and Kamchatka.

This unique Soviet state, half of which is located north of the polar circle and covered with eternal ice, has for more than two millennia been the home of one of the many Siberian peoples, the Yakuts, who have for centuries based their living on the reindeer. This faraway, almost hidden land has large dimensions and is a bilingual country comprising one-fifth of the Soviet territory, and corresponds in size to one-third of the United States. It is now being transformed, with the aid of investments of billions of rubles, into a key foundation of the modern U.S.S.R. Not only that—it seems destined to play an important role in the future world.

In this Soviet republic a fourth industrial center is being created, based on coal and iron. Furthermore, a third Baku is taking shape, which is predicted to become an oil supplier to the world of Siberia. The Yakuts are thought to have the chance of becoming leading producers of both gold and diamonds. Large gold mines are operating on the river Aldan, a tributary to the Lena. These mines are located in the icebound tundra region. Yakutsk, the capital, is situated on the majestic Lena River, and its population already has surpassed the 200,000 mark. At Yakutsk the Lena is more than twelve miles wide and has so far defied all bridge-building efforts. The valley of the river Kolyma, which flows north, contains gold and diamonds which even in the West are estimated as uniquely rich. A U.S. journalist who recently visited these regions reported that these mines do not consist of one but of a whole series of deposits. The leading mine is at Zelenij Nys (Green Cape) and is located as far north as the coast of the Arctic. The first gold bars were reportedly produced here in 1958.

Against Great Odds

It can be seriously questioned if we in the West really have grasped the enormous difficulties involved in human settling in these northern regions. The dead cannot be buried in this icebound soil, and water pipes cannot be laid down. One is faced with a whole array of obstacles and complications quite different from those we customarily have to cope with. Sewage and garbage cannot be disposed of by a charitable Nature. Special disposal units are needed. The heated homes melt away the permanent ice below, causing serious tensions in the ground constructions, finally ending up with destruction through almost explosive readjustments in the soil below. Roads are built from wood, resting as a special elevated structure on the ground. It is evident that under these conditions all modern technical skills, as well as pioneering scientific efforts, are needed to expand and fortify the realm of man against these serious odds. Several of the new mining towns on the Arctic coast, such as Norilsk and Nordvik, with more than one hundred thousand inhabitants each, are in this way built on the frostbound soils of the tundra. Even mining as such meets with strange technical problems under these climatic conditions. This frequently calls for entirely new methods and procedures. Most critical is the task of providing food to these northern millions. With the exception of what hunting and fishing yield and what can be grown in hothouses, all food has to be brought in to these regions much in the same way as a polar camp has to be supplied from the outside.

Against this background one might more clearly visualize the basic and decisive differences between the opening up of the U.S. West and the conquest of Siberia. Science and technology are—to a far greater degree than ever was true in pushing our "frontier" westward—indispensable partners in this great Siberian adventure; but more than that, they have been given the undisputed lead, equally imperative for success. Without the immediate and direct broad support of science and technology, development would hardly be feasible, or would in several instances constitute a hazardous gamble. Seats of learning, with academies, universities, and innumerable research institutes, are therefore being created in considerable numbers in these most remote places. The Yakut Republic today has the world's third-northernmost university (the northernmost is at Fairbanks, Alaska; the second is at Umeå, N. Sweden). The Yakut university has more than 2,000 students, half of which are classified as

Yakuts. These nomads have thus stepped directly from the hunting and fishing stage into the twentieth century. The new university in Chita is mentioned earlier.

The Soviet Far East

The Soviet Far East already ranks as the fourth, maybe fifth, center for the manufacture of steel, cellulose, and paper pulp. Plans visualize a future role for this center in furnishing the population-rich Asiatic markets in India, Indonesia, Japan, and China with these commodities.

The summer period in this Far Eastern region is warm and long enough to permit a rather diversified plant production and animal husbandry. Agriculture is largely concentrated on the climatically favorable and by no means small plains along the Amur valley, such as the Leya and Bureya regions, as well as the area surrounding the Lake of Khanka.

The importance which is attached to these regions is illustrated by, among other things, the new tunnel which connects Sakhalin with the Siberian mainland. According to British press reports, it has enormous dimensions. It is obvious that in the era of the airplane and missile warfare, one seeks to make sure that the lines of communication with an outlying island like this are protected. Sakhalin has rich resources of coal, iron, and oil. Many of these are already well developed, transforming this island into what amounts to an additional industrial base with considerable significance now and for the future. In addition, its fishing potential is basic to providing high-rate protein to the whole Far East region. The tremendous distances within Siberia make regional self-sufficiency imperative, from both the economic and the strategic points of view. This aim was clearly revealed in recent suggestions to Canadian wheat exporters to consider a long-time agreement for regular deliveries of grain to these Far East regions.

The Feeding of the Arctic Region

In spite of everything, the Arctic regions have a number of research centers for plant production and animal husbandry. The breeding of reindeer is given prime attention in order to improve yields, utilization, and meat quality. The reindeer herds may amount to several thousand animals on some *sovchozes*.* Breeding centers have been created, for reindeer, and also for the musk ox. Horses, cattle, hogs, and poultry are all fed on locally available fish resources as an exclusive protein source. There are any number of research reports on these undertakings. Pheasant-breeding is given special attention since it has been found that pheasant eggs have a longer storage life than the eggs from the ordinary hen, as well as a higher vitamin A content. The food shipments toward the north are mostly carried on the rivers and involve intricate organizational problems.

As to milk, little can be obtained locally. Adequate feed is lacking and far too expensive to transport so far from distant forage-producing pastures and feed-grain fields. Milk is therefore procured largely from the Ukraine in the form of condensed milk. A number of such milk plants are operating chiefly in the sugarbeet districts of that state. Preserved fish in cans provide another staple item for this northern region, and there are more than two hundred and fifty different types. Siberian rivers show an abundance of sturgeon, salmon, and whitefish, and are now commercially exploited. They are supported by a chain of canning plants. In areas where the construction of such processing units is not feasible for economic reasons, floating factories have been resorted to, for they move around to places where seasonal catches from sizeable fisheries can be obtained. The mighty Ob River has a sausage-shaped mouth with an area the

* State-owned farms, in contrast to *kolchozes*—collectively owned by the farmers.

size of the upper half of the Baltic. From this single body of water more fish is said to be extracted than from the whole Arctic coastal area, including that of the Bering Sea. It is a center for a drive toward a more intense exploitation of available fish resources chiefly in the fresh waters (rivers and lakes) heading toward the Arctic.

A Super Powerhouse

It seems justified and appropriate to insert a brief note on the large-scale energy powerhouse of Siberia, engineered by the Soviet planners. In many ways this might be considered the real key to the opening up of these slumbering and empty expanses. The hydroelectric plant at Bratsk, mentioned above, is only one in a vast network of similar giant installations under construction or in key planning stages such as:

Nizhne-Lenskaya	20	Ust-Ilimskaya	4
Sayanskaya	6	Belaya	3.5
Krasnoyarsk	5		

(Figures in million kilowatts).

The aggregate capacity of the Siberian electrical stations were in 1964 reported to exceed ten million kilowatts.

The Yenisey basin will have besides the Krasnoyarsk plant the giants of Sayanskaya and that of Ust-Ilimskaya. A chain of three gigantic stations—the Yakutsk, Mukhtuya and the Nizhne-Lenskaya—is planned for the Lena basin. The latter plant will be built at the mouth of this river by the Laptev Sea. The capacity of this station is projected at twenty million kilowatts, incomparably greater than any previous station. This giant will have twenty aggregates of one million kilowatt capacity each. Everything about this plant is unique—the 1.4-mile-long earth dam, the artificial lake, 23,650 square miles in area (almost

1,160 square miles larger than Lake Michigan), the industrialized country with a population of fifty million (the size of either the United Kingdom, West Germany or France).

On the Vitim, a tributary of the Lena, the Mokskaya station of 1.5 million kilowatt capacity will be built. A reservoir with a depth of 150 meters will make possible the regulation of the water discharged by the Vitim. A chain of three more stations of over one million kilowatt capacity each will bring the aggregate capacity of the Vitim up to five million kilowatts. A similar chain of hydroelectric plants is to be built along the Aldan. The largest one will be Belaya. The Aldan river basin is rich in iron ore and coal deposits. One station of a capacity of 2.5 million kilowatts is to be built on the Uchur, a tributary of the Aldan. A number of additional stations are planned for the middle and lower reaches of this river.

In the far northeast, on the Kolyma River, the construction of several large stations is envisaged.

Extensive plans have also been evolved for building thermal electric stations in Siberia, the capacity of the most powerful of which will be up to four million kilowatts. These will have more immediate effect, as power in this way becomes available more quickly. Seventy per cent of all the electricity in Siberia is in 1965 said to be generated by thermal stations operating on cheap coal from open-cut mines.

It can be seriously questioned if the history of hydroengineering has seen anything similar nor envisaged a planning on such a scale. These plants will make Siberia a veritable super powerhouse. This has already had a tremendous "breeder" effect on industrial developments. According to the English press, no fewer than forty-five large industries have been built in the valley of the Angara River, mainly because of the Bratsk station. It is further anticipated that when fully developed the energy resources of Siberia will be ample enough for Siberia to share its riches with the Urals and European Russia.

Siberia: Land of the Future

Many questions arise when it comes to evaluating and mapping Siberia's future. Will the exploitation of this vast area remain a Soviet monopoly? Will Siberia become the promising market of the future world as visionaries in the nineteenth century predicted? This image once lay behind the activities of a great many foreign commercial enterprises that were started up for the development of Siberia. Is the rapidly growing, mainly European trade with the Soviet Union merely the beginning of a far greater expansion? Will the U.S.S.R., even with a net population growth of approximately three million a year, have enough people to take care of all these Siberian riches? Or, before this region has had a chance of its own, will the Chinese millions pour in over the borders into this dreamland? Its dormant stage has persisted through history, owing basically to a shortage of people. This has unquestionably been the prime bottleneck of this immense heartland, and therefore the main prerequisite for an effective development is more people. Or is the world going to witness the third alternative: a still closer cooperation between the yellow and the white race, primarily represented by the U.S.S.R. and China? Will they join hands for this exciting venture, a mutual attack upon the Siberian expanses? Will this then in turn lead to a large-scale race mixture and the creation of a new world power, comparable in force and economic power only to a tightly knitted Atlantic Commonwealth? There are no clear-cut answers to these questions, but the march of history is not governed by fate alone. There is still a chance to affect this development. A great deal will depend on the kind of statesmanship of which the West may be capable.

Since these words were originally written in 1960 the rift between the U.S.S.R. and China has come out into the open. This does not change much, though it may make a closer Soviet-Western cooperation more likely. But this emphasis could rapidly switch through laggardness, dogmatism, or political shortsightedness by either one of the two major contenders.

But, whatever does happen, Siberia remains the New World. It is irrevocably the last frontier of mankind, which is now being pushed ahead in a dramatic, intense, and purposeful pioneer effort by the Soviet Union. In the light of future history the success of this undertaking may very well be judged as its greatest achievement.

It is conspicuously evident, furthermore, that we are running out of time. Already before the end of this very century the enormous Siberian heartland might well prove to be too small for the enormous demands of the rising population tide—in ten brief years the world population has grown by more than 750 millions!

The future will show if Siberia is to become the great armory from which the conquest of the world will take place, or if it will become an asset to all mankind and thus give this globe a breathing spell of about fifty years.

References

BARANSKY, N. N. *Economic Geography of the USSR*. Moscow, 1956, 413 pp.

CAMPBELL, E. M. J., and SHAVE, D. W. *Asia and the USSR*. London, Philip & Sons, Ltd., 1957, 310 pp.

CAROE, O. *Soviet Empire*. New York, Macmillan, 1953, 400 pp.

COATES, W. P. and L. K. *Soviets in Central Asia*. London, Lawrence & Wishart, 1951, 288 pp.

DAVIES, R. A., and STEIGER, A. J. *Soviet Asia*. London, Gollancz, 1943, 205 pp.

GOUSCHEV, S., and VASSILIEV, M. *Russian Science in the Twenty First Century*. New York, McGraw-Hill, 1960, 222 pp.

KOLARZ, W. *Peoples of the Soviet Far East*. London, Philip & Sons, Ltd., 1954, 300 pp.

LESSNER, E. *Cradle of Conquerors: Siberia*. New York, Doubleday, 1955, 774 pp.

LEVIN, M. G. and POTAPOV, L. P. *The Peoples of Siberia*. Chicago and London, University of Chicago Press, 1964, 948 pp. (Translated from Russian original, *Narody Siberia*, published in 1958.)

MACLEAN, F. *Back to Bokhara*. London, Jonathan Cape, 1959, 156 pp.

NANSEN, F. *Through Siberia, The Land of the Future*. London, Wm. Heineman, 1914, 480 pp.

SUSLOV, S. P. *Physical Geography of Asiatic Russia*. San Francisco and London, Freeman, 1961, 594 pp.

THIEL, E. *Sowjet Fernost*. Munich, Isar, 1953, 332 pp.

WHITING, A. S., and SHIH-TS'AI, S. *Sinkiang: Pawn or Pivot?* East Lansing, Michigan State University Press, 1958, 314 pp.

Also in this chapter information has been collected from a large number of Soviet Russian publications.

CHAPTER 13

The Soviet

Fisheries

Revolution

FISH has been given high priority in the Soviet efforts to improve everyday Russian diet. Among the many upheavals which have taken place in the Soviet union of republics during the last few decades, the happenings on the frontier of fisheries are not the least significant. In czarist Russia most fish came from the local resources of the inland seas, rivers, and lakes. A mere one-sixth of the catch emanated from the oceans and was largely consumed in the coastal regions in the east and west. The development of fisheries accelerated in the fifties, and for each year that went by, an increase in yield of no less than 10 per cent was registered. This growth would not have been possible if the resources of the oceans had not been increasingly tapped. Three-fourths of the fish landed today originate in the seas. In addition, the aquatic catch is now manyfold compared to czarist days (in 1963 a total of 4.2 million metric tons). The development of ocean fisheries has been given high priority and this huge investment has paid off well. Inland fisheries have been jeopardized by industrialization and thus have stagnated in spite of compensating measures to boost artificial fish-raising.

The Caspian Sea

The Caspian is for all practical purposes an inland sea. Prior to World War I it yielded 726,000 tons of fish, or about 65 per cent of the entire catch. It is still an important source. But the quantity of food fish from this water is now down to less than half of the amount harvested in those years. Its northern section is gradually vanishing from the globe. In the last two decades this part has shrunk about one-third and the water level is down

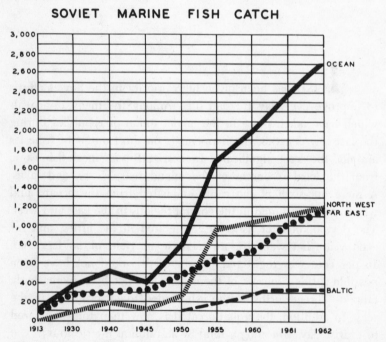

FIG. 38   Soviet marine catches surged ahead in the fifties. The Pacific is now taking the lead.

more than six feet. The sizeable irrigation projects in lower reaches of the Volga cover hundreds of thousands of acres and have deprived the Caspian of much of its normal influx. Salty marshlands now border the shorelines and cover hundreds of thousands of acres. The delta regions of the Volga and the Ural rivers have been considerably enlarged. Many former Caspian fishing villages have lost all contact with water and are now ghost communities. Changes of this nature and dimension take place in quite another time scale than do the secular changes observed and described by geologists.

The role of the Caspian as a food resource would have been even more precarious if permission had not been given a couple of years ago to use light-attraction in fishing. This brought about a considerable increase in sardine catches to the canning factories. With the desiccation, the salt level of the water gradually rises. This in turn has repercussions upon the composition of the fish fauna. This has for the time being favored the sardine, but at the expense of the Caspian herring, a special variety most closely related to sprat. This more valuable fish has been tapering off and is on the verge of disappearing. At one time this species accounted for half the annual catch or 363,000 tons. As late as the thirties it still exceeded 198,000 tons, but is presently reported to be down to about 55,000 tons per year. The Caspian is gradually being transformed from a rich to a poor water both in number of species and their quantities. In order to earn a living, the fishermen have resorted to the catching of feed fish, which is delivered to reduction plants for the manufacturing of oil and meal. To a certain degree this has averted a continued decline in the catch figures, by partly compensating for the drop in the harvests of fish for human food. In the long run, however, this development is likely to aggravate the situation, since in this way the balance is disturbed, if not upset. The food fish are in this way deprived of their feed.

Other Inland Waters

The Black Sea always was a poor fishing water. The salty Mediterranean water fills up the lower levels of the basin. There the sulphur bacteria reign freely. The lack of oxygen combined with the large-scale appearance of hydrogen sulphide practically extinguishes all other living organisms. Large-scale biological investigations have been carried out which paint the picture of a dying water. The annual fish yield is now approximately the same as from the Caspian Sea, which is of about equal size in surface area.

The northern bay of the Black Sea, the Sea of Azov, is shallow. It yielded good catches until, in recent years, similar detrimental factors as those operating in the Caspian were felt. The regulation by man of the river Don speeded up desiccation by extended use of its water for irrigation, a spreading and consuming of available water resources leading to increased evaporation. The Sea of Azov now renders only one-fifth of the food-fish quantities which were harvested there during the thirties. Also the fishing villages on the earlier shoreline have lost access to the sea. As in the Caspian, efforts have been made to compensate for this decline by larger takeouts of feed fish, but similar negative effects are reported.

The Side Effects of Industrialization

Like other industrialized societies, the Soviet Union is now experiencing the detrimental effects of an increasing water pollution. Hydroelectric plants are causing disturbances in the regular water flora. Rivers and lakes become recipients of undesirable chemicals, some toxic to fish. Paper-pulp factories and large metallurgic industries add to the plight. From an increasing number of fresh waters, declining fish catches and increasing fish deaths are reported. Even the Siberian expanses are threatened, and the Lake of Baykal, which seems to be so distant and well protected, was recently the object of a forceful rescue action by the Soviet Academy of Science to stave off a threatening suffocation, caused by the hurried industrialization of the region. Its distinctive and famous flora and fauna, including the fish resources, were imperiled.

Even the sturgeon fisheries, and thereby the precious caviar, are in danger in the Volga, the Ural, and other rivers. Countermeasures are now being taken, but so far without visible returns. The sturgeon is almost extinguished in the Lake of Aral. The total Soviet catch of this fish is presently down to half of what was landed prior to the Revolution. Thus, the inland fisheries of the Soviet Union are dwindling and pose many crucial problems. To compensate for the decline, well-planned and apparently successful endeavors have been launched for the promotion of fish cultivation. The artificial cultivation of carp reportedly renders more than 150,000 tons. This exceeds by 50 per cent the total salmon catch of the United States.

Fish Cultivation

Fish cultivation is actively supported by state authorities, and a series of stations for fish cultivation, so-called *rybchozes*, have been established in regions especially suited for this purpose. Furthermore, a network of fish hatcheries has been created. Extensive plans have been made to provide even minor regions with fish ponds, probably in order to relieve the transportation system of the country but also in order to be able to guarantee regional supplies of high-grade protein. This becomes particularly important because of the climatic hazards to which agriculture is exposed—affecting a dependable animal production. Usually these pond installations are combined with the rearing of ducks, whose droppings directly fertilize these waters and spur plankton production, thus providing more feed to the fish. Many cities are being furnished with establishments for fish cultivation as a means of disposing more efficiently of their sewage. Such a fish farm of giant proportions is under construction to serve Moscow.

The many hydroelectric dams and reservoirs for irrigation, which have given the country significant new water resources, have a combined acreage estimated at twelve million acres. Several of these waters are utilized for fish cultivation, but it will take many years to build them up to full productivity. So far the amount of fish obtained this way is minor, but considerable gain is expected in the future, when biologists have managed to build up fauna and flora into balanced and productive entities.

Thanks to all these measures, the U.S.S.R. has become one of the leading fish cultivating nations and now has at its disposal about half a million acres of producing ponds. This is an impressive achievement, although the country cannot by any means compete with China, which is much more favorably located for this kind of venture. According to the latest reports this country now has about seventy-five million acres for fish culture.

In the field of fish cultivation the U.S.S.R. is also cashing in on more than two decades of systematic research, as we shall see. Unhampered by preconceived notions, Soviet pisciculturists went beyond the traditionally cultivated carp and certain salmonids, trout, and others, and tried out a wide range of species thus far little used for this purpose, and even bred new fish varieties specially adapted for culture. In many cases these efforts have already been successful. To the fish combines in Moscow, baby sturgeon is regularly delivered from fish ponds. They arrive at these factories in live condition in refrigerated railroad cars of special construction and are there processed into ready-made foods. At the large industrial exhibit in Moscow in 1958 and later, these railroad cars could be inspected, and a detailed survey was presented of the various types of fish-cultivation ponds which have been developed.

A lively experimentation is also going on with fish transplantations. The species of the Lake of Baykal are transferred to the lakes in the west and the species of European Russia are tested in the eastern waters. The Baltic herring grew more than twice as fast when transferred to the Sea of Azov. Most spectacular has been the transplanting of the Pacific salmon and the king crab to Barent's Sea. This salmon seems to have established itself and has thrust southward, making king salmon a frequent prize in cod fishing off the coasts of Norway and occasionally around the British Isles. Other examples are the transfer of the Amur River species to the Baltic basin, the introduction of North Atlantic cod and herring into Antarctic waters. The result is not known in all cases. Hybridization has also been successfully carried out in several instances and resulted in useful new kinds of fish.

The Land Colossus Goes to Sea

The population growth which in recent years has amounted to more than three million annually, or fifty million or a whole England in a quarter century, has made it imperative not only to compensate for the decline in inland fisheries but also to procure more reliable and larger fish resources. The land colossus therefore became forced to move out onto vast ocean expanses. This created intricate and burdensome domestic transportation problems for railroads and highways. These appear to have been mastered. The success of this large-scale food procurement from distant waters may be considered in many respects the most important postwar accomplishment on the Soviet food front.

The U.S.S.R. holds the third place, after China and Japan, in terms of human food extracted from aquatic sources. In 1962 the Peruvian catch of anchoveta for fish meal in the Humboldt Current managed to exceed the total catch of the U.S.S.R.; almost all this tremendous takeout feeds the human race only indirectly. Soviet harvests per year from the oceans are in excess of three million metric tons, while inland fisheries amount to one million

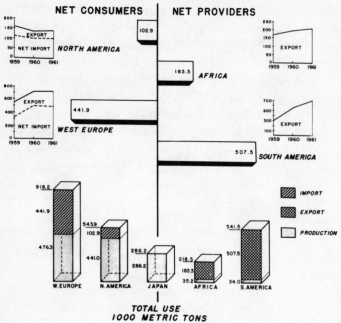

FIG. 39 The two well-fed continents of Western Europe and North America are the chief recipients of the protein riches extracted from the sea and converted into fish oil and fish meal. The two most protein-short continents are the providers. The hogs and broilers of the rich world eat far better than the malnourished of Latin America and Africa.

tons. Initially, main emphasis was placed on expanding the Atlantic fisheries; in the sixties the Pacific region received the lion's share of the investments. In this Far East region a tuna fleet is being put into action, fishing in the Sea of Okhotsk, particularly in Peter the Great Bay as well as around Sakhalin and off the shores of the Kamchatka peninsula.

Both in the Atlantic and the Pacific the landing ports are far from important population centers. Furthermore, a number of distant fishing waters are being exploited. Despite increased landings from the Pacific, these catches are insignificant in terms of filling the nutritional needs of this enormous land. Large fishing fleets are therefore dispatched on a growing scale to all the oceans of the globe and to all major fishing grounds. The strivings for world dominance are quite obvious also in this field of fisheries. They are, however, challenged in this area by Japan, the chief contender, although many large fishing vessels and factory ships are built on Soviet order by Japanese shipyards.

The Atlantic Operations

For a considerable time, the Pacific held the lead in marine catch, and not until the fifties did the Atlantic become the largest supplier of fish. In the second half of the fifties, the Soviet fleets started to fish distant waters systematically—the Davis Strait west of Greenland, the Flemish Cap (named the Sverdlovsk Bank by the Russians), and the Atlantic waters off equatorial Africa down to South Africa. These new fisheries were preceded by scientific investigations combined with extensive exploratory fishing. These started on a major scale immediately after Stalin's death in 1954. Each season, large fleets were dispatched to these distant waters, several thousand miles from the home shores.

In 1960, the Soviet Academy of Science requested that no less than fifteen research vessels be sent to the waters west of Greenland to map out the strange migrations, diurnal and seasonal, which several fish species of commercial importance undertook here. In 1961 considerable catches were reported from South African waters where a Soviet exploratory fleet then operated for several weeks.

The Soviet tuna hunt is primarily concentrated in the mid-Atlantic, ranging from the Bay of Biscay in the north all the way down to the coastal waters of African Guinea. Along the coast of tropical Africa—chiefly from Agadir and Cape Blanc in the north, southward to Abidjan on the Ivory Coast and Takoradi on the Gold Coast—other fisheries have been developed which so far seem to render a good yield. Large catches of mackerel, sardines, and other fish are reported from these waters.

Sardine fishes are light-attracted and then pumped on board directly. They are immediately chilled in basins (to reduce slime formation) and then bulk-frozen in blocks of fifty to a hundred pounds after having been densely packed with the aid of vibrating installations. Within an hour after the catch this rapidly spoiling fish is preserved and in a perfect way, probably while still alive. These blocks are shipped to canning factories in the homeland.

The Soviet fisheries of the southwest tropical Atlantic have been extended southward to include major operations off southwest Africa, particularly at Walvis Bay, and in the waters off South Africa, trawling for pilchards and various whitefish. Red Sea operations have been initiated by Soviet flotillas, even in this case after previous oceanographic and fisheries reconnaissance.

The Greenland Fisheries

In the winter of 1960–1961, more than 25,000 Soviet fishermen were busy fishing, freezing, and canning at the famous fishing banks of Newfoundland off the Labrador coast. This amounts to a whole Soviet working city comprising from 150 to 200 fishing vessels and three or four floating factories to take care of the catches. In addition to the units directly engaged in fishing, each fleet comprises some two or three search vessels, specially equipped to assist the trawlers in locating the fish shoals. Four modern salting factories and several freezing units are attached to this flotilla. Fleets of the same great size have been reported in subsequent years. Thus the Soviet Union outdid all other nations in these waters, which for centuries were visited by the Portuguese, Spaniards, Frenchmen, and later by Englishmen and Germans as well as by other nations. The processed products are brought back to the home bases by speedy transporting vessels, and when the ships themselves return home they are filled up. Ocean perch, cod, and haddock constitute the principal catches. Bases for these fishing activities are Murmansk on the Arctic Sea, Kaliningrad (formerly Königsberg), on the southern coast of the Baltic Sea, and recently also Riga, the capital of the Soviet Latvian Republic.

George's Bank

Since 1960, Soviet fishing fleets have been fishing the George's Bank off New England's coast with a constantly growing number of vessels, served by factory ships and freezing trawlers. The U.S.S.R. is currently without any doubt the largest catcher on these prolific fishing grounds. Smaller units have been seen on fishing operations along the entire Atlantic Coast of the United States, from Cape Cod in the north, in the waters off North Carolina, down to Florida, but carefully adhering to international waters.

Other North Atlantic Waters

Back in 1960 it was reported in the morning news in the United States that English fishermen had seen nearly one thousand Soviet fishing vessels in the waters north of Iceland. Although this figure seems somewhat exaggerated, possibly because that observation coincided with the push towards the Arctic of the United States Polaris submarines, English fishing journals, at this time expressed concern about extensive Soviet fishing activities north of Scotland, north of Ireland, at the Dogger Bank, and at the Faeroe Islands. From 90 to 100 Soviet ships were actually fishing close to the east coast of the British Isles during this same season. Between 150 and 200 have been trawling along the west coast of the Shetlands each year since the fall of 1959, normally accompanied by motherships and freezing vessels.

Since 1955 a number of Soviet ships have participated in the North Atlantic herring fisheries, both off Iceland and along the Norwegian coast. In later years they seem to have concentrated more upon the waters south of Iceland and around the Faeroe Islands. These fleets are regularly visited by speedy, combined supply and transport vessels. They deliver salt, barrels, food, spare parts, and medicine, and bring home catches. These large-scale Soviet operations have created considerable anxiety among the English, especially with regard to the North Sea where the yield from the herring fisheries has been small in recent years.

A number of Soviet ships have conducted exploratory fishing in several parts of the Gulf of Mexico and the Caribbean, partly aiding Cuba in building up its fisheries. Reconnaissance tours with exploratory fishing have since 1961 been reported from the waters off the Brazilian coast. Besides the small fleets which have been spotted off the coasts of North Carolina and Florida, some 120 trawlers are operating in the mid-Atlantic and the Caribbean and later will be using the new Havana base being built for the U.S.S.R.

The Home Bases

The main home base for the Atlantic Ocean fisheries used to be in Murmansk on the Arctic Sea coast. New installations and improved facilities have been made available here subsequent to World War II in order to meet the anticipated expansion. A high degree of automation has been introduced into the unloading and other handling of the fish.

Both Kaliningrad and Riga have also been moving forward as important fishing ports with large new freezing factories, refrigerated warehouses, and canning plants, greatly exceeding in capacity the limited fish resources of the Baltic Sea. In 1963 it was reported that a third major base was being erected in Tallinn, the capital of the Soviet Esthonian Republic. From these bases the fishing fleets and floating factories are regularly dispatched to the northwest Atlantic and the tropical Atlantic waters. The fleets are in continuous radio contact with their home bases. Their catches are all brought back as raw material, primarily for canning but also for salting and smoking. Some is defrosted and made into ready-made foods.

Kherson on the Black Sea, well known since ancient times, is another receiving port for the fish catches from the tropical Atlantic. There too the frozen blocks are converted, after thawing, into canned and smoked products.

The Pacific Scene

Many readers will recall the naval skirmishes between Soviet and Japanese units which frequently were reported in the daily newspapers of the thirties. Fishing interests were largely behind most of these incidents. At that time, Japan had put into operation several large floating canning factories which operated freely in the Sea of Okhotsk and also quite close to the territorial waters of the U.S.S.R. Primarily salmon was taken, on its way to spawn in the rivers of the Far East mainland and the peninsula of Kamchatka. Salmon fisheries both in the Sea of Okhotsk and in the Siberian parts of the Arctic have importance to the Soviet Union's Far East regions. The Japanese activities deprived these areas of important protein resources.

Nowadays the roles have switched. As before, the Soviet-Japanese fishing negotiations take place in a strained atmosphere, but now the U.S.S.R. dictates the terms. In our days the Soviet Union has the marine supremacy in these waters. The salmon quota has for each year been reduced. Japan can now operate only two floating canneries in the Sea of Okhotsk where as late as in the forties she used to have sixteen or seventeen. With Magadan and Nakhodka as new centers, Soviet flotillas are fishing these waters in addition to their coastal operations. Peter the Great Bay is completely closed to international fishing.

The northern parts of the Pacific Ocean have become centers for extensive Russian crab fisheries which have greatly expanded. Floating canneries, in quite a number, manufacture the well-known *chatka* crab, exported widely and sold in food stores around the world, including the United States.

Advances are being made southward, and the U.S.S.R. started in 1961 the building-up of a Pacific tuna fleet. Exploratory fishing has been pursued in the South China Sea, in the Indian Ocean (around the Chagos Islands) and in the Red Sea, combined with technical aid to Yemen.

The Bering Sea

One day in 1961 the radio news told the Americans that a big Soviet fishing fleet of more than one hundred units had been sighted at Bristol Bay just outside international territorial waters. This is a major fishing ground for Alaska salmon. The U.S.S.R. is now operating over the entire Bering Sea as if this were a Soviet inland water. Lately, Japan has appeared in these same waters as a serious contender. Several Soviet fishing fleets are active in these regions, however, and are often sighted in the eastern parts of the Bering Sea and around the Aleutian Islands. They have also penetrated this island chain and moved into the Bay of Alaska. Some units catch crabs in the Shelikof Strait, south of Kodiak Island. Several fleets have been spotted along the entire Alaskan peninsula. Others traverse the big gulf and catch close to the mainland around Yakutat. Here they get flatfish, cod, herring, and black cod. They have also started the catching of halibut.

United States fishing experts have reported from inspection trips in these waters during the winter of 1960–1961 that they were impressed not only by the modern Soviet trawlers, which in the spring of 1960 amounted to 129 in the eastern part of the Bering Sea, but still more by the many up-to-date freezing ships, no less than fourteen in number. The fleet further included two oil tankers, two transportation vessels, and several searching vessels. Each year since 1961, several flotillas of from sixty to eighty ships with accompanying freezing trawlers and crab-processing ships operate in different parts of the Bering Sea. Alaskan fishermen have looked upon the Soviet fishing activities as a kind of intrusion in what traditionally was their fishing domain. This resulted in 1960 in a proposal presented to the United States Senate that the United States government should obligate itself to build so-called supertrawlers for fisheries to counterbalance those massive fishing enterprises not only of the U.S.S.R. but also those of Japan.

Intense Research

A special fisheries commission has been active within the Soviet Academy of Science. Its main task is to lay the scientific groundwork for an expansion of the Pacific Ocean fisheries into new species, such as the scorpionfish and the sablefish. The studies have already yielded practical returns in the rapid development of one of the largest single fisheries in that ocean, namely the catch of the *saira*, a species closely related to the mackerel-pike. The Japanese have also created in their northern waters a flourishing saira fishery. The U.S.S.R. has built on the island of Shikotan—taken from Japan at the end of World War II—large plants for the canning of these catches. Close to the shores in several parts of the Bering Sea, Soviet fishing experts have established the existence of large stocks of flatfish. Findings of a similar kind in the thirties in Peter the Great Bay were soon depleted. Since then it has become important to establish the conditions for a maximum sustainable yield. These fish are of great age. Some live at great depths and require new intricate catching devices. In these waters the continental shelves are narrow. Much research, biological as well as technical, is now devoted to the mapping and utilization of these deep-sea resources in the trenches close to the coast, off Sakhalin and Kamchatka.

Floating Freezing Trawlers and Motherships

The Soviet Union, which at the end of the Second World War did not have more than three hundred good trawlers, now has at its disposal nearly three thousand and operates floating fish-processing factories on practically all the world's oceans. Freezing dominates, but the processing ships are also equipped for canning and drying of a certain portion of the catch, and in addition, fish meal is produced on board from the waste. Food technology knows few counterparts to this tremendous expansion which in many respects constitutes a pioneering feat.

The U.S.S.R. could build upon an old tradition both in moving their fish-processing to sea and in resorting to freezing. This latter development originated as early as in 1880 when freezing equipment was installed on barges which moved from the city of Astrakhan up the Volga River and back again and out into the Caspian. In the same way the fish catches of the Yenisey were utilized as early as 1904. With the modern freezing fleet in excess of three hundred units, of which some have a freezing capacity of fifty metric tons daily, similar activities now extend far away from the homeland shores.

Food-processing, then, is the key to the considerable success of this marine empire created in the brief postwar period. Without the concurrent enlargement of the processing facilities these extensive fisheries activities could not have taken on these proportions. A great deal of the credit for the progress made is due to Soviet research in the general field of food-processing.

Processing operations at sea encountered great technical and economic difficulties when tried earlier by various nations such as France, the United Kingdom, Germany, and the United States. The Soviet technologists had to overcome many intricate problems. In effect, twenty years of intense research and development lie behind the realization of this marine empire. Twenty-five to thirty years ago several fisheries research institutes were started, it appears, upon the initiative of the secretary of commerce Anastas Mikoyan—now elevated to the presidency. Throughout this entire period investigations were carried on in a number of areas, and not the least concerned floating processing units. One vessel after the other was built, launched, and scrupulously studied. The findings were applied in the construction of new model ships but in full-scale rigs—all with the aim of attaining maximum efficiency as well as minimum space. These experiments were not conducted on a kind of pilot scale but by the building of full-scale operating vessels. Utmost mechanization as well as automation has been the additional goal, in order to limit the size of the crew to a minimum. Most of the immediate postwar models required one hundred men, but in the latest ones the crew has been reduced to eighty.

When the war ended the U.S.S.R. was therefore in position to place on order immediately a large number of modern ships at shipyards over the world. Detailed designs and blueprints accompanied the orders. This was all possible because of the thorough, long-range research and development work. Many of these first series of ships (normally more than one of each) were built in West Germany, England, and Denmark. At the moment (1964) the technical buildup of the Soviet fishing fleet is pursued with still greater vigor. New modernized catching vessels and processing ships (for freezing and canning) are being built in France (3), Holland (4), Sweden (10), West Germany (17), Japan

(20). The figures in parentheses give the number of ships now on order (in 1964). West German shipyards built twenty-four of the so-called original Pushkin trawlers of 2,450 metric tons, a combined fishing-and-freezing ship with a stern chute for the hauling in of the catch. The new freezing-trawlers are larger— 3,000 gross tons.

It is obvious that the Soviets have drawn upon the English experiences with freezing vessels in operations in the thirties among them the trial vessel *Fairtry*. To a certain extent equipment from the West has been installed on these vessels, such as Baader's and Areneo's filleting machines and Norwegian freezers. But on the other hand, numerous new devices, machines, and equipment are the result of experimentation, development work, and improvements made in the U.S.S.R.

Japan is, as mentioned, an important source of new ships. These shipyards built several of the new herring-processing ships for the North Sea, and several tuna vessels.

Many new types of motherships have been incorporated into the Soviet fishing fleet. They serve as rallying points for fishing boats, take care of certain limited processing tasks, and are also supply ships. With movie theatres and other installations for entertainment on board, they also provide recreation for the crews on all the units of a fishing fleet. Most of them have in addition medical facilities including hospital services. Originally, rebuilt freighters were used as motherships, but of late specially constructed models have been introduced. Even larger ones, of 15,200 gross tons, are now reportedly under construction for testing in this kind of service. The best known among these is the Polish-built *Severodvinsk* which serves the Atlantic herring fisheries. It is 155 yards in length and makes 13 knots. It is equipped with a helicopter and a special landing bridge. A special type of mothership is the so-called workshop vessel for repairs at sea. Best known among these is the *Neva*. It was built in Arkhangelsk and is mostly on duty in the North Atlantic.

An Emerging Tuna Giant?

Most significant are the Soviet aspirations as to tuna. The U.S.S.R. is presently joining the big scramble for the migrating tuna shoals of the oceans and this on a very large scale.

Since 1956 the experimental ship *Nora* has been exploring the tuna potentialities of the Pacific. A number of specialized tuna boats are presently on order in Japanese as well as Soviet shipyards. Several are already moving into operation. A new 930-ton tuna vessel with a cruising range of 60 days, built at Leningrad shipyard, has been assigned to several units in the Soviet Far Eastern fisheries. More spectacular, however, are the huge 5,000-ton tuna ships built by Japan on order from the U.S.S.R. These giants are equipped with complete freezing and canning lines and carry on-deck catchers. They will operate in the South Pacific and the Indian Ocean.

The build-up of this tuna fishing fleet shows how justified it is to speak about a Soviet marine empire. Hardly anywhere do tuna fish come in the neighborhood of Soviet territorial waters in spite of the vastness of its lands, at least not in quantities which would motivate organized fishing activities.

Whaling Expansion

The U.S.S.R. has had a whaling fleet of its own operating mainly around the most western section of the Aleutian Island chain. Despite notoriously bad weather in these regions, with fog and heavy storms alternating, whaling factories are kept at sea accompanying the catchers.

In the latter part of the fifties a decision was made to join Antarctic whaling on a big scale. This must be seen in light of the fat and protein needs of the Soviet giant. In 1960, two top-flight whale factories, *Sovyetskaya Ukraina* and *Sovyetskaya Rossija*, each of 46,000 tons, were launched from shipyards on the Pacific and the Black Sea respectively. They are of record size and have three decks each. They measure 220 meters (240 yards) in length and can process no less than 75 whales per day or 4,500 each season. The freezing capacity per day is 110 metric tons of meat, liver, and other viscera for each unit. The holds for oil in each of the two ships carry 19,800 tons. A third equally large whaling factory, *Yurij Dolgorskij*, was recently delivered from an East German shipyard and became immediately the flagship of the Antarctic fleet. All three are equipped with helicopters. A smaller, also newly built, whaling ship, the *Vladivostok*, also with a factory on board, is now operating in the Pacific. When the whaling season is over, this ship is so equipped as to be used as mothership for the processing of regular fish catches.

Fish-Processing a Life-Saver

The capitals of the new Soviet fishing empire are, as already mentioned, Murmansk, Kaliningrad, Riga, and Kherson in the west, and Magadan and Vladivostok with Nakhodka in the east. Sakhalin and Kamchatka each has several important fishing ports. Murmansk, however, is the largest of all Soviet fishing ports and is presumably taking in more fish than any other port on the globe, at present more than 1.6 billion pounds per annum. The plans for 1965 anticipate that this will exceed 1.8 billion pounds. It is interesting to figure out how many trains leave Murmansk daily, loaded with fish for the many new population centers of the industrial giant. The official figures state that 250 railroad cars leave daily during the peak part of the season, from May to October, and from 100 to 150 during the remainder of the year.

In both the east and the west the fishing ports are far removed from the consumer centers. Fish-processing has therefore become a veritable life-saver since distribution of fresh fish almost forbids itself. Enormous obstacles have had to be overcome and large investments made to secure the additional fish supply for the nation's larder. A considerable expansion of the freezing installations of the country have taken place. The freezing capacity at sea, however, is still the largest. Special Soviet-built machinery is used mainly for so-called block-freezing. But only a small amount of the frozen fish is packed for retail. The fish is thawed out at the canning factories in continuous operation. Part of the fish is then smoked; a considerable amount is processed into ready-made foods. Fried fish fillets and boiled fish in plastic bags are two standard dishes. They are produced on conveyor belts in the large fish combines in Moscow, as well as in other cities. Each production line has a daily capacity of ten to twenty tons.

Canning

Traditional canning has received extensive support. Several hundred factories have been built in the postwar period in addition to those constructed earlier. These new plants are largely concentrated in the major ocean fishing ports. But quite a few are located at important centers for inland fisheries. It is particularly noteworthy that some are found at various points along the huge Siberian rivers and their tributaries. Large-scale single units—fish combines—are encountered in Moscow and other large cities. They operate as described above. It should be pointed out that even in this field, thoroughgoing research has been carried out resulting in a very wide assortment of canned fish products, either cooked, fried, or smoked. In addition to the fish species traditionally used for canning, the assortment includes other species such as cod, pike, and bass, and many species not known in the United States. Fish in combination with vegetables of various kinds are other popular items.

Floating Canneries

The Soviet Union early copied the floating factories of the Alaska canning industry. They were anchored in various regions around the Sea of Okhotsk. But, as already pointed out, Japan here launched floating factories operating at sea. The Soviet Union still sticks primarily to canning factories on land or moored at the coast, but Japan is kept away by virtue of the Soviet Union's military supremacy. The fisheries in the Sea of Okhotsk are under intense development also for species other than salmon, not the least for crab.

Floating canneries were further in use in the thirties both by Japan and by the U.S.S.R. to take care of the crab riches of the Pacific, mainly the king crab, but the Soviet Union has now out-distanced Japan in this respect. With Vladivostok as chief base, no less than ten such factories are now operating at sea. New modern units have been put to use also, the latest of them being the *Koryak*. In Leningrad a new diesel-driven ship of 14,000 tons is under construction for this purpose. The crew on board will comprise 130 men and 503 factory hands. The factory will be able to stay at sea for two months at a time and during such a voyage will can 25,000 cases of crab, 50,000 cases of codfish and in addition will produce fish meal and pack caviar. Such are the activities behind the Russian canned crab, which has become an article for the world market and is found on the shelves in many West European food stores under the name of *chatka*. The tensions in the North Pacific partly explain the considerable expansion of Japanese sea fisheries southward into the Pacific, into the Indian Ocean, and into the Atlantic (see also chapter 9).

A series of new 16,000–17,000-ton vessels are constructed as floating canneries and serve the fish and king crab fleets of the North Pacific. But still larger motherships are now joining the Soviet fleets. In 1964 a giant mothership was launched from the Admiralty shipyard in Leningrad. Mr. Khrushchev, in the summer of 1964, when naming Soviet freezing and transport vessels

(8,000 gross tons) built in Scandinavia, indicated the building of still greater units of 55,000–60,000 gross tons. Experiments are further under way for ships highly automatized both as to the catching and processing.

The Satellite Countries

Poland is rapidly building up its fisheries and creating, on the Soviet pattern, a modern fishing fleet including freezing trawlers and ships for salting operations. The bases for these activities in the Baltic—Swinoujscie, Gdynia, and others—are being enlarged and provided with modern facilities such as refrigerated warehouses, ice-making plants, canning factories, and reduction units. Polish shipyards have delivered several of the most modern Russian freezing trawlers, and the plans are to build at least seventy such trawlers for Poland's own use.

Polish shipyards, and also East German ones, have delivered both trawlers and canning ships to China. Poland together with East Germany also participates in the exploitation of the fish riches of West African waters. Besides, Poland supplies technical assistance and fishing boats to both Ceylon and Ghana. In the fall of 1960 the East German factory ship *Martin Andersen-Nexö* (named after a Danish Communist poet), a rebuilt banana freighter of 7,000 tons, made its maiden voyage to the waters of Newfoundland.

Both Rumania and Bulgaria are seeking to supplement their Black Sea catches by high-sea fishing in the Indian Ocean and the Atlantic. Bulgaria is doing this with Soviet support, and Rumania ordered its huge trawlers (more than 3,500 tons) in Japan. Two of these were delivered in the spring of 1964.

A Marine Empire

As already stated, there is every reason to characterize the gains of these peaceful conquests as the creation of a Soviet marine empire. The catch augments each year a quantity equal to one-fifth the United States catch of food fish. There was a slowing in the rate of expansion around the turn of the decade but the push has gained momentum, resulting in an adjustment upward of the goals set by the seven-year plan to 5.3 million tons. Despite these successes, the U.S.S.R. is purchasing additional fish on the world market, for example, from the United Kingdom, Scandinavia, East Germany, and Poland, and frozen whitefish from Iceland and Norway.

This is a reminder that even the seas, in spite of their vastness, have limitations in their fish-producing capabilities. The Baltic Sea waters show obvious symptoms of overfishing after a large-scale Soviet attempt to expand these fisheries during the postwar years. The North Sea and eastern parts of the Atlantic are under the pressure of heavy takeouts over a number of years, with evident signs of reduced catches. Basically the Soviet Union does not expect considerably increased ocean harvests, if any, from the northeastern Atlantic or the North Sea. Therefore, proportionately more effort and greater investments are used for the development of fisheries off western Greenland and in Labrador waters, the equatorial Atlantic, the Antarctic, and the northeastern and southern Pacific.

The U.S.S.R. will definitely not remain alone or unchallenged in this exploitation of the seas, although it has a considerable lead. The curtain has gone up on a new adventurous chapter in the history of mankind, decidedly more fateful and of greater consequence to man's future than the conquest of space will ever be. A number of countries have joined the race on both sides of the Iron Curtain. Besides Japan, the following countries in the West have followed suit and have acquired modern large trawlers combined with processing facilities or special motherships for this purpose: namely the United Kingdom, West Germany, France, Spain, Portugal, Italy, Greece, and Holland. Among the Eastern bloc the same is happening with Poland, Rumania, East

Germany, Yugoslavia, Bulgaria, and Cuba. Among uncommitted nations with similar trends are Egypt, Israel, India, Pakistan, Ceylon, Ghana and Nigeria.

Soviet Fish Research

A large institute for research in the general fields of ocean-ography, fisheries, and fish-processing is located in Moscow and has five hundred employees, half of whom have academic de-grees. Subsidiaries are located in Astrakhan on the Caspian Sea and in the Far East peninsula of Kamchatka. The Soviet Acad-emy of Science has in addition an oceanological and hydro-biological institute, also in Moscow. A fisheries experiment station and a fisheries college are active in Murmansk. The fish-eries in the Sea of Okhotsk are served by a central laboratory. In Leningrad a special institute for the mechanization of fish-handling is operating, a field in which Soviet research is particu-larly active. A special book has been dedicated to this research work and its results during the last few decades. Both Leningrad and Moscow have research institutes for refrigeration technology, which to a considerable extent are concerned with food research, including fish.

The Soviet Union has today more than fifty research institutes active within the fish field. Most of them have more than one hundred employees, some five hundred. Normally, half the staff are scientists. These facts, combined with the huge investments which have been made since 1955 and which are continued with-out interruption, testify to the strong Soviet position in world fisheries, now ranking third.

Research Vessels

The Soviet Union has at its disposal more than thirty oceano-graphic research vessels, especially constructed for this purpose, and in addition a number of service ships of various kinds. In 1957, twelve such units—converted fishing boats—were dispatched to map the herring migrations in the Atlantic. The majority of these ships are specially built or equipped for research purposes; several have been built in the fifties. The best known is *Vityaz*, launched in 1949, which is entirely devoted to deep-sea research. Reportedly it has already made thirty-five expeditions. Another well-known research ship is the *Mikhail Lomonosov*, of 7,000 tons, launched in 1959. This ship brought the Soviet delegation to the latest international oceanographic conference in New York and also participated in international research programs during the Geophysical Year. It has participated in the UNESCO studies in the Indian Ocean. It is named after the all-round genius of the Old Russia in the eighteenth century, the father of Russian oceanography. A specially constructed submarine, *Severyanka*, belongs to the research fleet.

The *Mikhail Lomonosov* was dispatched during 1962 for investigations of the winter fisheries for herring north of the Faeroe Islands. Together with another research vessel, *Akademik Berg*, the prospects for herring catches at various depths were investigated. Another research ship is named *Ob*, after the giant river. It is specially constructed for exploratory fishing and reconnaissance studies. Two new research units, each one of 4,500 tons and both built in Leningrad, were reportedly on trial trips in 1963. They are both equipped with deep-diving equipment, so-called bathyscaphes, and experimental processing factories.

The Pacific Commission

The so-called Pacific Commission of the Communist bloc holds regular annual meetings for presentation of papers and for the programming of joint research projects. It has organized a whole series of scientific expeditions, chiefly under Soviet management, for detailed stock-taking of the productive potentials of the major fishing waters of the western Pacific. This has given the Eastern bloc a lead in the Pacific fisheries advance. The annual meetings are held alternatingly in the capitals of the member governments—besides the U.S.S.R. and China—Outer Mongolia, North Korea, and North Vietnam. Energetic exploratory surveys are going on, as is fish-prospecting in the eastern part of the Chinese Sea, the Yellow Sea, and the South Chinese Sea. During the winter of 1960 the second joint Soviet-Korean expedition started mapping in detail the production biology of the Japanese Sea. The U.S.S.R. has started fisheries of its own in the China Sea.

Similar Soviet Commissions operate in the Black Sea and the Danube Basin, supporting fisheries research for the benefit of its partners in these waters.

Fisheries in Top Priority

Typical of this global race for food from the ocean is the fact that many protein-deficient millions in Asia, Africa, and Latin America hardly figure in the picture at all. Basically the "have" nations, the well-nourished, to which the Soviet nation essentially belongs, are those that carry through this gigantic exploitation. What Japan is not saving for her own population is sold only in minute amounts to the hungry of Asia or those of other continents—the bulk goes to the well-fed countries, such as the United States, United Kingdom, and West Germany. This is a kind of colonialism in a new marine setting. For the U.S.S.R. it is, however, somewhat more of a vital matter than to the West. The Soviet agricultural troubles are not wholly the result of fumbling government officials and a non-capitalistic economic structure. Far more powerful forces of Nature play havoc also with giants like the Soviet Union; nor is this merely a capricious play—there are quite concrete causal factors that exert their influence, as discussed in chapter 11.

If fisheries and agriculture are to be compared on the basis of how they fare in the grace of governmental planning, it is easy to note that fisheries are in favor. In proportion, far more resources are placed at their disposal. Awareness of the great climatic hazards to which Soviet agriculture is subject has presumably influenced these decisions and allocations. It looks as if the rulers placed greater confidence in the potentialities of the fisheries than in those of agriculture when it comes to providing the rapidly increasing population with animal-protein food. Nonetheless, the achievements of the fifties in the field of fisheries command respect and continue to do so in the sixties. There is even the possibility—in view of the great number of large new units being built, into which numerous new devices seem to be incorporated—that the sixties will be a still more important decade in the annals of Soviet fisheries. Giant trawlers, almost completely automated for both catching and processing, have been launched and are now coming from the shipyards outfitted for trial runs, which the whole world might well follow with greater attention than the cosmic feats and features are followed. They will surely mean more to man's future.

References

Numerous Soviet-Russian books have been published in the field of oceanography, biology, fisheries, and fish processing. Very few have been translated. A standard treatise, however, is the following translated into English:

L. ZENKEVITCH. *Biology of the Seas of the USSR*. New York, Interscience, 1963, 955 pp.

Readers are further referred to:

BORGSTROM, GEO., and HEIGHWAY, A. (eds.). *Atlantic Ocean Fisheries*. London, Fishing News Ltd., 1960, 336 pp.

1. Ovchynnik, M. M. "Development of some marine and inland Russian Fisheries, and Fish Utilization." pp. 267–281.
2. Borgstrom, Geo. "The Atlantic Fisheries of the USSR." pp. 282–315.

BORGSTROM, GEO. "The Soviet Fishing Revolution." *Food Technology* 19(2), 1965.

BORGSTROM, GEO. "The Soviet-Japanese Challenge to World Fisheries." *Proc. Gulf Caribbean Fisheries Inst. 18th Ann. Session,* 1965, 19 pp.

CHAPTER 14

Latin America—
The New Witches'
Cauldron

"**A**S a citizen of the United States let me be the first to admit that we North Americans have not always grasped the significance of this common mission—just as it is also true that many in your own countries have not fully understood the urgency of the need to lift people from poverty and ignorance and despair. But we must now turn from these mistakes—from the failures and the misunderstanding of the past to a future full of peril, but bright with hope." (John F. Kennedy, March, 1961.)

World Record in Population Growth

What may be the reasons for the President of the United States to talk in such stern terms and to air such misgivings? Latin America is swiftly developing into the new witches' cauldron of our generation, much more explosive than ever the hungry millions of teeming Asia or the tribal peoples of Africa, involved in nationalistic ravings and agitation for freedom. Latin America has natural resources far greater than these two other continents but holds at present a dubious record in population growth. Even when successful, comprehensive large-scale development plans—whether pertaining to agriculture, industry, or education—are undermined from within because the presumptive beneficiaries multiply in numbers in the meantime. In several countries and regions a doubling takes place within twenty-five years, something that demographers, economists, and politicians for decades have declared an impossibility. But this is now common in South America, in Central America, and in the Caribbean islands.

The year 1960 will in future historical writings mark the passing of an important crossroad in the history of the Western Hemisphere. In that year the number of people south of the Rio Grande, the border river between the United States and Mexico, passed the 200 million mark. The United States and Canada together were 197 million. The English-speaking North irrevocably lagged behind the South, those speaking Spanish, Portuguese, and some hundred Indian tongues. There is every indication that Latin America will rapidly gain in numbers on Anglo-America. Despite the fact that Anglo-America holds the record for population growth among western nations, Latin America increases almost twice as fast, and unfortunately in many key areas the proportion of destitute people grows at an even greater rate. The resources in soils, forests, and fuel are simply no longer adequate and cannot be mobilized fast enough.

With good reason Latin America has been called the plundered continent. During five centuries its riches have been grabbed, chiefly by the western nations, less in terms of precious metals which the conquistadors sought so stubbornly, more in terms of food, cotton, coffee, bananas, cocoa, bonemeal, and timber. The excess millions in Europe—coming from Italy, Portugal, Spain, England, and Germany—took hold on this continent and sent back home primarily agricultural products. Europe created around the turn of the century a feeding bastion at the mouth of the La Plata River, exploiting the cattle kingdom of the Argentine pampa. The end of this episode in history is already in sight. A new social order is emerging. The continent's own millions are gradually demanding their legitimate share at a time when the population growth is at a record high. At the present rate the population figure for Latin America will pass the half billion mark as early as the 1980's. Even if rigorous birth control measures are applied, which at present seems unlikely, a population figure of this magnitude appears inevitable. Forty per cent of the people living in this southern part of the hemisphere are below fifteen years of age, compared to one-fourth in countries like the United States and Scandinavia.

Islands of Abundance in a Sea of Poverty

But is there any real need to worry—is not South America the huge continent of the future with enormous riches and unlimited resources? A British journalist wrote a few years ago that South America, figuratively speaking, could have been the Land of Promise which the devil pointed out to Christ from the mountain of temptations. It has more tropical soils than any other continent, per person three times more tilled land than Asia; it possesses the largest timber resources of the world. Hidden beneath the mountains slumber enormous treasures of oil, iron ore, copper, tin, silver, and zinc. The list could be made almost endless. South America has also large untapped resources of hydroelectric power. The population growth provides an almost unlimited labor force.

Against this stands the fact that Latin America is one of the poorest and most exploited regions of our globe. The riches, to the extent they have been utilized, have largely been to the benefit of the few—a minority of the growing masses of this southern hemisphere. The food shortage, malnutrition, and deprivation in general are in several critical regions worse than in Asia. The grain and meat of Argentina and Uruguay have not been used to feed the continent. A French writer once observed: "South America is no continent, it is a large archipelago." This holds true in more than one respect. The overflowing food produce of the pampas has created in the Province of Buenos Aires a stronghold of gluttony, an island of abundance in a sea of poverty. In the mountain regions of the Andes as well as in areas located in their rain shadow, a large semistarving empire is encountered. Bolivia and Guatemala get one-third of the protein they need, Ecuador and Colombia one-half. If the latter country should take seriously the urgent task of feeding its people, the present agricultural acreage would have to be doubled or the per acre yields increased twofold. In the fertile valleys which largely belong to the owners of the large *estancias*, the cattle thrive and provide meat largely for the rich. On the slopes of the mountain ridges hard labor and sweat extract a starvation diet for the people, consisting of manioc (cassava), corn, and beans. Malnutrition is common. There is not sufficient food for the whole population, nor is it within reach of the purchasing power of the many. Yet, plans are discussed to attract foreign capital to build up on the luscious pastures of the valleys an export trade in thoroughbreds. The grim truth is that the present livestock of this country consumes in protein what would be sufficient for 130 million people. A realistic adjustment, including a radical reduction of the excessive number of livestock, could presumably give all the fourteen million Colombians an adequate diet. We are horrified at the cattle of India, but in South America the situation is relatively much more serious. Brazil is inhabited not merely by about seventy million people, but its cattle, hogs, poultry, and other livestock correspond as protein consumers to almost one billion population equivalents. In the same manner, Argentina's total livestock equals more than 1.5 billion and those of Mexico close to 380 million.

As was shown in chapter 3, the ratio of livestock to man in this continent is today three times higher than the world average. An adjustment to reality by correcting this ratio, largely a remnant from a colonial pattern serving transoceanic needs or a privileged few, seems both inevitable and advisable. Paradoxically enough this is presumably the only way to improve the nutritional standing of the exploding millions of this huge continent rapidly enough. Latin America has for too long lingered in the past and needs to catch up to its future.

Latin America—South America, Central America, Mexico, and the Caribbean islands—represents a total living mass, which has to be fed, of almost three billion population equivalents. By the same method of calculation, the United States and Canada together have merely one billion and in addition a population which is by and large well nourished. To carry out an adjustment in this respect in Latin America is a revolutionary and intricate task, but appears inevitable.

Latin America inherited through its colonizers a pastoral agriculture, largely run for their own benefit with amazingly little regard for the domestic needs of these vast and increasingly populous countries. Profits were easily made by dispatching the fruits of the soils to distant prompt buyers.

Monocultures

Large acreages of Latin American soil are used, not to feed their peoples, but in dubious efforts to procure foreign exchange. This constitutes the reverse side of the plantation system. Monocultures, such as coffee, cocoa, and bananas take up a considerable portion of this continent's tilled land and, in addition, often its best soils. The British importation of meat and grain from Argentina claims for its production approximately one-third of the tilled acreage and pastures of this country. There is little wonder that Latin America has feeding difficulties. Add these circumstances to the frightening reality of malnutrition and the overall situation takes on almost terrifying dimensions. The quantities of protein that could be obtained by Brazil through switching from growing coffee to growing soybeans would not suffice, however, to remove the present malnutrition of this rich nation even if this were done on the entire present coffee acreage.

Conditions like these justify speaking about South America as one large shadow colony of the West. Economic dependence and integrated continental thinking are still to come and will force agriculture into diversification on a big scale. Monocultures supporting distant beneficiaries are doomed in the light of the immense unfilled domestic needs, not the least in food but also in feed.

Venezuela is an extreme case, with oil as the dominating export article, largely U.S.-owned, with a multibillion-dollar investment. This influx of capital does not stimulate Venezuelan enterprise and hardly reaches the people. The annual importation from the United States amounts to a full billion dollars at high prices, not the least for food (eggs, wheat, dry milk, etc.).

This is the brew in the new witches' cauldron which is simmering here. Although twenty countries are involved, the entire continent is penetrated by a growing nationalism, also among the so-called leftist groups. This movement has a legitimate and highly understandable motivation, to develop—and for the first time in the history of this continent—an agriculture and an industry designed to satisfy the needs of its own people and to put an end to foreign exploitation, be it by the West, the Soviet Union, China, or Japan.

The United States of South America

Historical research may one day give us the explanation why the two victorious generals José de San Martín and Simón Bolívar, at their private encounter on that fateful day in July, 1822, parted without having taken advantage of that unique opportunity to unite the large continent into a United States of South America. Bolívar had as early as 1818 spoken about the urgent need of an "American" pact which brought the South American republics together in one single political unit which would "let America stand to the entire world in all its majesty and glory." Our generation now witnesses the birth pains of such a creation. The Castro experiment, which unfortunately is jeopardized in a political whirlpool, has sent an electric shock throughout the continent. The masses represented by labor, farmers, middle-class people, and intellectuals are no longer inclined to acquiesce to the starvation and misery which marks the everyday existence of the overwhelming majority of the broad masses of this continent. They are prone to create their own alliance for progress, the interests of which may not coincide with those of the United States. In no part of the globe is United States diplomacy and statesmanship put to a more severe and meaningful test than in this very hemisphere. Will we recognize in time the true nature of these signals and will we constructively participate in this new American revolution? There are many indications that we have not realized the real magnitude of the malnutrition in this southern part of the hemisphere, nor recognized the dimensions of the distress facing major portions of this continent. Islands of abundance, such as the city of São Paulo, have been built up largely with foreign capital and have attracted the millions like magnets. This Chicago of South America stands as a symbol for revolutionary progress, but nobody mentions that long ago the city exhausted available water resources. Industries and homes have to be content with electric power during only 40 per cent of the productive period of the day. It is a healthy sign, however, that so many United States and European industries have started factories there to supply the large and rapidly swelling Brazilian market—so far a largely urbanized minority.

Twenty-one million people, called the "flagelados" (the flagellated ones, hit by the scourge of drought), live in the dry areas of the Brazilian hump. Thousands die in this region from starvation and thirst. In large droves the people migrate to new regions, only to return home sooner or later, to regularly face new ordeals and new catastrophes. The deforestation which followed the colonization of this continent is one reason for the water shortage. Subversive agents find fertile ground for their preachings among these harassed victims. Almost one-third of the nation is involved in this drama. In spite of their extreme poverty and serious distress, they carry considerable political weight. They actually are, in this respect, far more potent than the 3.5 million residents of São Paulo. This city has had, in addition, the good fortune to be located in the midst of one of the most fertile red-soil laterite regions of the entire continent. This flourishing center also reaps the benefit of the coffee business. Most of these profits move into their hands. São Paulo boasts of having several hundred millionaires among its inhabitants. Its population consists of 1,250,000 Italians, 1,000,000 Portuguese, 400,000 Spaniards, 250,000 Japanese, 100,000 Lebanese and Syrians. It has 60 per cent of Brazil's industry. Foreign capital, from the United States, France, and Italy, and above all from West Germany, keeps pouring in.

The great question remains to be answered: Can this beachhead of wealth colonize the remainder of Brazil? The country has been compared to the United States in its great thrust toward the west, but it is highly doubtful if a new California or Oregon looms at the western horizon. Before the end of this century, the population of Brazil will exceed two hundred million. It already is and will remain the giant of the continent in numbers, but unfortunately it must be looked upon as a colossus with clay feet when food is taken into account. Decades ago it was already evident that the native soils were poor and inadequate for feeding the country. Not even grain could be produced in sufficient quantities, but had increasingly to be bought and to be imported from Argentina, the United States, and Canada—despite the constant breaking of new soil, various kinds of subsidies, purchasing programs, and unemployment compensations for those toiling on the farms. Surprisingly enough, even the U.S.S.R., in the postwar period, has been one of the grain suppliers to Brazil. The southern province of the country, Rio Grande do Sul, has constantly expanded its wheat acreage and limited its meat production. A fierce battle is raging here between the plough and the pastures. As in so many other nations of the earth, the plough comes out on top when everything is mobilized to secure food for the millions.

The fact remains that the overwhelming majority of the Brazilian producers are subsistence farmers. They are simply not able to produce enough from the soils to relinquish anything at all to the growing urban millions. In most regions the diet is dominated by tapioca, which gives a flour rich in starch but low in protein. Widespread malnutrition followed by deficiency diseases is the sad outcome of this monotonous and inferior diet. The stomach may be filled with starchy food, but this does not provide building material for the body, nor does it release adequate energy.

The Caribbean Islands

Lloyd George, the famous English politician of the early part of this century, coined a phrase about the Caribbean islands, calling them the "slum of the empire." Already in his days, this whole region was threatened by devastation induced by overpopulation. Since then, conditions have not improved. On the contrary, they have become seriously aggravated. On many of the larger islands, such as Jamaica, Barbados and Puerto Rico, the forest cover has been reduced to a minimum; merely a pittance of some 1 to 3 per cent of the land area is retained in forests.

Their function of protecting the soils is wholly lost. The once rich bird life has vanished. The green sea-turtle, which at the time of Columbus's arrival grazed the vast underwater meadows and as meat-provider held the role of the bison in the prairie provinces of North America, is for all practical purposes extinct. (See chapter 17, p. 389.) Protein deficiency is reported and recorded from all regions and has in several places reached critical dimensions. Three-fourths of Haiti's children are seriously undernourished and thousands are starving outright.

Operation Bootstrap

There is a great deal of talk about the Puerto Rican miracle, resulting from the so-called Operation Bootstrap, where all the Western patent medicines have been administered. There is no question that considerable progress has been made within the framework of this undertaking. Large sums have been invested in a number of projects, several of which have been notably successful. Yet poverty, malnutrition, unemployment, and illiteracy have not yielded. The mounting population wave is overwhelming. Chiefly owing to the airlift to New York and later to Philadelphia, Chicago, and other midwestern cities, the population pressure was somewhat relieved. Each seventeenth New Yorker today is a Puerto Rican, yet the population density of the home island is so great that with the same degree of density the United States mainland could house the entire world population.

The 1930 census showed Puerto Ricans living in all of the then forty-eight states, and by 1940 New York City had 63,000 of them. Not until after World War II did the stream of emigrants have an appreciable effect on Puerto Rico's population problem. In 1947, 35,000 left the island. The number rose to an all-time high of 75,000 in 1953 and then declined again to 14,000 in 1961. Today, more than one million of the mainland population is

actually born in Puerto Rico. Only in 1962 did this massive outflow taper off, owing to the impact of the rising race tensions in
the United States. It was suddenly realized that living in slums
at home might not be worse than living in slums in the United
States. Energetic efforts are being made by a number of social
welfare organizations to stem the population tide by an effective
birth control.

The importation of food has steadily been mounting. If this
purchased food were to be produced on the island, it would
require an acreage two and a half times the present tilled acreage
of the island. In addition, Puerto Rico has a second footing in
the sea from which no insignificant quantities of food are extracted. The fish corresponds in terms of protein to about two-
thirds of the tilled acreage. This would be required to produce
an amount of animal protein equivalent to what fish is providing
today, whether it is landed by the fishermen of the islands or
bought from the United States and other sources. Operation
Bootstrap is therefore more of an illusionary trick than an economic miracle.

The population of the island continues to grow at a rate of
70,000 a year. Up to 1962 the annual emigration siphoned off
a major part of this increment.

The Peruvian Feeding Bastion of the West

In the postwar period the Western countries, largely with
United States leadership, have created a new feeding bastion in
Peru, in recent years extended to northern Chile. Through
massive investments by European and United States business
interests, a fish-meal industry has been created within a rather
brief period of a few years. Recently Japanese, Norwegian, and
South African investment capital has entered this scene. This
industry is now the world's largest of its kind.

The rich "anchoveta" resources of the so-called Humboldt

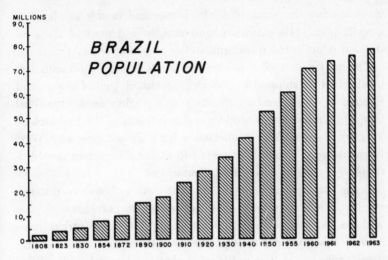

FIG. 40

Current, moving along the coast from the cold Antarctic, are exploited. This current is rich in fish, owing to the upwellings it causes and the mineral nutrients it carries. In 1963, the amount of fish scooped up of this single species exceeded the total world-wide catches of the U.S.S.R. The catch was 6.4 million tons, to which now can be added another 100,000 tons from the Chilean coasts. The guano-producing cormorants are thereby, to a considerable degree, deprived of their food. This, as such, might be quite a smart move, as in this way food is obtained directly and not indirectly from agricultural lands around the globe. But man is still going about this business in a rather roundabout way. Only a fraction of this invaluable fish catch reaches the Peruvian or any Latin American market as food to alleviate the wide-spread malnutrition of this country. Both those inhabiting the coastal regions of Peru and those living in the high Andes suffer extensively from lack of food, particularly of protein, and to an amazing degree, also of fat.

The pattern is exactly the same when this exploitation

wave reaches the north of Chile. Plants and vessels are built at a swift pace. The catches mount rapidly and most of the production is delivered to distant, well-nourished people.

The major part of this sizeable catch is converted into fish meal which is shipped to the well-nourished United States and Europe to be utilized as livestock and poultry feed. One-third is fed to United States broilers and two-thirds to the livestock of Western Europe. The Netherlands buys 28 per cent and West Germany 25 per cent. This means to Holland a protein contribution larger than its entire meat production.

Japan emerged in 1960 for the first time as buyer of this fish meal and has constantly been increasing its purchases in pace with its budding animal production. So far, these orders have been a modest 3 per cent of the total Peruvian outflow of fish meal (1962), but it is anticipated that these purchases will increase considerably. No less than seven Japanese companies have started reduction plants of their own in Peru.

This is another striking example of how the well-nourished nations, in the name of traditional economy, grab what others so badly need. Converted into dry fish or fish flour and used as protein concentrate to enrich bread, these catches would be quite adequate to raise the nutritional standard of these protein-hungry Andean regions of South America to West European standards. In all the hustle and bustle surrounding this fish-meal undertaking, so impressive in scope and magnitude, there is little recognition of the basic fact, known to every biologist, that these fish resources, at the moment seemingly limitless, are indeed limited. Already several fishing vessels complain about diminishing catches. These catching efforts are no longer rewarded to the same degree as when these operations started from three to five years ago.

Most operators however, look only to the immediate future and certainly do not involve themselves in any kind of long-range planning in order to safeguard the availability of future raw material on the basis of a maximum sustainable yield. Fish management is still further away and, in general, beyond the scope of their concern.

During single years, minor deviations take place in the flowing direction of the Humboldt Current. This strongly affects the fish shoals and thus the catches. The fish no longer come close to the coast, particularly when a warm southward current—el Niño —gains the upper hand and manages to squeeze in between the Humboldt Current and the mainland. This is a reminder that in the hunting stage of ocean fishing we are still at the mercy of Nature.

At any rate, the people that live in this part of the world should have the right to demand their share of these riches off their shores. They should also have a chance of voicing their opinion before it is too late. One of the greatest protein assets of this continent is being tapped, exploited, and depleted—in one word, risked—to the short-range satisfaction of others. Even from the narrow point of view of simple profiteering, it can be seriously argued whether this handling of the matter is prudent. Far greater profits would unquestionably accrue from taking the long-range view and catering to the huge food markets of this southern hemisphere of the Americas with their truly immense demands. This becomes almost self-evident if public health and adequate food are listed as capital assets. This should be the aim of the national policies of almost every Latin American country. If we are serious in our proclaimed aims of the Alliance for Progress, then we should focus our attention upon what is for the benefit of these countries themselves. We need to take a serious look at the world from their vantage point, not ours. There is in my mind no doubt about the urgent need to allow full priority to their necessities. A new, constructive way of thinking must be introduced. The outmoded terms of communism, social-ism, and capitalism completely lose their meaning when facing reality in this context.

A National Economy

Economists will have to devise new methods and rules for exchange of goods. Something is fundamentally wrong when a country like Mexico, so desperately short of critical proteins and even calories, is devoting a major portion of its agricultural efforts to feeding the United States and a few other countries. Meat and live cattle move in a continuous stream into Texas from northern Mexico, while the food markets of Mexico City and other cities are critically short of meat. The prime beneficiaries of the impressive accomplishments in Mexican agriculture should be the Mexican people. This is only partially the case.

This imbalance becomes still more obtrusive in the utilization of the ocean harvests. Nine-tenths of the shrimp catches are sold to the United States. This alone would suffice to give each Mexican an additional amount of animal protein corresponding to one-fourth of his present intake. In other words, from this source alone, standards could be improved by no less than 25 per cent. For each ton of shrimp captured, seven tons of fish are taken on board but are discarded and immediately returned to the sea. The shrimpers want to fill up with their precious catches. Most of this discarded fish is equally valuable as food and if utilized on the Mexican scene could give the entire population a vastly improved diet in terms of animal protein—twice the present figures. This would give Mexico a standard which, if not up to the United States level, would at any rate place the country next to Uruguay and Argentina as one of the best fed in Latin America. It is to be hoped that the new development program for Mexican fisheries will serve to remedy some of these absurdities, so detrimental to the nutritional well-being of Mexico. Degree of profitability is a poor guide to rational measures.

Similar examples could be given from other Latin American countries. Whether further planning will go in the direction of creating national economies or the creation of a common Latin

American market, we can be certain that this crucial area no longer will be one for exploitation.

A Long-Range Program Indispensable

A leading Latin American journalist recently wrote: "Half of us Latin Americans have never slept in a bed, have never had enough to eat, have never seen a classroom." This is by and large a true statement and illustrates well how throughout four centuries traditional economic gauges have failed to cope with the realities of this continent.

Since the Second World War ended, revolutions have taken place in Bolivia, Brazil, Argentina, Colombia, Haiti, Venezuela, and Cuba. One and a half per cent of the Latin Americans are in possession of half the agricultural land. In Venezuela 3 per cent own nine-tenths of the land, and in Brazil three-fourths of the agricultural acreage is in the hands of 1.4 per cent of the people. Land reforms are therefore indispensable, but a redistribution involving the splitting up of the land is not always the most commendable countermeasure. Efficient cultivation and sizeable crops for marketing frequently hinge on large-scale operations, but ownership, motivated by a sense of responsibility, remains a crucial issue.

The shortcuts to the economic millennium proclaimed by the Communists naturally offer considerable enticement. Their program is simple and seems to present devices for remedying a desperate situation. The Catholic Church, on the other hand, is said to favor growers owning their farms. Here we encounter the philosophy of the have-nots as against that of the haves. Nevertheless, one Latin American leader of the Catholic Church once stated so rightly, "It is not the will of God that the few shoud enjoy extravagent riches while others are lacking the most elementary necessities for life." A new era is evolving where social revolutions will take the place or political upheavals. The Mexican Revolution, including confiscation of property and followed by nationalization, inaugurated this new era in 1910 but has not until now been followed by other nations. *thank goodness.*

The many eruptions now threatening in many countries can only be met with a farsighted reform policy, but even this is doomed to defeat if the rising tide of human beings is not abated. Otherwise the riches of this continent will prove wholly inadequate.

The Expanding Ocean Fisheries

Like so many other nations on earth, the peoples of Latin America now reach to the seas in order to alleviate their pressing protein shortage, particularly since the soils either have failed in this respect to provide adequate amounts or have been degraded, mainly to supply energy in the form of carbohydrate calories. The ocean harvests have increased threefold since the end of the last world war. Largely with Japanese help, Brazil and Argentina are now building up their Atlantic fisheries and organizing distribution and marketing along modern lines.

The Humboldt Current, moving northward along the Pacific, is extremely rich in fish. As already mentioned, Peru and Chile are increasingly exploiting these resources, but here the smallness of the globe becomes clearly evident. In these same waters the United States has already created a tuna empire. Nine-tenths of the United States tuna catch delivered to the California canning plants come from waters south of the Rio Grande and as far south as Chile. This is, however, no longer sufficient to meet the needs of the growing United States population with its high preference for tuna—two pounds per person a year. With Puerto Rico as a new operational base, the United States is now supplementing its needs from the Middle Atlantic. Puerto Rico has already four major canneries. United States tuna ships operating in the Atlantic are aided by deliveries from Japanese, French, and Spanish vessels. Some of this tuna comes from the Latin

American sector of the Atlantic. The day, however, is not too distant when the millions south of the border will not only want their tuna, but will also demand priority in the disposition of these catches.

The Caribbean and parts of the Gulf of Mexico have, as far as present knowledge goes, rather scanty fish resources. The productivity of these waters is rated as low. In addition, the sharks, the lonely hunters, reign fairly supreme over vast expanses.

Shrimp is another important food, but Mexico, Surinam, Panama, and others direct their efforts primarily to supplying the shrimp-hungry United States in order to procure dollars. In most cases, these fisheries are conducted with U.S. capital and U.S.-built ships. The waters of the Mexican Gulf are already seriously overshrimped, and to an increasing degree both Mexico (for its catches) and the United States (for its supplies) are now turning to the Pacific Coast. Shrimping is here also conducted by Japanese vessels, operating from Mexican ports, but, even in this case, mainly to serve the United States market. Nowadays, the United States takes a major part of its menhaden catch in the Gulf. This provides fish meal for United States broilers and oil to the margarine industries of West Germany and Holland.

Future historians will undoubtedly study the role of the dried cod and stockfish in world history. They will then discover that these fish products constituted the protein base for millions. Today they still carry this unique responsibility. The stockfish is being deposed and no longer manages to feed the many new mouths added to the population of this southern flank of our western hemisphere, in added numbers expected to exceed those of an entire United States by 1980.

Chronic Water Shortage

Tourists, businessmen, and sailors have for centuries praised the gorgeous scenery and beautiful mountains of Rio de Janeiro.

Only a few have mentioned the *favelas*, the miserable shacks built by using discarded tin plate and waste wood. These hovels cling to the slopes of the some thirty hills which make up the transition to the inland high plateau. More than one hundred thousand people live here without organized water provision and sewage disposal. It is bitter irony that a considerable majority live around the water tower which provides the elegant homes and luxury hotels of Copacabana with abundant water even for shower baths, while a few public water faucets are available to these poor ones. In addition, the water delivery is shut off for several hours daily. There is simply not sufficient water to care for the many. They have to stand in line for hours—God help anybody who tries to break the queuing rules. Those at the end of the line frequently do not get to the faucet during the few hours water is available. They have to wait for their turn and better luck the next time.

Similar outrageous conditions prevail in the "rich" city of São Paulo. Life in these favelas, with their many thousand destitute living in abject poverty, has recently been the subject of a jolting description in the naked narrative of a mother of three: *Child of the Dark*. (See references for this chapter.)

Let us transfer from Rio to Mexico City, where the tower of the Loretto Cathedral is leaning in oblique angle against the sky because its foundation is sagging, largely owing to the excessive tapping of the subterranean water resources. The authorities have great difficulties in keeping abreast of the city, now number two in Latin America (six million in 1964), and swiftly reaching the critical point where the amount of available water is inadequate. Rationing has already been a common feature of daily life in this capital, once famed for its lagoons and abundance of water.

In recent years large irrigation projects covering an impressive acreage of no less than two and a half million acres have been installed, but this does not go far toward meeting the needs of a population growing by more than one million per year. According to estimates, the total acreage which may be irrigated in Mexico, and at considerable costs, amounts to twelve million acres. Even this figure dwindles in significance in the light of the fact that fifteen to eighteen million more people will demand food ten years hence. A decade is no long period for the planning, construction, and starting up of a major irrigation project. Malnutrition is still the scourge of the broad masses, despite impressive agricultural accomplishments in both increased yields and more tonnage. More than one million go north from Mexico each year to seek employment as migrant workers. Others move to the rich neighbor of the north more permanently. Temporarily (1964) migrant workers are not encouraged. The sad fact is that in spite of extensive industrialization—in many respects very successful—and continued social reform activities in the spirit of its famous revolution, Mexico continues to be a seething volcano.

One of the leading magazines in the United States commented recently, with reference to the exorbitant increase of the Mexican population from 24 million to 35 million in the twelve years from 1950 to 1962, the following: "The secretaries (members) of the government know that they all are involved in a race with catastrophe." Despite Herculean efforts to cope with the situation, 60 per cent of the Mexicans live in seriously inadequate homes or lack shelter completely, as in the gravel pits of Mexico City, which this author saw with horror when visiting there in the summer of 1964. Thirty per cent of the population are still listed as illiterate; tens of thousands of children are critically undernourished or malnourished.

The Overflow from the Andes

So far it is little recognized that hundreds of thousands of South Americans participate in a major migration eastward, down the slopes of the Andes. They are moving in a direction opposite to that of the North Americans when they pushed westward. In Venezuela, Colombia, Ecuador, Peru, and Bolivia the people are abandoning the depleted soils of the Andean high plateaus and moving thousands of miles eastward traversing the intricate and wide system of mountain ridges. Entire families leave, taking their cattle, in order to settle in the tropical forest regions immediately east of the Andes, in those areas where the springs of the large rivers of Orinoco, Amazon, and Madeira are located. A number of new frontier cities, often with more than ten thousand inhabitants, have suddenly sprung up over the last two or three decades. The Andean valleys are overflowing, and the stream of migrants is increasing rather than decreasing. The population growth and the dwindling yields of the depleted soils at high elevation are interrelated factors which are the driving forces in this migration. The dull and languid population, largely Indian, which nowadays inhabits the majestic world of the Andes has lost its cheerful creativity described by the conquistadors. These people in the highlands get fewer and fewer calories; the malnutrition becomes chronic, their hunger and cravings for food are increasingly quenched by chewing the coca leaves with their poisonous effects. The dried leaves contain approximately 1 per cent of cocaine. The Peruvians and Bolivians are said to consume together at least 12,000 metric tons of these ominous leaves each year. In order to fill the medical needs of the entire world, 500 to 700 tons is an ample quantity.

Jeopardizing Soil Fertility

One of the most stubborn myths about Latin America is that it comprises large open expanses which are awaiting mass immigration from an overpopulated world. A major proportion of the soils of this continent are surprisingly poor. Despite the vast areas opened up through ploughing and new cultivation, the net increase in tilled acreage in this century is insignificant. One-fourth of this gain has lost its topsoil through erosion. This large-scale destruction is encountered in those parts of the Argentine pampas which have been plowed and tilled, in the *campos* of south Brazil and in the Venezuelan *llanos* as well as in the wake of the massive Mexican deforestation. Each year the erosion is estimated to destroy almost three-quarters of a million acres in Latin America by moving topsoil, on the average, four feet in depth. This corresponds to the crop-producing soil of 3,000 farms of 250 acres each. To visit the abandoned coffee acreage of Brazil is almost like looking at a lunar landscape; and to travel through the once fertile Bío-Bío valley in Chile, recognizing the frightful devastation caused by deforestation on the slopes down to the valleys and by too extensive ploughing, is both a perturbing and thought-provoking experience. At least, this was my own re-action.

The Brazilian coffee plantations have succumbed to disastrous soil erosion, and in the Chilean valley the rainfall has carried away the topsoil into the Pacific not leaving untouched even the oyster and mussel banks along the coast. A mere 13 per cent of the Chilean soils are reported as unaffected by the cancerous soil erosion, and almost half the tilled acreage is seriously damaged by such destruction.

The Mexican scene can be summarized in the following way: For each century that has passed since the conquest, one-fourth of the forest lands have vanished. The Spaniards started this destructive game and the present generation is now nibbling on the last quarter—by and large, second-rate forests. Desperate efforts are made to turn the tide, but only with partial success. Four centuries of soil destruction have taken their toll in terms of land, which hardly ever can be paid back and certainly not as long as constantly increasing millions are clamoring for food. These soil losses are directly attributed to the interaction between the loss of protective forest cover and the ensuing upset water balance, accelerating runoff, and evaporation.

A recent German investigation* established through field studies that more than one-fourth of the vast virgin forests, which in the Peruvian capital of Lima have been mentioned as future assets, no longer exist. Under the pressure of the population growth, new land is constantly broken up and these forest soils are the chief remaining source. Devastating erosion ensued from this removal of the forests followed by ploughing.

The coastal plains where corn, cotton, and bananas are cultivated are losing water, furthermore, since the rivers dry up and the highly limited vital rainfall comes from the east—as melting water or catch-water from the high Andes. The many new lands which have been put under the plough have not managed to increase the tilled acreage of Peru. This is because the building of roads, cities and industries gulp up more land than is added— lands which have, by and large, far better soil than those newly opened up for cultivation.

In no less than twelve countries in Central and South America the erosion damage is so serious that a total of between 70 and 140 million acres have become unsuitable for cultivation. The wide discrepancy depends on where one draws the line and considers a badly eroded land no longer suitable for crop production. In several regions the eroded acreage amounts to 60 per cent of the total land area. In some places, soil erosion is so intense that new hydroelectric dams become filled with sand, soil, and silt within a brief period of ten to fifteen years.

If the present exploitation continues in Brazil and Mexico and other countries, and the land is misused as in past centuries, the huge resources of this seemingly rich Latin American continent will be wasted long before this southern part of the Western Hemisphere has ever had a chance to create decent living conditions for its own people. If those millions who now constitute this continent's labor force do not get a larger share of the avail-

* G. Kunkel, "Über die Bodenzerstörung in Sierra und Selva Perus." *Zeitschrift für Wirtschaftsgeographie* 3 (3), 1961, pp. 65–68.

able resources, then Latin America will remain a dream which will never come true. The potential value of the Amazon basin, a highly controversial topic, is analyzed in detail in chapter 15. Ultimately the point will be reached—and this is not far off— where the total resources of these lands no longer suffice to create a decent living for their teeming millions. No continent is limitless, no matter how reassuring the situation may appear at the moment.

If nothing unforeseen happens, the population of Brazil will have grown within fifteen years from the present 70 million to 100 million, that of Mexico from 37 million to 56 million. The 35 million of Peru, Venezuela, and Colombia combined, will almost double and reach 65 million. As things now stand it is in this very continent that the real population explosion will reach its highest intensity and take on grave dimensions.

Therefore there is every reason to call for a little more realism in the appraisal of the world's food situation and a better recognition of the magnitude of the difficulties this poses; this applies to all parts of the globe, but especially to Latin America.

In spite of Operation Bootstrap in Puerto Rico, around 40,000 people moved to the mainland each year in the fifties. To create jobs for these—if they had stayed on the island—would have meant an outlay of close to half a billion dollars for a ten-year period. Newly created jobs in industry cost from ten to twelve thousand dollars each in investment. This may be contrasted with the half billion dollars which the United States appropriated for all of Latin America when launching the Alliance for Progress. The present minimal needs are many times larger if efficient remedies are to be provided for the rapid continued deterioration of the major cities into enormous slum areas, for counter-measures against soil erosion, and for water conservation to meet the real needs of crops, of industry, and for domestic use. The water situation is in too many regions chronically critical.

At present the entire South American continent applies an

amount of commercial fertilizer approximately to what little Holland is using. Obviously, the true requirements are many times larger. In addition, most of these fertilizers are used on cash crops, and only a trifle is employed for the raising of food crops which feed most of the people. If the immediate needs are formidable, how much less will the chances be to improve the situation, when by 1980 another United States of 195 million people will be added to the Latin American population, a doubling of the present number? And by the turn of the century, with the present rate of growth there will be more than half a billion to take care of!

Measures of an entirely different dimension than those to which we have resorted so far are required, but also a better awareness of the fact that the rich resources of South America will be in short supply when the masses rightfully step forward to demand their due share. When politicians and economists of Latin America come to realize the true magnitude of their plight, little will remain for the United States, Europe, the Soviet Union, China, or Japan to extract. This adjustment to reality may already have started. The original pledge of the Alliance for Progress had quickly to be revised upward. Two billion dollars were pledged at the conference in Punta del Este in August, 1961; large additional funds have been appropriated for Brazil and Argentina. As of now (1964) Brazil appears to have received two billion alone—in any case only a fraction of the more than twelve billion dollars Latin America maintains it lost through the price reductions which took place during the latter part of the 1950's on coffee, copper, tin, grain, and other Latin American staple goods.

It is this unilateral price squeeze more than anything else which has created resentment and which goes a long way to explain the delay in social reforms long overdue. There is more than loose talk and more than the search for a rallying slogan behind the widespread denunciation of this plunder.

Another sore point is the twenty or more billion dollars pocketed by a small minority, the operators and executives in government and business, and hidden away in bank accounts in Switzerland, New York, and other places. This is the result of a totally inefficient taxation system. The need of drastic reforms in this respect is well recognized by United States experts as well as government policy makers.

The most recent eruptions in Cuba, Panama, and Bolivia, all are signs of an upheaval which is likely to involve the whole continent unless drastic measures are taken to cope with these fundamental issues. This unrest reflects the prevailing tensions and the political and economic imbalance posed by the absence of social justice. Nobody should lure himself into believing that only leftist students and bearded Communists are behind the agitation and unrest. It is almost universal in this continent. The dismal picture of incessant military coups have done little to remedy this continent's social and economic ills. We therefore see the rising expectations among the masses creating new revolutionary patterns.

Will we in the West grasp what is needed in time? Some signs of awakening are to be seen but are far from adequate to affect the political scene. Are we prepared to make the huge efforts that are required both in the name of justice and humanitarianism? Latin America desperately needs for its own use every pound of meat, grain, shrimp, fruit, coffee, and bananas that it now sells. The coffee and cacao acreages are also required for any efficient move against hunger. Outmoded economic patterns have long ago lost or outgrown their usefulness and are now largely detrimental to progress in this southern hemisphere of ours.

A recent book published in the United States carries the title *Latin America—The Eleventh Hour*. This is the true issue bluntly stated. (See reference list—MacEoin.)

References

ALEXANDER, R. J. *Today's Latin America*. Garden City, N.Y., Doubleday, 1962, 263 pp.

BENHAM, F., and H. A. HOLLEY. *The Economy of Latin America*. New York, Oxford University Press, 1960, 169 pp.

BENTON, W. *The Voice of Latin America*. New York, Harper and Bros., 1961, 204 pp.

CONSIDINE, J. J. *New Horizons in Latin America*. New York, Dodd, Mead, 1958, 379 pp.

ADAMS, N. *et al. Social Changes in Latin America*. New York, Harper, 1960, 353 pp.

DE JESUS, C. M. *Child of the Dark*. New York, E. P. Dutton, 1962, 190 pp.

DOZIER, C. L. *Indigenous Tropical Agriculture in Central America*. Washington, NAS, 1958, 134 pp.

GALINDEZ SORAREZ, J. *Ibero-Americas*. New York, Las Americas, 1954, 620 pp.

GERASSI, J. *The Great Fear: the Reconquest of Latin America by Latin Americans*. New York, Macmillan, 1962, 451 pp.

HANKE, L. *Modern Latin America*. Princeton, Van Nostrand, 2 vol., 1958. Vol. I, 420 pp.; vol. II, 440 pp.

HERRING, H. *The History of Latin America*. New York, Knopf, 1960, 845 pp.

JAMES, P. G. *Latin America*. 3rd ed., New York, Odyssey Press, 1959, 942 pp.

KALIJARVI, T. V. *Central America: Land of Lords and Lizards*. New York, Van Nostrand, 1962, 128 pp.

MACEOIN, G. *Latin America, the Eleventh Hour*. New York, P. J. Kennedy & Sons, 1962, 224 pp.

MARTZ, J. D. *Central America, the Crisis and the Challenge*. Chapel Hill, University of North Carolina Press, 1959, 356 pp.

NEHEMKIS, P. *Latin America, Myth and Reality*, New York, Knopf, 1964, 286 pp.

PAHLEN, K. *Südamerika, Eine neue Welt*. Zürich, Orell-Füssli, 1949, 394 pp.

PARKER, F. D. *The Central American Republics*. London and New York, Oxford University Press, 1964, 348 pp.

PLAUM, J. P. *Arena of Decision*. Englewood Cliffs, N.J., Prentice-Hall, 1964, 334 pp.

SOULE, G., EFRON, D., and NESS, N. T. *Latin America in the Future World*. New York, Farrar & Rinehart, 1945, 372 pp.

STARK, H. *Social and Economic Frontiers in Latin America*. Dubuque (Iowa), W. C. Brown, 1964, 464 pp.

TEICHERT, P. C. *Economic Policy Revolution and Industrialization in Latin America*. University (Miss.), University of Mississippi, 1959, 270 pp.

UNITED NATIONS ECONOMIC COMMISSION FOR LATIN AMERICA, 1960. *Economic Survey of Latin America—1959*. Santiago, 220 pp.

WITHERS, W. *The Economic Crisis in Latin America*. New York, The Free Press of Glencoe, 1964, 307 pp.

YEARBOOKS:

Pan American Yearbook
The South American Handbook

CHAPTER 15

Brazil—

A False Eldorado?

IN the fall of 1960 Brazil suddenly appeared in the world news as a buyer of Russian wheat, a quantity of 150,000 metric tons. The trade statistics reveal that Brazil regularly buys food from many countries and has done so far many years. How is this to be explained? Brazil, the enormous country, about equal in size to the United States (including Alaska), has for centuries been described as the huge immigration country which would be able to feed hundreds of millions. Does not this rich nation manage to feed the 80 million now living there? Does the bright picture of Brazil as a future Eldorado, with the gigantic Amazon as a life-giving artery, merely represent wishful thinking? Is this image but a fallacy cherished through the centuries? Or had mankind possibly neglected to take possession of this paradise? How is it to be explained that a country largely spanning the warm tropical latitudes and with an area one-tenth larger than that of the United States (excluding Alaska) does not manage to feed a population only slightly more than one-third (80 million as against 192 million)?

In Brazil, as in so many other nations on earth, reality emerges as very different from the image which mankind's dreams and hopes have constructed. A single purchase of grain does not tell anything in this context, even though poor harvests often have forced Brazil to look around for supplementation.

Considerable Wheat Importation

More revealing about the actual food situation of Brazil is the fact that the country for more than two decades has been forced to purchase wheat from Argentina, and this in increasing quantities despite commendable efforts to increase wheat production and its own wheat acreage. More than one million tons of wheat harvested from around two and a half million acres of tilled land, mainly in Argentina, are required per year, on the average, to fill the immediate needs and safeguard daily bread for the Brazilians; and yet, during several years wheat flour has had to be extended with the addition of cassava flour and other less valuable ingredients. The tiny neighbor of Uruguay, too, used to be a Brazilian granary (1956 more than 300,000 tons), but since its own population has grown, this flow to Brazil stopped in 1958, and on the whole its wheat export tapered off to terminate completely in 1960. In the fifties, Argentina and Uruguay furnished Brazil with three-fourths of her imported wheat.

But off and on, even these grain-producing countries used to experience crop failures. In such critical years Brazil was obliged to scan the world in order to fill in this grain deficit.

Crop subsidies, the breaking-up of new land, support purchases, and other government measures were not sufficient to remedy this situation and in any way to reduce the need for importation.

The United States became in the fifties the major supplier of supplementary wheat, subsequently in the sixties, moving into the position of chief provider, on an average 1.4 million metric tons per year. U.S.S.R. has also become a regular source of about a quarter million metric tons of wheat annually.

TABLE 27

Major Wheat Imports to Brazil

(1,000 METRIC TONS)

	1953/54	1954/55	1955/56	1956/57	1957/58
U.S.	7.6	243.5	482.7	378.4	289.9
Argentina	1,115.4	883.4	933.8	1,039.9	732.9
U.S.S.R.	—	—	—	—	—
Uruguay	141.3	241.5	309.1	279.2	8.1

	1958/59	1959/60	1960/61	1961/62	1962/63
	475.5	917.6	1,069.7	1,432.0	1,407.2
	1,433.0	910.5	684.4	551.3	472.2
	—	3.9	256.9	299.7	260.0
	—	—	—	—	—

Source: World Grain Trade Statistics, FAO

United States deliveries are almost a continuous ferrying operation. The annual volume is equivalent to what the United Kingdom is purchasing annually in the form of wheat and approaches the amount India has been receiving from the United States up to the most recent step-up in deliveries (1964). Brazil's annual requirements amount to almost three million metric tons of wheat. During the latter part of the fifties, barely one-third came from its own soils despite increased acreages, and during the sixties the situation is worse, with only one-fourth provided from Brazilian soils—and yet the acreage has gone up. New lands have been opened up for wheat. Naturally, the ploughing-up of pastures in order to raise wheat in the southern state of Rio Grande do Sul has meant a decline in the livestock feeding of this area. This is where Brazil's pampas are located. As indicated earlier, the plough always is given the priority when the cry for more food becomes urgent from the urbanized industrializing millions. Market farming has to take the place of subsistence farming.

Natural Growth, Not Immigration

The malnutrition as well as undernutrition of Brazil is less surprising when it is taken into account that the population has grown by more than twenty-five million since 1939. It is no easy task to care for an additional two million people each year, when the major portion of the population already is short of food and lacks most of the essentials of life. An improved standard for those now living would require exceptional measures.

TABLE 28
Brazil Immigration Data

		(1000 PERSONS)			
1954	72.2	1957	53.6	1960	40.5
1955	55.2	1958	49.8	1961	43.6
1956	44.8	1959	44.5	1962	

Source: U.N. Demographic Yearbook

It is a common but false notion that Brazil is an important immigration country. Since 1884, altogether around five million people have arrived from abroad. Italians and Portuguese each make up one-third of this influx. Compare this with the population growth: the birth rate as well as the annual net increment supersedes that of India. Five million is more or less the number of people that came into the United States during the ten-year period from 1880 to 1890. In eighty years Brazil has received about the same number, but one-fourth of these departed, disenchanted. During the fifties, when refugees and displaced persons from the whole world were looking around for a haven, less than fifty thousand on the average entered this huge country per year. This is an insignificant number compared to the natural population growth, around 3 per cent of the annual increment of 1.6 million per year. Since 1963 the net growth has exceeded two million per year. Brazil can hardly be classified as an immigration country. Only the refugee pressure from Europe and elsewhere after the Second World War led to the establishment of a modest immigration quota (as a rule, 2 per cent of the total from each ethnic group in the previous fifty years). In relation to its size and natural resources, Brazil has received the smallest number of any major immigration country (see table 21, p. 177). In none of these cases, inclusive of Brazil, did the number of immigrants in any significant way serve to ease the pressure of the growing world population.

Even if the influx of people from abroad has been a trifle, Brazil can nevertheless best be characterized within its borders as a migrating country. Currently, three such movements are essential features of the socio-economic development in this country, namely (1) the search of the drought-ridden, mainly from the northeast, for employment or land, (2) the influx from rural areas to urban centers because of industrialization, and, not the least important, (3) the march westward for pioneer colonization. This latter *marcha para oeste*, has been inspired by the success of its North American precedent, when the "frontier" was pushed across this northern continent. But this parallel is highly misleading, as it overlooks the many geographical differences coupled with climatic diversities. The exploitation of the prairie and the penetration into golden California were, in spite of all sufferings and tests of endurance, easy tasks compared to the penetration of the interior of Brazil. This explains why the westward drive has progressed so very slowly, and is several hundred years behind, although it started almost at the same time.

A population map of Brazil shows how people today still cluster on a narrow strip along the coasts. This is slowly changing. It is true that the march toward the central regions of the country did go on persistently through the centuries but has now reached a point where it is becoming increasingly inevitable. The inland has to be conquered in order to make space and to find food and employment for the growing millions, now more than two million per year. There are many signs of a mounting population pressure becoming excessive in the coastal areas. Therefore "the march toward the west" is nowadays better designated as "the pressure toward the west." It is in effect no longer a voluntary migration in a spirit of optimism and exciting adventure but a reluctant penetration under severe deprivations, that yields meager returns to the victims of these changes, also in terms of excess food to provide for the millions in the coastal cities. This migration is primarily directed toward the sparsely populated expanses in the heartland of the continent belonging to the huge states of Goias and Mato Grosso. Though these regions are much less attractive than those of the coastal areas, nonetheless their population is growing twice as fast as the rest of the country, reflecting the higher net growth and also this pressing drive to relocate people.

Those politicians who count national strength in numbers of millions have felt justified to speak about Brazil as a great power of the future, which, alongside China and India, would one day be able to compete with even the United States and the Soviet Union. This can be strongly disputed; almost the reverse is true. The chief weakness of this great country is its failure to provide for its millions. No force is more disruptive of Brazilian economy than the oversized population pressure which in the postwar period has constantly grown worse.

Two Worlds

Brazil, like so many of the Latin American countries, is falling apart into two distinct spheres; one is represented by those living in a largely urbanized and industrialized world—around twenty-five million, one-third of which are inhabitants in the two cities of Rio de Janeiro and São Paulo. The remaining fifty million are spread over the wide expanses, basically rural. This majority is living under conditions completely different from those of the more fortunate minority. They have, however, one thing in common, a sizeable slum population which is incorporated into neither of these two spheres.

The differences between these two orbits can be characterized in many ways: market economy as against subsistence economy; mobility as against rootedness; wage incomes as against a barter economy. This is not the place to analyze this further, but rather to underline the fact that recognition of the existence of two Brazils seems to be the only way of formulating aid programs that would not benefit unilaterally one or the other group but would aim at the amalgamation and coordination of both spheres into one nation.

Despite the city slums, the urban industrial spheres are more or less the sole beneficiaries of the modest prosperity improvements that can be noted. Most of the major capital investments, and particularly the foreign capital that has been attracted to the country, have landed in this sphere. A large proportion of the masses—the fifty million in the other world that also is Brazil —have been affected very little. Suffering and poverty is their lot, and in particular this is true of the more than twenty million living in the northeastern part of the country. Three-fourths of the population live in three southern states, and most significant is the fact that almost forty million of the total population are children below the age of fifteen.

The Pantanal

In the boundary areas between Bolivia and Paraguay a controversial region is located which throughout the centuries often changed ownership. It consists of vast marshes formed by the

Paraguay River and its tributaries. Through drainage a major portion has been converted into a new agricultural area called the Pantanal, about the size of Portugal. The capital is Corumbá. Pantanal nowadays supports 2.2 million head of cattle, twice as many as Portugal. These cattle are largely of the Brazilian zebu stock: nellore and gur. But the number of human inhabitants is merely 40,000; Portugal has 9.3 million. So far the exploitation of the region is only in its beginning stage, and the land is almost exclusively used for agriculture. The plans are to increase the number of livestock to fifteen millions for a combined milk and meat production following the French pattern. This would mean an increase of 16 per cent in the present cattle stock of Brazil, an important addition, yet inadequate to eliminate the present malnutrition of Brazil. It further seems likely that in five to six years this additional meat and milk would be wholly swallowed up by the present population growth of Brazil. At any rate, Brazil has in this distant corner not only a new granary but also a larder for the entire nation. The plans are to construct refrigerated warehouses and processing factories, but so far this is on a minor scale although such facilities are indispensable in order to utilize fully this production to the benefit of the entire country.

Brazilian Soils Poor

With regard to soil productivity, Brazil is a poor country. This is the bitter truth. On the whole, the tropics are not a cornucopia as until recently they were generally assumed to be. Only in the two southern states, Rio Grande do Sul and Santa Catarina, is the agricultural potential fairly good, more or less comparable in this respect to that of Central Europe. Brazil has in this region pampas of its own. The grassy land expanses further to the north, the so-called *campos*, provide pastures which are, however, highly seasonal and in addition seriously deficient in minerals (lime and other key plant nutrients). They also decline rapidly under the impact of permanent grazing. The animals in these pasture herds usually become smaller and smaller in body size with each succeeding generation, and new "blood" has to be brought in constantly from outside.

The enormous South American grasslands, which were once looked upon as one of the large food potentials of the globe, have lost their gloss. The poverty of Brazil's *campos* as well as of Venezuela's *llanos* is gradually becoming evident. The animals can be fed only by roaming long distances over extensive areas. In the central part of the Brazilian heartland lies *El Planalto Central*, from which the Amazon flows toward the north, and where the La Plata and Parana rivers toward the south originate; the soils are depleted and dried up and represent some of the poorest ones of this globe. The subsoil can be penetrated only with the aid of dynamite or strong tractors of the bulldozer type.

Despite creditable efforts by a series of modern agricultural experiment stations in the south, in the west, in the east, and in the center of the country—partly with considerable economic and technical aid from the United States—Brazil has not been able to raise its overall yields per acre and enhance the output of food and feed. The natural obstacles are formidable and have dictated for a long time the history of the nation. They will probably always do so. Plant production and animal husbandry are too much of a hazard, and the gifts of Nature are, contrary to general belief, rather frugal, with the exception of the volcanic soils, *terra roxa*. Rightly managed, these are as a rule fertile, and the problems of the binding of certain plant nutrients in these soils can generally be mastered.

Most of the agricultural lands of Brazil suffer from mineral deficiency; the experts estimate the need for commercial fertilizers to be about fifty times higher than what is now administered. Therefore, paralleling what happened earlier in India, a depletion of the soils of considerable proportions is going on.

It is understandable that under such circumstances deficiency diseases become commonplace in the crops and, through the feed, also among the livestock. Many devastating fungal diseases and insect attacks are directly linked to reduced crop resistance, which in turn is due to the lack of essential minerals, including trace elements. The reserves of these substances in the soils soon become depleted, as only a fraction is returned through conventional fertilizers.

Food Losses Considerable

Cold storage and refrigerated transportation require large investments and are expensive to operate in such a vast, sparsely populated country, and especially because of the hot climate. The low population density has had a direct detrimental effect upon the economy of railroads and the outlays for highway constructions. Both these factors have contributed to a seriously inadequate transportation system. Heavy losses are incurred on meat, poultry, fish, fruits, and vegetables, frequently exceeding 50 per cent. It is also costly to protect grain, beans, and rice against spoilage by fungi or insects. This is true almost everywhere with the year-round high temperatures, aggravated by ample rain in other regions. Food processing is a paramount problem which so far has not been solved satisfactorily. In many cases the lack of such facilities has not even been recognized. For grain, the staple food, the government maintains a network of silos. These storage costs are not borne by the consumers, since it would unduly increase the price for basic foods. In 1954, the grain losses due to deficient storage were reported as 260,000 metric tons, thus corresponding to approximately one-fourth of the then imported quantity.

More than four-fifths of the livestock is found south of the sixteenth latitude. The majority of the slaughterhouses are also located there. Animals which are raised on the poor pastures north of this latitude must often be marched for 90 to 120 days before reaching the slaughterhouse. To transport animals using their own muscle-stored energy as fuel is a costly method. Therefore, air transportation of slaughter animals according to the Australian pattern is now being studied. Essentially the problem is the same, that of vast open expanses of low fertility. By means of improved livestock breeding, especially by cross-fertilization with Indian zebu cattle, the Brazilians have been able to produce their own meat races, humpbacked and gray-skinned, which are adapted to the hot regions of the country. Similar efforts to breed milk-producing animals for the same areas have so far had little success. In any case, the introduction of breeding animals for high milk production from Europe and the United States has largely failed. The production level could not be kept up under the climatic strains. Only in the southern part of the country, where the climate is cooler, has a considerable dairy industry been developed. Even meat-producing animals, fed on pastures, grow at a slower pace in the southern regions of Brazil than on the Argentine pampa. Further to the north this is even more pronounced. The production per acre often drops to approximately half that of the south.

On top of this there is the constant menace from insects and from animal diseases. In some years hog pest and cholera decimated the hog population of the country by half. The gadfly larvae bore through the hide of the cattle. To combat these harmful insects has proved much more difficult than in our latitudes, and this is only one of the many malicious flying creatures that attack cattle.

The Brazilian high plateau offers a rather pleasant tropical climate with cool summer nights. During wintertime the temperature rarely falls below +50°F (+10°C). This sounds perfect, but the rainfall is adequate to raise a normal crop during only four months of the year. Then, luscious pastures spring up, but for the remainder of the year the grass cover becomes decimated and frequently burns. The cattle herds then starve, having almost nothing to eat, outside of a scanty ration of this grass preserved through natural drying.

People living in temperate latitudes often entertain the false notion that it is only the severe winters that cause high costs for the harvesting and storage of hay and the building of barns, feed storage, and feeding installations. But the heat and the drought of the tropics cause the same high expenses. Feed storage is equally indispensable here and under far less favorable conditions, not to speak of the fact that normally the return from the animals is less. The farms usually have little financial means to acquire such facilities.

The Treasure Chest of the World

Brazil has been named the world's treasure chest. Besides its diamonds, some of the globe's largest deposits of iron ore are to be found on Brazilian territory. Still more valuable are its manganese ores. It was only natural that the exploitation of these enormous resources expanded rapidly during the Second World War. The list of ores mineable in Brazil is impressive, and several new minerals have been added recently, such as beryllium, zirconium, chromium, nickel, mercury, and platinum. Finally, monazite has been found, which is extremely valuable to modern nuclear technology as a raw material for the plants manufacturing the radioactive matter.

The exploitation of many of these ore resources is currently carried on at such a rapid pace that they are quickly being depleted. The rich deposits of manganese in the state of Minas Gerais are already heavily taxed, and it is estimated that less than ten years production will remain if these operations are not slowed down. Indeed, the safe is filled, but it is one of the few left in the world, and it may not be so wise to go ahead like the spendthrift and squander our last assets in the way we now are doing. Viewed in terms of the self-interest of Brazil and its potentialities as a land of the future, this rapid depletion is both alarming and unfortunate.

The enormous oil dome, the Blue Goose, at the foot of the Andes, which stretches along this mountain chain underneath a large portion of the South American continent, is also gradually being tapped, but so far to a very little degree within Brazilian territory. Oil has also been found, though in more limited quantities, in other Brazilian states, which at present provide the country with 70 per cent of the domestic oil consumption. This helps to save currency exchange. Large deposits of oil shale constitute another important energy source, but they are located in regions where water is lacking, which renders processing difficult. Shortage of sulphur is another handicap for the future, which will affect the development of both agriculture and industry.

Wood Civilization

In spite of everything, the vegetation cover remains Brazil's largest asset. But prudent exploitation is required if another instance of ruthless devastation is not to be added to the many examples of this kind which the world has already seen. The question is how to put this production potential to good use while avoiding the gigantic losses in humus, water, and minerals which have occurred in other parts of the globe. The Brazilian development so far provides little encouragement in this respect. It is of little avail that the Amazon region possesses in the oil palms the largest source of vegetable oils found on earth, if continuous production cannot be guaranteed for the future.

Four-fifths of Brazil's energy consumption is derived from wood, that is, from the vegetation. The country has a wood civilization which can most adequately be compared with that of Europe in the seventeenth and eighteenth centuries and toward which that continent was again pushed back during the two world wars. In Brazil the trains are for the most part run with wood fuel; wood is also commonly used in the mining operations, and many metal plants depend on wood for energy. As once in Europe, the forests of Brazil are rapidly dwindling. The forests along the railroads are pulled down in order to keep the trains running. Tens of thousands of acres have been planted with eucalyptus and acacia for the purpose of supplying wood to the engines. Several iron works have to use charcoal in the extraction of ore and have extended the eucalyptus acreages. Even up on the bush steppes, the so-called *catinga*, the hunt for wood has made its marks. Around the cities the bush vegetation has been reduced to a cover of thorny brush which tears up the hides of grazing cattle and goats. Coal constitutes merely one-fifth of the energy consumption of Brazil and the quality is poor. Therefore coal is imported, especially for the huge iron works at Volta Redonda in the coastal region between Rio and São Paulo. Part of the coal for these steel plants is supplied, however, from deposits in the state of Santa Catarina in the south, which involves costly hauling.

Water Power Mobilized

There has been a great deal of boasting about Brazil's enormous potential for hydroelectric power. Theoretically, however, it is merely half of that of Europe. More than one-fourth is found in distant parts like the Amazonas and therefore is hardly exploitable. Because of the mounting population pressure and the simultaneous industrialization, ever larger power stations have been built. But they have not been able to keep pace with the growing needs in the amount of power produced. Merely 2 per cent of the total energy consumption is obtained from water power. The swampy Tietê River in the mountain chain Serra do Mar on the High Plateau provides three-quarters of a million horsepower units to the industries of São Paulo. In its natural stage this river, after a great deal of meandering, finally reaches the Paraná thousands of miles away. It has been forced to flow backwards and to throw its water masses down the slopes of the plateau from a height fifteen times that of Niagara —directly down toward the Atlantic. This is the often described Cubatão power station with its large artificial lake reservoir, Santo Amaro. Another one of the largest power stations ever constructed, the Alfonso on the São Francisco River, has contributed invaluable additional energy to the entire northeast region. It provides fifteen million people within a radius of 275 miles with electric power for household use. A considerable part of the available power is used, however, for the pumping involved in the irrigation in these areas, so intensely harassed by constantly recurring droughts.

The large cities, Rio and São Paulo, have grown at such a rate that both water and electricity have become shortage commodities. The sum total of this admirable hydroelectric expansion thus becomes less impressive when the mounting population figures are brought into the equation. Per person, the Brazilian has at his disposal merely one-twentieth of the electric power used by an average American. A French study* recently stated that Brazil very soon will meet a serious crisis in the field of energy. Another two and a half million kilowatt/hours are needed during the period 1960–1965 and an additional four million from 1966 to 1970; thus huge additional power quantities are required which in spite of the present expansion will be hard to provide.

It is therefore only natural that Brazil places its hopes for the future in atomic power and is rapidly training experts of its own. Several reactors are under construction, so far, however, not for power production.

* Leloup, "La Production d'énergie électrique au Brazil," *Ann. Géogr.* 69 (No. 376), 594–611.

The Forest Protection Rapidly Dwindling

It is imperative to economize with the soil-protecting and water-preserving forest cover to the degree that it can be saved from being cut down to provide tilled land whenever this is urgently needed. Averages are misleading when it comes to such a huge country as Brazil. Of its total area, 58 per cent is registered as covered by forest. This sounds reassuring, but in the more densely populated coastal states along the Atlantic Ocean the situation is much less favorable. There civilization is taking over, and the forests disappear in the so-called development process. Originally more than 80 per cent of the country was protected by forests. What is left are mostly so-called second-class forests, that is, forest that grows on second-rate soils of low fertility. The colonizers early discovered that the forest soils were far superior to those of the savannahs and other grasslands. They had no choice. In order to obtain reasonable productivity and sufficient food they had to pull down the forests.

It is thus of little help that Brazil has one of the world's largest forest resources. In the rich southern states, the forest acreage has in a hundred years been reduced from 34 to 12 per cent, with serious disturbances in the water balance as a consequence. In Bahia, the cocoa state, the reduction is from 36 to 19 per cent. In the drought-plagued Paraiba on the hump, the situation is catastrophic. Originally one-third of this area was protected by forest. By now it has almost disappeared, the forest cover being reduced to less than 1 per cent of the land area. The same applies to the nearby state, Sergipe, to the south, where the forest acreage has been reduced from 40 to 10 per cent.

Undoubtedly, this deforestation is to a high degree responsible both for the intensity of the drought as well as for its frequent recurrence in these regions. According to the forestry journals, the forest has nowhere in the world been ravaged as terribly as in the state of Paraná to the south of São Paulo. This is probably an exaggerated statement in view of the vandalism of the forests in New Zealand and in the Mediterranean region. Yet, the destruction of the Brazilian forests provides food for thought. Gradually as the water-conserving forests disappear, the drought ravages have become more pronounced. Considerable forest acreages have been converted, presumably forever, into savannahs or bush steppes. Climatic data from the last fifty years show that the winter and spring rains have diminished in the forest-deprived areas, and thus the crops planted there receive much less water. This has in turn brought about the need for irrigating the coffee and citrus plantations during the winter, the dry season. On the whole, growers who irrigate have been forced to extend irrigation to areas which earlier were not considered as dry regions. Feverish attempts to achieve a reforestation through planting have so far had little effect. Several reforestation projects command great respect but they should be five to six hundred times larger to be effective in compensating for the huge losses inflicted by deforestation. In spite of ambitious plans for reforestation through planting and improved forest management, wood and paper pulp are being imported by Brazil in increasing quantities. Even on this battlefront for existence, the Brazilians have not managed to cope with the demands raised by the mounting population and the ensuing increase in paper requirements. In 1956 the deficit amounted to 92,000 metric tons; by 1960 it had reached 195,000 metric tons, and it is still rising. Brazil is even in this regard depending on outside acreages to a growing degree.

Forest Burning and the Milpa System

The clearing of forest by burning is still common all over the country. Large and small trees are cut down with the machete, a special knife. The maze of trunks, branches, twigs, and leaves are left to dry for a while and then set on fire. This is done immediately before the rainy season arrives. With the hoe or the digging stick, the two major implements in primitive agriculture, the soil is worked lightly and then sown. The method is called *derruba quemada*. The forest is destroyed in order to gain a few bushels of manioc flour. The jungle takes on a ripped appearance. The virgin forests in Brazil look frayed when seen from the air. Inadvertently this makes one think of a boy who has tried to give himself a haircut. A number of open spaces are discernible. As one flies over the regions around Rio or São Paulo in the months of September and October, which is springtime in these latitudes, one sees hundreds of patches from which the smoke ascends and almost as many brown areas where the forest is cleared and the trees and bushes lie withered, ready for burning. Finally, several hundred black patches are noticeable where burning already has taken place.

It goes without saying that this is a wasteful system in regard to labor, forest resources, and soils. But it still remains to be proven that continuous cultivation does work on Brazilian soils. Many lamentations are to be read about the primitivity of these methods—often accompanied by good advice and an assurance that modern mechanization after the United States or European pattern would be the remedy. A great many of these plaintive comments show that the author is little acquainted with the topography and soil conditions of this country. To take one example: no less than two-thirds of the sugar-cane acreage of the northeast hump is located on soils where no machinery so far known or invented would work; either it would get stuck or would seriously damage the topsoil. Furthermore, the sugar acreages in the state of Pernambuco are seriously eroded because of single-crop cultivation over a long period of time. Coffee-growing is on the whole not suited for mechanization and is an important part of Brazilian plant production. Several other examples could be brought up. Consequently, mechanization is not a universal remedy as is frequently maintained. This is proven indirectly by the fact that the present campaign for mechanization is successful chiefly in the southern part of the country, where soils and crops are more amenable to such developments. There are, nevertheless, only about 70,000 tractors in the whole of Brazil, which is one-tenth of the number agricultural economists consider desirable and feasible.

Nomadic Life

A reminder for all those who speak about the large future feeding potential of Brazil is the fact previously mentioned that an incessant migration goes on, which largely has remained little noticed or unheeded. Millions of families are forced to move every year in order to secure daily food. This applies to those who depend upon the milpa system in the forests, as well as to those tied to farming along the rivers in the Amazon basin. The soils become depleted so rapidly. Therefore a great many farmers are constantly on the move in the enormous country, in constant search for new land to "mine." The severe droughts which often strike, especially in the northeastern region, are another factor which contributes to these hordes of almost eternal migrants. In this hump the land is sparsely populated, as it consists largely of bush steppe. Every tenth or fifteenth year rain does not fall during the normally rainy season. Then rivers and lakes dry up completely. The wells also run dry and the plant cover withers away. The livestock animals succumb and die off in the thousands as they gather around the empty watering places.

Such droughts sent people in droves into the Amazonas region towards the end of the 1890's. For the same reason hundreds of thousands flocked to the cities. The flow of humans from the interior of the northeast culminated again in 1951 and 1952 when a new catastrophe hit, as severe as the one of 1899. A similar fate befell these regions during the Second World War. No less than 236,000 *flagelados*, the flagellated ones, then fled southward in boats, on trains, and in substandard trucks along worn-out roads—with a heavy accident toll as a tragic consequence. Another catastrophe scourged this region in 1957–58 when 70 per cent of the crops were lost.

The Tragedy of the Hump

Each time this happens, agitators get new grist for their revolutionary mills. A special government body, called SUDENE, was created after the last disaster (1957–58) in order to plan long-range countermeasures, but was soon shunted out in the constant political reshuffles of the country, with new bodies taking its place who were no more effective than the earlier ones. The dilemma is here unusually serious. What can really be done in the way of industrialization, when no water is available? To store up large quantities of food in order to cope with new catastrophes is expensive and difficult to carry out in the trying climate. One Brazilian secretary of finance came to talk the United States Government into financing the transfer of this population to the Amazonas. However, far better guarantees are needed for the success of such a plan in order to avoid the same outcome as when this was tried earlier. Then the migrants returned home, disenchanted with the alleged paradise of the Amazonas.

More recently a costly irrigation project has been developed for this region at an estimated cost of two billion dollars. This is seemingly a better alternative, although few seem to take the enormous costs into consideration. A more realistic approach would unquestionably be to reinstate the forest cover of these states and thereby restore the water balance at large, which presumably would reduce both the intensity and the frequency of these recurring droughts.

The ominous population growth has such dimensions, however, that neither economic prudence nor long-range planning seem feasible. In this part of the world, as in so many other places, man has long ago gone beyond the reasonable limits for his existence.

Seasonal Nomads

Seasonal changes too have their effect upon the movements of these seminomads. Many of them come from the north to seek work as cattle herdsmen in the huge expanses of Mato Grosso and other regions. Because of the seasonality and inadequacy of the pastures, they wander with the cattle herds over immense areas, in constant search for more feed. Thus, a considerable part of these migrants consists of an agricultural population continuously on the march, unsettled, primitive, and abandoned. They appear on the coffee plantations; sometimes they are found in the mountainous west; during the rainy season they find their way back to the north. Their own cattle are sometimes brought along with them. These wandering hordes of humans without permanent abode represent to a considerable degree an adjustment to the hard-earned existence which large regions of the so-called rich Brazil has to offer. Food is inadequate and Nature yields a parsimonious return.

The Giant Empire of the Amazon

The Amazonas has been called both the green hell and the paradise of the future. Many travelers and visitors have been impressed by its enormity and expressed extreme confidence in its potential as a future haven for the excess millions of the world. From a vessel out in the middle of the Amazon River one may see the river upstream and downstream for several tens of miles, but the shores are not visible. If land is sighted, it is mostly islands being passed by, often at a long distance.

Utter failure, accompanied by human suffering beyond measure, is the tragic outcome of efforts spanning over no less than four centuries to substantiate all these fanciful notions about the potential of the Amazon basin. This immense area has today a total population of approximately two million people, of which 350,000 are listed as Indians.

Minnesota is often spoken of (as is Finland) as the state of the thousand lakes. The Amazon basin could in a similar way be called the River of the Ten Thousand Islands. Many of these are large in size. The Amazon has sometimes been described as a giant dragon lying with its tail end far up in the Andean valleys and spewing out into the Atlantic from its mouth enormous water masses, around sixty billion gallons per hour. In the grasp of its jaws it holds several big islands; the largest one exceeds the size of Denmark, Switzerland, or Belgium.

The mouth of the Amazon is ten times wider than the English Channel between Dover and Calais. Sharks, tarpons, sawfish, and swordfish go all the way into the heartlands of Brazil via this water system. The tidal waves are often several feet high and regularly cause damage and expose the shoreline to constant strain and destruction. The Indian tribes who live along the river have—with good reason—named it *El Mar Dulce,* the fresh-water ocean. It has more than one hundred tributary rivers and provides the Atlantic Ocean with one-fifth of all the fresh water which all other rivers together in the whole world furnish to oceans. More than five hundred miles out at sea from the Amazon delta, the Atlantic waters are diluted and consequently brackish. Ten tributaries are larger than the Rhine. One tributary, the Rio Negro, is twenty miles wide where it joins the Amazon in the central part of the country. Speaking in geological terms, long before the Andean Mountains were folded and when South America still was divided into two separate islands, this whole region was covered by an enormous inland water.

The great diversity of fish species in this green kingdom is often pointed to as an asset. But in such discussions quantity is often mistaken for quality. That a greater number of fish species live in the Amazon than in all other fresh waters of the world taken together, does not in any way reflect the productive potential of these waters. Biologically, it may rather be interpreted as a sign that nature has been forced to develop a wide range of forms in order to sustain life. It also seems likely that this Amazon region harbors more insect species than the whole remaining world.

The Amazon basin constitutes 59 per cent of the Brazilian land area. In addition, the Amazon region covers considerable land areas in Bolivia, Peru, and Colombia. These regions are even more sparsely settled than those constituting parts of Brazil. It is presently (1961) estimated that the Brazilian section of the watershed area of the Amazon has a population of around 3.5 million.

Gradually, research has mercilessly revealed the facts about the Amazon basin, and they are certainly not encouraging. As can be expected in a region so leached through the constant rains and by the river water, the soils are very poor in minerals, and in addition, over the centuries they have gradually become very acid. Of the area which has been classified as cultivatable only one-twentieth is above the water level during the rainy season, and at the most, one-tenth of the periodically flooded regions may be cultivated with a reasonable return. The Amazon empire is an area larger than Europe or mainland United States, but according to estimates made by the Brazilian government, it contains a total of only around 160 million acres of cultivatable land—one-third of the present United States acreage of tilled land. Furthermore, the hazards for crop production are overwhelming. The abundance of butterflies which enchant the tourist means as many larvae, which voraciously attack the vegetation, including the tables which the pioneers set for them in the form of newly planted acreages. Fungal diseases spread in a disastrous way. Ants and termites turn loose on plants and soils. Poultry and other domestic animals have to be protected by means of specially constructed cages hung high up in the trees. The hogs must be confined to elevated pigsties to keep away snakes and numerous predatory animals.

Crops Yield a Parsimonious Return

Most of the farmers in the Amazonas barely manage to take care of their own subsistence; much less are they able to produce a surplus for the urban population. The cities in this part of the vast Brazilian land are by and large provided with some food from other parts of the country. Yet the Amazonians do not get adequate amounts of protein. Besides, their food is low in iron, zinc, calcium, and practically all other mineral nutrients as well as vitamins essential for good health. This is true despite the fact that the regular flooding provides fertilizers in the form of silt, free of charge. These inundations are beneficial by killing off several fungi and insects detrimental to the vegetation. On the other hand, the annual floods cause considerable damage. The shoreline is constantly changing as the water makes its cuts. This renders any kind of area-planning in these regions almost impossible. In the major part of the lower stretches of the Amazon, the river level drops less than one inch in ten miles (1 mm. per 100 meters).

The soils of the Amazon basin are normally hidden under an almost impenetrable canopy of trees. When the ground is cleared for cultivation and thereby made accessible to the scorching sun, the soils soon become less usable for cultivation. The temperature rises twenty to fifty degrees, accelerating the breakdown of organic matter and chemical oxidation of soil constituents. All binding humus is gone within a brief period of time.

The soil of an Iowa farm, in this climate with its daily heavy rain downpours, would most likely be leached of all minerals within three to four years and would be completely washed away in five. The lower Amazon basin is drenched with one to two hundred inches of rain annually. During the rainy season the river swells in places to a width of four hundred miles and the water level rises thirty-six to forty-eight feet.

Many have asked why the rubber tree has not become the great economic life-saver to the Amazonas, its country of origin. In the natural vegetation the rubber tree appears in single specimens spread among other trees in the extensive forest areas. Efforts to bring it into plantations have shown, however, that cultivated in this way, the rubber tree, despite being a native plant, yields only half of what the same species and varieties produce in Malaya. On an average they can be tapped only seventy times a year in the Amazonas, but one hundred and fifty times in Malaya. The cocoa tree, too, is indigenous to the Amazon region but yields far less there than in Africa. This is chiefly because of the mineral deficiency of the leached soils, which simply are not capable of producing more.

The Sauva

Brazilian plant cultivation is harassed by a host of serious pests. The arch enemy is the vociferous leaf-cutting ant, the *sauva. Ou a Brasil acaba com a sauva, ou a sauva caba com a Brasil*: Brazil must destroy the sauva ant; if this is not done, the sauva will destroy Brazil. It cuts up the leaves in small pieces and uses them to develop its own subterranean plantations of fungi. On its march over the land it ravages all kinds of crops, depriving crops and wild vegetation alike of all their leaves. Continuous and costly chemical warfare has to be carried on against these pests, which appear in armies numbering millions. Despite an unrelenting fight for their annihilation, every year they destroy crops worth millions of dollars. The sauva do not spare much; forest and agricultural plants are equally attractive to them. Coffee bushes, cocoa and orange trees are deprived of their leaves year after year until they finally succumb. Plants of cassava, beans, and potatoes are stripped of their leaves in one single attack. The subterranean living quarters, the sauva anthills, reach considerable dimension, from 2,500 to 3,500 cubic feet, 80 to 100 yards in diameter, subdivided into thousands of chamber sections.

The sauva constitutes the enemy number one of Brazilian crop production. But many other pests and diseases take a heavy toll each year. Insects destroy regularly 25 to 50 per cent of the cocoa harvest, and fungi destroy at least one-tenth. The coffee bean is bored through by an insect which often causes damages of disastrous proportions; this, the so-called "broca" disease, is fought by radically removing through pruning all lateral branches carrying infected berries. Frequently the whole tree has to be sacrificed. Termites penetrate woods, books, and food. The ant-eater is a highly valued domestic animal. He is the only effective ally man has in this battle against these insect armies.

Animal husbandry, too, is subject to hazards which a United States farmer can hardly imagine. On the big island of Marajó at the mouth of the Amazon River, there are quite a few rich pastures, some of the best in the whole country. But the croco-dile, or cayman, takes a yearly tribute of hundreds of thousands of young cattle, especially during the floods of the rainy season.

The Mineral Nutrients of the Soils

In spite of everything, the soils of the inland regions of north-eastern Brazil to the southeast of the Amazonas are better pro-vided with minerals than soils in wetter regions. The drought causes the soils to retain their mineral nutrients. In latter years nearly one billion dollars have been invested in various irrigation projects in these regions. Large silos have been built for grain to be stored as reserves for the drought periods. The exploitation of the mineral resources of these soils has consequently started in quite an organized manner.

Shortage of phosphate soon revealed itself as the most severe deficiency of Brazilian soils. Sometimes the shortage exists because these leached soils bind the phosphate that is available. Sometimes it can be explained by the low natural phosphate content. Through importation and by exploiting newly discovered phosphate deposits, the Brazilians try to compensate for the shortage, but high transportation costs present a significant and often insurmountable obstacle. This explains why such a gigantic country uses less than half a million metric tons of commercial fertilizers (potassium, nitrogen, and phosphate—NPK). About three-fourths of this quantity is imported. The need for commercial fertilizers has been estimated at about nine million metric tons per year, not including lime. The requirements are consequently enormous and can probably be met only through government subsidies. Commercial fertilizing on a major scale, however, would be highly wasteful in the Amazon basin. Most of these added nutrients would be lost through leaching before they had a chance of being taken up by the plant crops. The lion's share of the imported fertilizers goes to the southern state, Rio Grande do Sul. It is particularly important that nitrogen, which yields the vital protein, is not wasted. In several agricultural areas the nitrogen can be retained only by resorting to discarded oil cakes as fertilizers. In this case the nitrogen is released very slowly and at a rate which allows a gradual pickup by the plants during the course of several weeks in the hot soils. The commercial Chilean saltpeter, on the contrary, is rapidly dissolved and carried away by the seeping rainwater. It is, therefore, more than a coincidence that protein deficiency is the number one nutritional problem of the tropics, and not the least in Brazil. The original nitrogen content of these soils is normally, in round figures, one-tenth of that in temperate regions. The added nitrogen fertilizer often bypasses the root system of the plants owing to the intense leaching, before these have had a chance to absorb this invaluable nutrient. The growth is correspondingly slow, and the return of protein small. Nor are the livestock capable of magic.

Without sufficient protein in the grass of the pastures and in the feeding grain, the production of milk, eggs, and meat remains low. This explains why beef cattle in Brazil need twice as long a time to reach slaughter size than similar cattle on the Argentine pampas or on the prairies of the United States.

Pirarucu—the Food Fish of the Amazons

It is understandable that a country with such an extended coastline and such a vast river network as Brazil has made efforts to meet the protein needs of its nation through fish. When the soils have fallen short, the sea and the inland waters have been called upon to perform this function. In the heartlands of the Amazonas lies Manaus with Brazil's largest fresh-fish market, averaging thirty metric tons daily for a population of only around 125,000. The entire inland fisheries are estimated at 27,500 tons and ocean fisheries at approximately 132,000 tons annually. In both cases Nature raises severe obstacles. The tremendous number of species in this river and its mouth is a serious drawback to any regular commercial fisheries. Only one single species appears in large quantities in fairly concentrated catching grounds—the Brazilian "cod," the gigantic pirarucu. It is sold fresh, salted, or dried, usually in fillets.

Tropical waters on the whole are not very rich in fish. The Brazilian fisheries therefore are best developed in the cooler regions. In the north, fish-eating sharks dominate and are the basis for processing industries in the state of Maranhão, north of the hump. Vain efforts have been made to save foreign currency by procuring through native fisheries a quantity of pirarucu amounting to 55,000 tons, corresponding to what is being imported each year as dried fish. Around half of this importation is dried cod (klipfish, bacalao), coming primarily from Canada and Norway. Both Scandinavia and Japan have provided experts whose efforts have resulted in somewhat increased catches but so far not on an adequate scale. The hot climate and the shortage of salt complicates preservation, and in large areas sun-drying is not possible even when fish species suitable for drying are available. This is because of the high moisture content of the air. Drying has also been tried repeatedly with the pirarucu but largely without success. Canning has given a better result, but the extended floodings paralyze inland fisheries for months at a time and particularly in the Amazon.

Exploitation Efforts

Many efforts have been made throughout the years to utilize more efficiently the riches of the Amazonas. Out of the colonies which immigrants from the southern United States founded after the Civil War in the interior of Brazil along the Amazon, came the rubber-tree plantations. This later induced Henry Ford to start his capital-consuming venture, extended over several years at the river Tapajós, a tributary to the Amazon. The difficulties finally became overwhelming and the plantations were sold in 1945 to the Brazilian government. The Hylaean Institute, a special research institute under international management for the development of the resources of the Amazonas, has largely had to confine itself to activities in the abstract level of theoretical analyses of studies on paper.

A great deal of publicity has been given to the chain of isolated jungle cities which, with the airplane as the only connecting link with the outer world, are located right across the enormous Amazonas realm on the diagonal between Rio and Caracas, the capital of Venezuela. The hope is nurtured that these new creations will become centers for new colonization. The capital expenditures have been enormous, but there is a great risk that this chain of modern cities will become—like Manaus in the heartland of Amazonas—partly ghost towns, particularly when the modern jets bypass them. If these cities created by air traffic are not capable of finding other bases for their economic activity as well as for their food production in the radial exploitation of the vicinity, they will partly die off as Manaus has.

The agricultural experiment station located in Tingo María in the Amazonas high up at the foot of the Andes in Peru carries on far more purposeful activities than the Hylaean Institute. Here in the tropical rain forests efforts are being made to find ways of satisfying the food needs of the hundreds of thousands who, along the entire Andean mountain chain, are abandoning the overpopulated high plateaus. Progress can be noted in several areas but the limitations are the same as found in the Congo. The soils do not stand up under the strain of permanent agriculture, and when the forest is cleared they suffer terribly. It is important to keep in mind when judging Brazil's food-producing potential that nine-tenths of the country is located within the tropics.

The Amazon region is especially rich in various palm trees which yield oil-rich fruits. The babassu palm is considered the most valuable of them all. In the state of Maranhão the number of babassu palms, yielding oil-rich nuts, has been estimated at two billion. Also in the state of Piauí, like Maranhão located between the mouth of the Amazon and the hump, these valuable palm trees grow. Within the framework of President Truman's Point Four Program a company was created for the exploitation on a large scale of this valuable oil source, but so far it has had little success. Many of these palm oils are not suitable for food purposes but yield first-rate industrial oils and are expected to provide Brazil with a possible new export article, which in the future might become more important than coffee. Much more significant, however, are the experiments now being carried out to cultivate on a large scale other oil palms as plantation crops. This might possibly provide the tropical soils with a crop which protects them. Besides, if species are selected which yield oils and fats suitable for human consumption, they might create a new food resource and possibly solve the problem of permanent cultivation of tropical soils.

Priority to the Residents

Even if Brazil and the Amazonas should in a distant future prove capable of taking care of their future millions, we Westerners are definitely not first in line to receive these crops. The continent's own semistarved peoples must in all fairness be given the opportunity to share in an eventual abundance. Moreover, are not the excess millions of China and India equally justified in demanding their emigration quota as well as Europe? The Asiatics already have a Japanese beachhead in Brazil of more than a million people, the descendants of about 300,000 immigrants.

But we ought to think further ahead. Does not the first right really belong to the many American Indian tribes and peoples who in the great lottery of history were given these areas? In the interior of Mato Grosso and along the banks of the Amazon they created highly diversified cultures, often ingeniously adjusted to the caprices of an overwhelming Nature. Are we entitled to count them out?

Powerful civilizations were once created along the great rivers: the Nile, the Thames, the Hwang Ho and the Tigris-Euphrates. The Volga and the Yenisey are giving birth to new cultures, still under development. The Congo River is just beginning to shake off the jungle. But as far as we know today, the Amazon region is a mock paradise.

A Brazilian nutrition expert recently asserted that without food the Amazonas would remain a demographic desert. Traditionally coffee has been given precedence over food. In the tug-of-war between nourishment and foreign exchange the latter was always given the priority. This is not so surprising, as the decision on these matters only rarely lay in the hands of those trying to eke out an existence on this continent.

Coffee on the March

When the coffee prices are rising, the economists in Europe and the United States overbid each other in sagacious explanations about price manipulations, changes in consumption, purchasing strikes, and stock exchange manipulations. These reasonings may be partially true but Nature's own stock exchange is habitually overlooked. This exchange makes quotations of its own. The almost predatory exploitations by the coffee planters have ruined a considerable portion of Brazil's soils. In many areas, these abandoned coffee lands are so ruined that they can hardly ever again be restored to crop production. In others a varying portion of the topsoil has been removed, or the humus content of the soil has been seriously reduced. In most regions, a mere one-tenth now remains of the amount of humus present when coffee cultivation was started. Therefore the coffee plantations have always been on the march, grabbing new land and leaving behind eroded or impoverished soils. Coffee has climbed even higher along the slopes of the Brazilian high plateau and has finally reached up there. In search for new soils to take the place of those that had been destroyed, coffee-growing moved toward the south and west as well as into entirely new states.

Each time, however, the coffee plantations were forced to move to less favorable regions, where especially the frost risks have turned out to be considerable. They have also been compelled to abandon the fertile red soil, *terra roxa*, where uninterrupted production is possible for from forty to sixty years. Poor sandy soils have been put under cultivation where the life span of the coffee bushes is only half as long. As a last resort, still poorer soils in the state of Espírito Santo have been used, where the bushes render reasonable yields merely for eight years or so.

This march of the coffee plantations over the wide expanses of Brazil has been likened to a devastating giant wave which has now reached the river Paraná, where cultivation takes place under much more unfavorable conditions compared to the time when the coffee bushes flourished in the vast Paraíba Valley, west of Rio de Janeiro. Here the pioneers burned enormous forests in order to obtain room for the largest possible number of coffee bushes. Behind them the coffee-thirsty peoples of the world have left poor pastures. Here and there a grove of eucalyptus trees, imported from Australia, may be seen. The humus has not stood up against the strain. The soil has deteriorated and has subsequently been damaged on quite a scale in a man-induced erosion. Centuries of forest growth would be required, to restore an adequate humus layer.

Europeans and Americans pay, in today's coffee prices, not only for a commodity which is costly in acreage and labor requirements, but also for this long-range damage inflicted on Brazilian soils. In other words, we not only have to pay for the coffee we now consume, but we are indirectly taxed for the soil that was destroyed when the coffee of our parents and grandparents was produced. But we should, in effect, also pay for the repair and restoration of the soils to full productivity. In some of these early coffee regions the abandoned soil is so crisscrossed by ravines and gullies that it almost resembles a lunar landscape. The cattle cannot go in there to graze the sparse wild vegetation which barely covers the wounds of the ground, without risk of breaking their legs. The pasture forage is deficient both in quality and quantity. A famous geographer once said, with Brazil primarily in mind: "It is not in the old countries with time-honored civilizations that the soil is most worn, but rather in the most recently colonized."

Cattle as Fertilizer Producers

In many regions of Brazil, as well as on the west coast of southern India, cattle are held primarily for the production of fertilizers and in order to fill the needs of the coffee plantations. There are *fazendas* (large farms) which have thousands of animals gathered in primitive barns for this purpose. They are daily fed leaves and twigs from the virgin forest nearby.

Bedding is also gathered from the forest. Straw (haulms) and grass are utilized as supplementary feed. In order to secure a permanent feed supply a special kind of sugar cane, *taquera*, is sometimes grown, or fields with melass grass are harvested and put into silos. In the course of a year, a considerable amount of natural fertilizer in the form of manure is produced at these specialized farms. Per year, one thousand cattle yield sufficient manure for 150,000 coffee trees, which corresponds to about twelve metric tons per acre. In this way it takes three years to go over a coffee plantation of half a million bushes, providing it with adequate fertilizing.

Malnutrition and Poor Health

Diseases have shortened the life of the Brazilians to the extent that almost half the nation is under fifteen years of age, in spite of a high infant mortality. Every fifth baby dies before completing his first year. Those who have seen the seemingly healthy people which throng the *praias* (beaches) at Santos and Copacabana, may have difficulty in imagining that the prime worry of the country is undernourishment and poor health. Good health is almost an exclusive privilege of the well-to-do.

It is worth noting that the major health problem is not the tropical diseases. These have gradually been put under control, primarily through the important work by the world-famous physician Osvaldo Cruz at the beginning of this century. No, the crux of Brazil's problem is hunger and malnutrition which alone slowly enfeeble and undermine the health and resistance of millions. In this respect there is a great similarity between the masses in Brazil, in India, and in China. In all three countries undernourishment is basically caused by an overall lack of biological balance, an overestimation of the productivity of the soils. According to nutritional surveys made in several Brazilian states, not more than about 1,600 calories can be procured of the 2,600 which are the daily minimum for each individual.

According to the recent FAO (Food and Agriculture Organization) figures (1960) the average calorie supply per person is given as 2,710 (3,100) and the consumption of animal protein as 18 (66) grams and total protein as 67 (92). The figures in parenthesis refer to the United States. This classifies Brazil as one of the world's poorly fed countries. How population growth comes to exceed the available food supply is best illustrated by the gradual deterioration of the protein standard. Since the 1930's the per capita intake of animal protein has dropped one-third. Plant protein has taken its place. Rice and beans have been substituted for meat.

Officers of merchant-navy ships often make fastidious comments about the laziness of Brazilian stevedores and longshoremen. The sad truth is that inadequate calorie intake in most cases is the underlying cause. They simply cannot work harder. The food supply is not sufficient for a six-day work week. In addition, the deficiency—according to the above-mentioned nutrition surveys—is especially great in regard to proteins and minerals, above all calcium and iron, and a series of vitamins. The diet of the poor is largely composed of manioc (cassava) flour (or sugar!) and beans, possibly supplemented with a small amount of dried meat (*xarque*). As explained above, the mounting population pressure has forced an increased vegetabilization of the diet, reflected in the ploughing of pastures to find land on which to grow wheat, beans, and manioc. This has resulted in steady reduction in cattle and meat livestock—in turn affecting a drop in the meat consumption since the thirties.

Only a small upper class can afford the luxury of drinking milk. However, most of the milk is less nutritious than ours and is especially low in calcium. Magic is not possible, and the feed contains no more calcium than the lime-deficient soils allow. Large quantities of lime supplements must therefore be added to the feed in order to obtain milk with a reasonable amount of calcium. The public food control has a difficult task, moreover, in preventing milk from being diluted with water.

As already pointed out, the protein content becomes low in the nitrogen-poor tropical soils. The mineral content is also below normal—not surprising in the light of the leaching and depletion that take their toll. Nor is it surprising therefore to find that so many apparently healthy bodies and faces show such obvious traces of tooth decay. Nutritional deficiencies are important causes of widespread tuberculosis and also aggravate other diseases such as malaria, hookworm infections, and perhaps also syphilis. The Brazilians are as able to work and have as much initiative as any other people, including ourselves, if they are adequately nourished. This was proven by the Brazilian army units during the Second World War and is also evidenced by those among the modern city dwellers and well-to-do who, thanks to higher purchasing power, can secure a greater share of the inadequate food supply or can supplement their food by imported articles.

It is true that the cultivated acreage has trebled since 1920, from about fifteen million acres to almost forty-seven million. However, this is not as impressive as it may seem. Despite the fact that eleven million acres were added during the ten-year period 1940–50, the sad result is that this has, by and large, managed only to compensate for the drop in yields per acre; this applies to most crops. The yield per acre of cocoa for example is miserably low compared to that of most other cocoa-producing countries. Only cotton shows good yields compared to other countries.

During the forties the number of mouths to feed increased by almost twelve million. This explains the factual deterioration in nutrition despite the overall improved economy of the country. From 1945 to 1955 the population increased 25 per cent and the agricultural production, measured in tons, 19 per cent. Yet the harvest figures were pushed upward primarily through increased sugar production, a calorie swindle. The vital protein production in the form of animal products increased merely half as much as plant products. The nutritional standard was further pressed toward a vegetable consumption.

Food Crops Essential for Balance

It is often pointed out that the cultivated acreage of Brazil amounts to a pitiful 2 per cent of the land area. But it is rarely mentioned that in spite of this notably low figure a high proportion of the tilled acreage is located on slopes (10° to 35° angle), resulting in varying degrees of detrimental erosion. This reflects the basic shortage of good lands for crop production. In order to obtain sufficient tilled land, many agricultural regions have therefore been compelled to resort to utilizing so-called marginal soils which do not even possess a fertility considered normal for Brazil.

One-fourth of the tilled land is used to grow corn accounting for one-third of the daily intake of plant protein. Almost one-third of the cultivated acreage is equally divided between coffee and cotton. It is easy to prove that the total tilled acreage would be needed for food crops in order to provide the Brazilians with a minimum nutritional standard.

The arms required in the labor force also represent mouths, and it has been too often overlooked that arms are little effective if the needs of the stomach are neglected. Balance in this respect constitutes Brazil's chief problem. If larger areas cannot

TABLE 29

Wheat Balance of Brazil

(ANNUAL 3-YEAR AVERAGES)

	1934–38	1940–43	1943–46	1946–49	1949–52
Area (1,000 hectares)	151.0	280.0	315.0	516.6	729.0
Yield (1,000 kg/ha)	9.6	8.0	6.9	8.1	7.5
Production (1,000 metric tons)	144.2	223.8	217.0	412.0	549.0
Import (1,000 metric tons)	915.2	—	—	494.7	1,222.7
Population (millions)	38.6	—	—	48.5	53.3

	1952–55	1955–58	1958–61	1961–62	1962–63
Area (1,000 hectares)	1,013.0	1,162.0	1,258.0	1,022.0	743.0
Yield (1,000 kg/ha)	9.0	6.9	5.2	5.8	9.1
Production (1,000 metric tons)	915.0	752.0	604.0	545.0	676.0
Import (1,000 metric tons)	1,570.2	1,456.4	1,803.3	1,886.8	2,199.8
Population (millions)	57.1	62.0	70.6	75.3	77.5

be put under cultivation and the total agricultural output increased above the present one, some kind of change is mandatory in view of the mounting nutritional needs.

Several nutritional experts have recommended that an adjustment be made at the expense of coffee, but the results of such a move are uncertain. It has been said that Brazil could replace coffee with steel as a source of income and that if this were done, enough grain could perhaps be produced within the country. In order to achieve this balance it is necessary, however, to leave the realm of wishful thinking and return to reality. The total production from Brazilian soil has increased by 56 per cent since the thirties, while the exportation has gone up only 7 per cent. This clearly points to the fact that the nation needs a higher and increased share of the agricultural production as food—first, to satisfy minimum nutritional needs, and second, to keep up with the population growth.

Coffee has always been Brazil's most profitable crop, in many years accounting for as much as 80 per cent of the income from foreign trade, and wherever it can be cultivated the coffee bush has been given precedence over food. Today this is still the case, though, as discussed above, the frost limit has been reached in the northern part of the state of Paraná. Corn, beans, and feed crops have been made a second choice, and largely grown only where the "cream" of the soils had been reamed—when depletion and erosion started to affect coffee yields. It is symptomatic that in the present plans for federal investment in irrigation projects, 75 per cent is allotted for use in coffee plantations. Santos is gradually diminishing as a coffee port, and large sums are now being earmarked for the construction of new roads and railroads as well as for the enlargement of the harbor in Paranaguá in order to organize shipments directly from the state of Paraná, where about 60 per cent of the coffee has been produced since the beginning of the 1950's.

The Protein Production

Aside from fisheries, the raising of meat-producing animals—cattle, hogs, sheep, and poultry—constitutes the means by which efforts are made to sustain, though in a scanty way, the protein needs of the nation. This protein production, however, takes place under rather unfavorable circumstances. The subordinate position of dairy products in the Brazilian diet has already been pointed out. Protein-rich feed is as difficult to come by as is protein-rich human food. According to recent statistics the number of cattle amounts to sixty million—more than in Argentina—and the hogs to fifty million, but the latter are raised more for the production of fat than for meat. If the total livestock is taken into account, its feed consumption in terms of proteins corresponds to the consumption of 1,030 million people. This brings Brazil at once into the ranks of the most populated countries on earth. Its vegetation cover has the task of feeding a domesticated living mass corresponding to 1.1 billion people! The vegetarians and the traditional economists, who do not want to face the nutritional realities, recommend, of course—as they do for India—a drastic reduction of the cattle production. This would be feasible only if the areas feeding these could be put into efficient crop production. So far it has not been possible to secure vital protein in adequate amounts from alternative sources. Two expedients have been tried but both have so far proved less than promising.

The fisheries were discussed earlier. Among the nitrogen-fixing crops, the soybean occupies a special position. It constitutes one of China's life-savers. But numerous experiments carried out at the agricultural research stations of Brazil have early borne out the fact that only restricted areas offer the rather demanding soybean a satisfactory mineral nutrition. This is probably the chief explanation why its cultivation is limited to about half a million acres and chiefly in the favored southern state of Rio Grande do Sul. Beans of other kinds—which also take their nitrogen from the air—have long held a prominent position in the raising of crops—more than 1.25 million acres. But these sources do not go far when the population figures are pushing upward by more than 1.5 million per year. This production must be increased tenfold barely to fill the present protein gap.

The Coffee Enchantment

Not until the coffee enchantment threatened to topple the Brazilian government through enormous, non-saleable surpluses, did reason prevail. In 1934, planting restrictions were instituted, and interest was aroused in producing food, which at that time had to be bought from abroad to a considerable extent. When the government regulations were abandoned a few years later, the number of coffee bushes continued to diminish—now as a consequence of the decreasing yields. Devastating attacks by fungi and insects were primarily explained by the reduced vitality of the bushes, which was due to deficiencies in several essential soil nutrients. The rate at which new plantings were made was substantially reduced—despite the economically favorable situation—because of the limited availability of new soils suited for coffee. In 1947 there was a reduction of no less than half a billion coffee bushes compared to 1934; this was one-third of the total stock of bushes.

Brazil seems to move inevitably from one coffee crisis to the next one. One occurred in 1960–61 and a second one in 1963–64. The unilateral dependence on coffee for its foreign trade is a serious weakness in the national economy. The unrestrained hunt for foreign exchange each time seems to lead to renewed massing of coffee surpluses, with the risks of a collapse of the market.

The economic thinking, which is unable to free itself from these simple causal circles, and fails to consider the health and nutritional standard of the people as invaluable economic assets, will constantly be fooled by facts and reality. A flourishing industry with well-nourished workers would bring considerably higher returns to the nation than coffee ever did or could. This holds true especially on a continent which is lacking in most of the things which are essential to a decent life, even such simple commodities as bicycles and furniture, including beds. Brazil could easily become the industrial giant of this continent if food and health were adequately taken care of.

Presently Brazil produces on an average 70 per cent of the world's coffee, but frost, drought, and damages cause greater yield fluctuations than in any other coffee-producing country. The dominance of coffee in the trade balance has therefore made state regulations necessary for more than a century. Fluctuations have in turn brought about social unrest. The statement that coffee has been and is a powerful factor in Brazilian politics is thus well founded, but it need not necessarily remain so.

Nowadays, Brazil has in all no more than two and a half billion coffee bushes. It is highly indicative of the increasingly precarious climatic conditions under which they now are forced to be cultivated that in 1953 no less than half a billion bushes were lost through a series of frosty nights. Sixty million bushes are labeled as overaged, and over 300 million are not yet in a productive stage.

It was during the reconstruction period in the thirties that large-scale burning of coffee took place and the railroad engines were fueled with coffee. This measure is often recalled as an indication of the earth's abundance but also of man's lack of wisdom. In any number of magazine articles the concurrent starvation in the world has been discussed, but it has rarely been pointed out that this coffee was extracted from Brazilian soils for an addicted, well-fed world, but at the price of malnutrition and undernourishment for the producer nation. Coffee surpluses were never any evidence of abundance; rather, they point to grave defects in international marketing.

Tons and Calories

Like so many other nations in the world, Brazil has committed the grave error of looking more for quantity than quality in its agricultural production. Sugar production has been pushed high in tons and even caused surpluses which have had to be converted into alcohol or used in rubber production. In 1954 the sugar "surplus" was used to produce more than seventy million gallons of industrial alcohol. The yield statistics have been impressive, presented in tons and calories, but the nutritional needs, especially in terms of protein, vitamins, and minerals, have been disastrously neglected.

In this same light Brazil's stubborn fixation on the high-yielding manioc, sometimes called Brazilian tapioca or cassava, is to be judged. Its protein content is a mere 1 to 2 per cent as compared to the 10 to 12 per cent in corn. The yield per acre for manioc, which is primarily a starch-producing crop, is at least ten times as high as the yields for corn and wheat. For myopic agricultural economists, who count solely in tons and calories, manioc is, like the sugar cane, a godsend, but to an under-nourished people it constitutes a scourge. When efforts are made (as they were for a long time and especially during the last world war) to compensate for huge shortages of bread grains by compulsory adding of cassava flour in the milling, the nutritional base of vital protein is further seriously undermined. Cassava flour has 0.5 to 0.6 per cent protein and consists mainly of starch. During the Second World War the cassava flour addition was raised to no less than 30 per cent—almost one-third.

Development Plans

Few countries have presented such a cavalcade of magnificent plans as Brazil for the coordination of projects to increase food production. At least six large-scale projects have been born since 1943. Economic means have not been lacking for their realiza-tion. Most of them have also been put into effect. But by and large they have all fallen short of the goal, not, as is often said, because of political strife alone. To a considerable degree the country's potential for food production has been overestimated. Most planners have been deplorably unaware of a whole series of basic factors which limit the possibilities of Brazilian soils to attain European, or even North American, yields: primarily, poor soils, water shortages, and inadequate nitrogen resources. It is tempting to predict for Brazil a glorious future under the banner of industrialization. But those millions who gather in the cities and flock to the industries must also be fed, and Brazil cannot, as Europe once did, resort to massive importation of foodstuffs.

Despite laudable efforts to the contrary, about 60 per cent of the nation's labor force is still toiling in agriculture. Much food is purchased, but, despite large volumes, in wholly inadequate amounts and yet economically back-breaking.

The so-called SALTE plan was the one which reflected a more thoroughly conceived, forceful attack on the ills of Brazil. It was geared to a coordinated action for improved health (*Saude*), nutrition (*Alimentacão*), communications (*Transporte*), and electric power supply (*Energía*). Only by encompassing in this way the whole field is there a chance to put an end to malnutrition and to slow down the importation of foodstuffs. It remains doubtful, however, if the country's actual status as the major deficiency area of the globe can be changed. In any case, all talk about Brazil as a land of abundance, a Canaan for the many excess millions of the globe, is far removed from reality. Each government is vigorously trying to improve the situation and setting up the obvious goal of drastically increasing the food production by 25 to 50 per cent. Mostly they realize the need for major investments in canning factories, machine and tool production of all kinds, in other food industries, packaging industries, and so forth. In cooperation with international capital, efforts are being made to reduce the present storage wastes. These reportedly reach 20–40 per cent of the food produced. Before the food reaches the consumer, that much is irretrievably lost. Considerable gains could be made in this area. But only by putting a brake to the population growth is any kind of progress within reach.

The Eternal Utopia

"If Paradise exists anywhere on earth, it cannot be far from here." Amerigo Vespucci is reported to have uttered these words when he first saw the beautiful façade of Brazil toward the Atlantic—a façade of exuberant green. This was one year after the Portuguese navigator Cabral had discovered this land. This quotation contains a great deal of truth, but we must keep in mind that the paradise is not identical to the land of promise for millions of people. Our wasteful economy is hardly compatible with a paradisiacal existence, a way of life where all values are kept in harmonious balance and in continuous circulation through plants, animals, and microorganisms. With our accelerated tempo it is certainly not possible to maintain a Garden of Eden. If we persist in pursuing the present exploitation, and if in the future a predatory course is followed as during past centuries, then the great resources of Brazil will be wasted long before the country ever has had even a fair chance to create human welfare. If the millions of Brazilians who now constitute the nation's labor force are not conceded a greater share of its own resources, then Brazil will remain for generation upon generation a mirage looming on the horizon, a dream that will never be fulfilled—an Eternal Utopia.

References

BRAZIL

BASTIDE, R. *Brésil, terre des contrastes.* Paris, Hachette, 1957, 343 pp.

CAMACHI, J. A. *Brazil—an Interim Assessment.* London and New York, Royal Institute of International Affairs, 1954, 123 pp.

FREYRE, G. *New World in the Tropics.* New York, Knopf, 1959, 385 pp.

————. *The Masters and the Slaves,* 3rd ed. New York, Knopf, 1960, 537 pp.

FURTADO, C. *The Economic Growth of Brazil.* Berkeley, University of California Press, 1963, 285 pp.

GRACA, A. *Economía politica e economia Brasileira.* São Paulo, Saraiva, 1962, 339 pp.

HILL, F. L. (ed.). *Brazil.* Berkeley, University of California Press, 1947, 394 pp.

HUNNICUTT, P. H. *Brazil Looks Forward.* Rio de Janeiro, 1945, 522 pp.

KUZNETS, S. S. *Economic Growth: Brazil, India, Japan.* Durham, Duke University Press, 1955, 292 pp.

LOEB, G. F. *Industrialization and Balanced Growth with Special Reference to Brazil.* Groningen, J. B. Wolters, 1957, 159 pp.

MEIJER, H. *Rural Brazil at the Cross-roads.* Wageningen, Veenman, 1951, 208 pp.

MEIJIDI, P. A. *Brazil, la gran potencia del siglo XXI.* Porto, Santiago de Compostela, 1957, 270 pp.

SMITH, T. L. *Brazil, People and Institutions.* Rev. ed. Baton Rouge, Louisiana University Press, 1963, 667 pp.

WAGLEY, C. *An Introduction to Brazil.* New York, Columbia University Press, 1964, 390 pp.

AMAZONAS

BROWN, J. *Two Against the Amazon.* New York, Dutton, 1953, 247 pp.

CLARK, L. F. *The Rivers Ran East.* New York, Funk & Wagnalls, 1953, 366 pp.

HAMON, G. P. *The Amazon—a New Frontier.* New York, Foreign Policy Association, 1944, 92 pp.

HASKINS, C. P. *The Amazon—the Life History of a Mighty River.* New York, Doubleday, 1943, 415 pp.

HERNDON, W. L. *Exploration of the Valley of the Amazon.* New York, Grosset & Dunlap, 1952, 201 pp.

HOFF, W. *Tropisches Südamerika.* Berlin, Safari, 1949, 262 pp.

KATZ, R. *Auf dem Amazonas.* Zürich, Rentsch, 1946, 292 pp.

PERRIN, M. *La Tragédie du Haut-Amazone.* Paris, Denoel, 1954, 270 pp.

PRICE, W. *The Amazing Amazon.* New York, John Day, 1952, 306 pp.

SCHURZ, W. L. *Brazil—the Infinite Country.* New York, Dutton, 1961, 346 pp.

SEITZ, G. *People of the Rainforests.* London, Heinemann, 1963, 208 pp.

SNOW, S. *My Amazon Adventure.* London, Odhams, 1954, 224 pp.

ULLMAN, J. R. *River of the Sun.* Philadelphia, Lippincott, 1951, 444 pp.

WAGLEY, C. *Amazon Town—a Study of Man in the Tropics.* New York, Macmillan, 1953, 305 pp.

WAVRIN, R. *L'Amazonie et ses Indiens.* Namur, Ed. du Soleil, 1958, 188 pp.

CHAPTER 16

United States

Food Surpluses—

A Brief Episode

MORE than 150 million people on the globe today
get their food needs filled from acreages which have been made
available for the production of food instead of feed, thanks to
mechanization. This is a one-time device to which first Western
Europe and then the Soviet Union have resorted in order to take
care of their food needs. In the case of North America (the
United States and Canada), however, it was not the threat of
food deficiencies that was the driving force. Instead, replacement
of the horse with mechanization constituted a necessary measure
in the rationalization process. Nevertheless, the fact remains that
after the Second World War the United States broadened its
agricultural basis of tilled land by about sixty-six million acres
through mechanization. This corresponds to almost one-fifth of
the total tilled acreage of the country. It is evident that such a
significant contribution to the food-crop production could not
take place without considerable disruptions of the market. No
country could swiftly expand its acreage by one-fifth without

noticeable repercussions. The politicians reinforced this effect even further by putting restrictions on cotton cultivation. President Franklin D. Roosevelt limited the cotton within the framework of the "good neighbor policy" in order to help Brazil's cotton production. This gave the United States in one stroke another twenty-five million acres to utilize fully for other purposes, including food-producing crops.

Favorable Climate

During the forties and fifties the climatic conditions in the United States were what may be termed abnormal, which means that they deviated from the average figures for the last 150 years. The thirties have been labeled "the terrible thirties" in the annals of U.S. agriculture, as drought and subsequent dust storms devastated millions of acres. Drought is an integral feature of the climate in the United States. The forties enjoyed an especially favorable climate and are therefore generally called "the favorable forties." Only two or possibly three times since the thirties has there been a tendency toward such conditions as prevailed during the middle years of that unfortunate decade. In the sixties serious drought has been a recurrent phenomenon, in one major region or another and to the degree that several agricultural districts have each year been declared catastrophe areas, and thereby eligible for financial aid.

It is of interest to note that by and large Europe experienced the opposite. The record yields of the thirties caused Hitler to overestimate tremendously the feeding potentialities of that continent. The forties, especially the first war years, were characterized by extremely harsh winters.

Tilling Pushed to the Extreme

Another important factor which partly explains United States surpluses is the Federal program of subsidizing with parity prices and other similar measures, thus making grain production most attractive. This stimulated extensive ploughing to gain land for grain-cropping. This was carried far beyond what was prudent with regard to soil protection. As is well known, the "dust bowl" catastrophe hit the country in 1934. This was primarily caused by such excessive ploughing for the raising of larger crops. In drought years and with the winds prevailing over the prairies, this gave rise to extensive soil erosion accompanied by dust storms. In the sixties special measures have been taken to reduce the wheat acreage through government contracts—the so-called Soil Bank Program, still in full operation, but frequently misconstrued. Besides reducing the wheat surpluses, this arrangement was made to avert a new dust bowl catastrophe and to reduce the risks of a new large-scale loss and destruction of invaluable soils. This protection was attained by limiting cultivation to those soils which can stand tilling and grain cultivation over a number of years. Surpluses which are bought at the expense of devastated soils, with accompanying acreage losses, are basically illusions for they represent the squandering of capital assets.

High-Yielding Grain with Less Protein

Over the years a switch on a major scale has been made to what is termed high-yielding varieties of corn and wheat. Together with the factors mentioned earlier this constitutes a key factor in creating the U.S. surpluses of which so much has been written. In chapter 2 it was pointed out that if the protein content of the present corn and wheat crops is to be equivalent with that found for corn twenty years ago and for wheat as late as 1948, these crops must be supplemented by a substantial portion of the present U.S. soybean crop. Quantity has been bought at the price of quality.

By and large the same situation is prevalent in Europe. Despite considerably increased nitrogen fertilizing, it is the exception rather than the rule that the protein level in terms of percentage of protein has been maintained in winter or spring wheats. As a rule, high-yielding varieties show lower protein figures, and with each new variety bred to yield more, the protein content has usually been reduced. This causal relationship can also be formulated in the following way: the gradual increases in total yields per acre have, as a rule, exceeded corresponding increases in the yields of protein per acre. The cells have become more filled with bulk, chiefly carbohydrates, that crowds out the protein. Only in rare instances has it been possible through late fertilizer dressings to counteract these effects.

Surplus—A Relative Concept

It should further be kept in mind that every country could easily obtain surpluses by steering its agriculture in one direction through either state planning or excessive profiteering. From time to time one or another country in Western Europe expresses concern about one kind of surplus or another. West Germany has reported a butter surplus despite the fact that more than half of the nation's food fat has to be imported; English producers showed a surplus in eggs in spite of the country's great dependence on importation of animal protein and feedstuff; Austria has spoken about surpluses of agricultural products although in order to feed the nation it is forced to buy food from abroad in quantities which, if produced within the country, would require an acreage corresponding to 40 per cent of its present tilled acreage. A great many similar examples could be given. It is high time that economists and agricultural experts agree upon an acceptable definition of what is meant by surplus. If this term is used as soon as something non-marketable is produced, both the public and the politicians are misled.

Butter Surpluses

The discussion about the butter surpluses is especially distorted. A few rich countries utilize the cow as fat-producer and put on an astonished face when the poor world cannot afford to buy this expensive fat. Even in the rich countries themselves, for instance the United States and West Germany, large segments

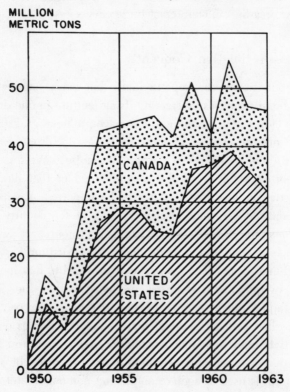

CARRY-OVER STOCKS OF WHEAT, NORTH AMERICA, 1950-63

FIG. 41

of the population are not able to buy butter, aside from the fact that margarine has now become so well integrated in the total fat provision of the western world that a return to butter is unthinkable. In other words, present agricultural production could not manage without a considerable downgrading of the daily diet to procure these supplies of butter fat. It is no exaggeration to say that at least two hundred million people in the United States and Western Europe depend upon margarine, and thus on vegetable fats and marine oils, for their fat provision, and this number is steadily increasing. The cow has its justification as a protein producer. However, this may not be interpreted in such a way that the "have-not" nations, in spite of their enormous protein deficiency, are willing or able to pay the "have" nations' high costs of milk production, partly caused by expensive, long-distance feed purchases or price manipulations based on agricultural policies.

Stored Quantities

At the beginning of 1960 the United States had in storage a quantity of corn corresponding to two years' consumption and wheat enough for one year. The stored surpluses have been reduced somewhat in recent years by extensive sales and relief deliveries during the sixties, but there are still in these two commodities considerable amounts (see Figure 41). These may look like large surpluses, but already from a national point of view a buffer of this magnitude would seem a necessary precaution. No American President, familiar with the climatic conditions of our country and in view of the present world situation, can afford to count on average yields. Buffer storage of the present size seems to be a reasonable safeguard. As an historical parallel it might be of interest to note that a Chinese emperor regarded as most successful was the one who managed to hoard in the state stores rice and other crops adequate for twenty-seven years of

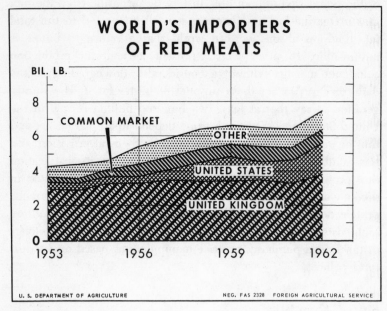

WORLD'S IMPORTERS OF RED MEATS

BIL. LB.

COMMON MARKET

OTHER

UNITED STATES

UNITED KINGDOM

8

6

4

2

0

1953   1956   1959   1962

U. S. DEPARTMENT OF AGRICULTURE   NEG. FAS 2328   FOREIGN AGRICULTURAL SERVICE

FIG. 42

consumption. With the hundreds of millions in our day this would simply not be feasible, either from a technical or an economic viewpoint. Nonetheless, it would definitely be less prudent even for an economically strong country like the United States to make itself wholly dependent upon one year's crop. It is sobering to realize that no part of the world, in the event of serious crop failure, is more than one year away from critical starvation, and even the rich United States with all its surpluses is not more than two years away. Purchases on the world market may alleviate the sufferings, but no grain movements on any major scale are really feasible. There are simply no merchant navy or port facilities available for such gigantic undertakings.

During the latter part of the 1950's there was a great deal of fuss about the butter and the nonfat milk solids which were then being stored as surplus. In relation to the actual consumption of these items within the United States they were rather insignificant, but when considered in terms of world trade they constituted a threat of disturbance to these markets.

World trade in foods never amounted to more than a fraction of the total production, and on the whole its role in relative terms has been steadily declining with the mounting needs for domestic consumption which have accompanied the population increase within the various producing nations themselves. Australia already speaks about the day when it will be forced to import food in order to maintain its standard. The same applies to Argentina. Even though this may seem exaggerated, it illustrates the fact that when evaluated in terms of protein quantities, the surpluses were always minor. This was highlighted in a couple of recent instances. When the Kennedy Administration undertook to distribute food surpluses to the unemployed in the depressed areas, only corn and wheat were available. The stores of protective foods such as eggs, meat, and milk were either non-existent or wholly inadequate.

When UNICEF started its worldwide rescue operation for the world's children, this was looked upon as an ideal way to dispose of the United States milk surpluses. Within three months, however, the stores were emptied and the large-scale plans had to be revised. UNICEF had to scan the globe to find any considerable amount of excess protein. In the many projects which formed part of the Food for Peace program it soon became clear—much to the surprise of some economic circles—that the stored grain would not go far when converted into milk, meat, and poultry. Even minimal plans for efficient and nutritious aid to undernourished countries would, if put into effect, soon lead to considerable shortages on the U.S. market. A study of the protein consumption and its distribution in the present world quickly makes this abundantly clear, almost self-evident.

The Fisheries Crisis

The United States fishing grounds, its lakes, rivers, as well as coastal waters, are threatened like those of other industrial nations. Many rivers have become sewage carriers; lakes and coastal waters are increasingly polluted. Hydroelectric dams have a disturbing, even an obstructing effect on spawning and fish migration. As in the U.S.S.R. and Europe, efforts are being made to compensate for this destruction by controlled fish cultivation, particularly in the southern parts of the country. Ponds can be operated there the year round. Their number already exceeds one million. Even the rice fields in the south are increasingly combined with the raising of fish, following the Southeast Asian pattern.

The serious crisis in U.S. fisheries is evident in the steadily increasing reliance on importation. Since the end of World War II the total aquatic catch has dropped by no less than 550 million pounds and the United States has become the world's largest importer of fish, 1.2 billion pounds per year, and is scanning almost the whole globe for shellfish (shrimp, lobster tail, etc.). The population growth has such dimensions in the United States that in order to keep pace the fish catch would have to have been extended by 800 million pounds since 1945, and yet this would have done nothing to raise the low average intake of fish.

Protein Importation

Less noticed is the fact that considerable protein quantities reach the U.S. national household through the back door, so to speak. Meat is imported from Mexico, Argentina, New Zealand, and Australia. Young cattle are increasingly taken from Canada for finish-feeding in the United States. Cattle are marched from Northern Mexico.

Attention was finally focused (1964) on this unique phenomenon as this importation exceeded one-tenth of the consumption and continued to mount, to the detriment of U.S. meat producers. Congress intervened and tried to put a damper on this development by introducing import quotas and freezing imports at certain prefixed levels.

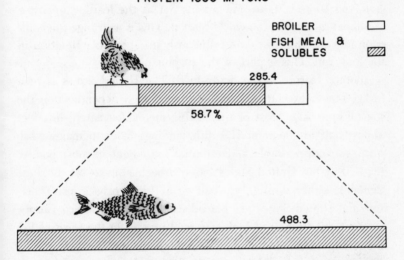

U.S. POULTRY BALANCE
PROTEIN 1000 M. TONS

BROILER

FISH MEAL & SOLUBLES

285.4

58.7%

488.3

FIG. 43 Most fish meal and fish solubles go into the manufacturing of poultry feed. This graph elucidates the significance of fish protein to the raising of U.S. broilers. The data are based on the assumption of a high conversion efficiency of 1:3, largely applicable to the broiler industry and the high-grade feed proteins.

How to provide the United States market with fish is nowadays a leading question in foreign fisheries' journals (in Japan, the United Kingdom, Norway, for example).

More than half a million tons of fish are now being absorbed from the world market since our own fisheries have fallen behind the population growth and no longer manage to provide the modest consumption in the United States of a little more than eleven pounds per person a year. Shrimp is imported from more than forty countries, partly by air, and from some undernourished countries such as Taiwan, India, Mexico, and Ecuador, to meet the needs of U.S. luxury consumption. It would seem to be a wiser move to render U.S. aid in mobilizing and utilizing these shrimp fisheries to the benefit of these countries' own needs. It is almost incredible, as well as inconceivable, that next to England, the United States now stands out as the leading importer of animal protein on the world market. This is a strange phenomenon in a starving world and obviously an untenable situation in the long run. This is part of the surplus picture.

Another feature is the ocean-feed. The United States is to a far greater degree than is usually recognized dependent on the sea (Figure 30). Most of the sizable menhaden catch—in effect almost half of the total U.S. fish landings—goes to making fish meal, an indispensable and essential ingredient in most poultry feeds. But the United States has not been able to satisfy these demands either through agriculture or its own fisheries. Therefore the United States has placed itself next to Western Europe as the largest buyer of high-rate feed-protein in the form of fish meal. Figure 43 shows to what a high degree the U.S. broiler industry today is "seaborne." If this sizable influx of protein were cut off, this would have a major effect on available feed surpluses. Considerable adjustments would be needed in agriculture, faced in this way with the need to devote considerable acreages to providing no less than half a million tons of high-rate protein, comparable in feeding value to this fish meal. Menhaden, incidentally, would be an excellent raw material for the manufacture of fish-protein concentrate, presently strongly advocated as a possible U.S. contribution to the filling of the serious global protein gap.

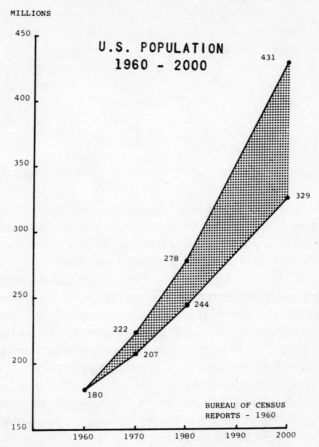

MILLIONS

U.S. POPULATION
1960 - 2000

431

329

278

244

222

207

180

BUREAU OF CENSUS
REPORTS - 1960

FIG. 44

Inadequate Forest Resources

The United States—holder of the world record in paper consumption—is not capable of filling its own enormous needs from its own vast land. Also in this respect the U.S. market is almost insatiable. A recently published inventory shows the critical situation:

TABLE 30

U. S. Lumber Balance

	Year 1975 (billion board-feet)	Year 2000 (billion board-feet)
Timber Needs	68.2	105.4
Assets with Present Methods	58.6	25.2
Shortage	9.6	80.2

The above estimate is based upon the present rate of population growth and of increased purchasing power. Most notable, however, is the fact that this is based on the assumption that the United States will continue to earmark for its needs enormous forest acreages in Canada, Scandinavia, and other countries. Present reforestation does not keep pace with the removals, despite the fact that U.S. forests, as mentioned, fill only part of the country's needs. The forest is hardly a bright page in United States history, and exceptional measures are required to replant the deforested areas (not used for other purposes) which as of now amount to above fifty million acres. Furthermore, many additional millions of acres would be needed to balance the national consumption and in this way make a contribution to the lumber and paper-starved countries of the world by placing more at their disposal. At present the Soviet Union has in this respect a tremendous potential which at any time could give it world dominance in this key market.

Even in this respect a sobering is needed. A considerable amount of marginal land in the United States should be removed from agricultural production and be planted with forests. This would benefit the economy of farms, local communities, and states, to say nothing of its value in restoring the water balance and counteracting soil erosion. In one word, such measures would greatly contribute to the economic stabilization of U.S. agriculture.

Export Volume

Recognizing certain shortcomings in calculating the acreages required to produce what is exported to a given country (see pp. 70 ff, 82–83), certain safe and valid conclusions may nevertheless be drawn. It may thus be inferred that the total U.S. export of agricultural products (in 1958–59) corresponded to about 65 million acres out of the country's total tilled acreage of 450 million acres. Against this stands an importation corresponding to around 25 million acres. Consequently, U.S. contributions in net figures was 40 million acres to the world household. England, with considerably higher yields per acre than the United States, still requires what corresponds to 54 million acres in importation. This allows the conclusion that the total U.S. export of food (inclusive of aid delivery) was thus not sufficient to keep England supplied with food on the present diet level of that country. In case of a military conflict, the United States would consequently not be capable of sustaining Western Europe on its present diet level. It can barely fill the present importation needs of West Germany and Italy. Of considerable interest is the fact that England's 54 million acres corresponds to about two-thirds of Argentina's tilled acreage. If converted to the much lower yields of the key crops in that country, this means that the United Kingdom nowadays is relying on more than all of Argentina can produce as its "nutritional colony."

Population and Tilled Land

At present the United States grows each year by about three million (1.6 per cent). This implies that the United States holds the record for rate of growth among developed countries.

(This rate has unexpectedly dropped in 1964.) It surpasses in this respect countries which traditionally are estimated as having an unreasonably rapid population growth, such as India, Indonesia, and others. In order to feed this yearly net increment on the present high nutritional level, an additional seventeen million acres would be required each year. Through highway construction, airfields, industrial development, and sports fields, for example, up to five million acres are lost each year. Add this to the acreage required for feeding of this added population, for a total of some twenty-two million acres of new tilled land needed each year—but under the assumption that the yields per acre were unchanged. As they improve, this demand figure may be adjusted downward. This would mean that in two years the present net exportation acreage of the United States—forty million acres—would be eaten up.

Since in the United States the yields per acre in most crops are considerably below those of Western Europe, it might seem feasible to raise U.S. agricultural production more through higher yields per acre and less through the breaking of new lands. Nevertheless, new acreages will sooner or later be needed in view of the fact that large regions constitute dry areas where high yields can be obtained only through costly irrigation installations in order to bring the water supply to a level more comparable with that of Western Europe. It is, however, thought-provoking to realize that already at the present stage most dam constructions and irrigation installations are erected not in arid regions but in areas with a dependable average precipitation—where it pays better per acre to reach for yet higher yields by using still more water.

Even though individual areas show per acre yields on a par with those of Western Europe, the average yields are considerably lower in spite of the more favorable climatical location of the United States.

But the United States handicap is of serious dimensions. On

the average, the rainfall is only one-third that of Europe. This explains why serious consideration is given to tapping the Great Lakes to raise still further the entire level of agricultural production in the Midwest. But are we really prepared to pay that price—the loss of the Great Lakes together with that of the St. Lawrence Seaway for the dubious pleasure of having still more millions as our neighbors? Despite significant agricultural advances—greater use of commercial fertilizers, more irrigation, more effective control of diseases and pests—during the post–war period the yields per acre have not gone up in terms of percentage weight to a corresponding degree. This might indicate that we are closer to limiting factors than we normally realize. Are we hitting the ceiling?

The Surpluses in Global Context

The United States stands out to the world as a country with large food reserves. If, however, its food importation ceased, far-reaching adjustments would be necessary in order to secure the present nutritional standard. Measured in metric tons, the present (1962–63) importation of animal protein to the United States corresponds to one-fifth of the average annual wheat crop. In other words, the entire wheat crop would have to be used as feeding stuff, if a quantity of animal protein were to be produced which equals what the United States presently is importing in terms of food and feed. The latter chiefly consists of fish meal, but also copra and oilseed cakes. This is one way of elucidating the scope of this matter. No livestock can be raised merely on wheat; furthermore, only through a highly efficient animal husbandry, avoiding poor converters like beef cattle, would it be possible to obtain this large quantity with a conversion factor of five.

In order to illustrate the rather modest size of the "enormous" U.S. surpluses, placed in a global context, the following figures may suffice. If all the wheat now stored in the United States was promptly distributed to the underfed and malnourished of the world, it would only give them a minimum diet for a period of two and a half months. If all kinds of grain surpluses were included—besides wheat, also corn, barley, rice, etc.—they would last for seven months. If a part thereof was utilized to produce a modest quantity of eggs, milk, and meat—about as much as the East Indians eat today—this period would be reduced to four months; with the average U.S. diet, to less than one month. The huge grain deliveries to India, mentioned in chapter 8, constitute per year about 5 per cent of that country's grain consumption (wheat and rice). What is adequate for 196 million Americans would feed only 107.5 million East Indians (40 per cent of the present population) and 61 million Egyptians (see Table 31). This brings up the additional aspect that the needy world is eating proportionately far more grains and plant products in their daily food. One year's consumption in the United States context, therefore, means far less wheat than it would in India, where the intake of cereals in terms of protein is almost twice as high.

Public Law No. 480

Here should be included a brief survey of how the United States tries to dispose of its present surpluses in the most efficient way. In 1956 a special law, called *Public Law No. 480*, was passed which gave the Federal Government the authority to dispose of the stored surpluses in needy foreign countries. Until the present time, agricultural products valued at five and a half billion dollars have been delivered abroad under this special law, chiefly outside the present world food trade. It has not been possible to conduct this large-scale aid delivery of food entirely without repercussions in such affected areas as competing trade partners, domestic agricultural production in recipient countries, and nutritional complications. These difficulties have

TABLE 31

Per Capita Intake of Cereal Protein (g/day) and Millions Possible to Feed by U. S. Cereal Protein Intake.

	Wheat	Corn	Rice	Others	Total Cereals	Number Fed* Millions	Ratio to Present** Population
U.S.	13.5	1.5	0.5	0.7	16.2	192	1.0
Japan	7.3	—	19.2	4.7	31.2	99.5	1.0
India	5.7	1.4	12.1	9.8	29.0	107.5	0.4
Egypt	22.0	17.0	5.2	6.7	50.9	61	2.1
Brazil	11.2	4.3	7.0	0.1	22.6	138	1.7

* On U.S. annual intake of cereal protein (if completely interchangeable)
** In respective countries listed above.

been most obvious in countries with very low purchasing power. By and large, however, it has worked well. A special clause of this law allows payment in non-dollar currency and thus also in the national currency of the recipient country.

Among the countries which have received aid within the operational framework of this law are Poland, Spain, Yugoslavia, South Korea, Israel, Syria, and Egypt. Both Pakistan and India have been able to avert regional hunger catastrophes through PL 480 deliveries. In other words, this law has been an efficient instrument for the disposal of stored surpluses. It ought to be kept in mind, however, that the transportation costs often have exceeded the value of the delivered commodities.

Food for Peace

Public Law No. 480 has several limitations, however. President Eisenhower therefore launched another plan for the disposal of U.S. food surpluses, which by and large coincided with a proposal made by then Democratic Senator Hubert Humphrey. This plan was considerably enlarged by the Kennedy Administration and was also provided with an executive branch directly under the President. The stored surpluses were thereby given a central position on the world scene. An impressive five-year plan was presented, implying costs in the neighborhood of eleven billion dollars. For the first time in a long while, these food surpluses were looked upon not merely as a burden for the taxpayers or as a pressing agricultural issue but as an asset to the United States and the world. In this plan, called the McGovern Plan after the head of the new bureau, the task is not merely seen as a mission to get rid of the cumbersome surpluses which the farmers or the agricultural organizations see as profitable to produce. Instead, the long-range goal is to produce what the world most urgently needs. There is no doubt that primarily this is protein.

UNITED STATES FOOD SURPLUSES 363

The intention is therefore to stimulate the production of food such as eggs, poultry, and milk-powder according to various plans which have been developed. In this process the planners have experienced a most healthy and concrete confrontation both with the modest size of the surpluses and their onesidedness when it comes to the production of high-quality protein, regardless of whether this is done by the cultivation of "protein" crops such as soybeans to a larger extent than now is the case, or by utilizing the grain surpluses for animal production.

According to the McGovern Plan, U.S. aid in several countries would take the form of food deliveries rather than money, which is more easily pocketed by others and may never reach the needy people. However, this involves economic problems and also difficulties with the exchange convertibility. Payments in national currencies have already piled up in considerable sums in United States funds abroad, and efforts are being made at present to utilize these for research and technical-development programs in the respective countries. Such funds are to a more considerable extent available in India, Poland, Japan, and Indonesia.

World Food Development Program

Under the auspices of the Freedom from Hunger campaign led by the Food and Agricultural Organization of the United Nations (FAO), new life was blown into the old dream by the founder of this organization, Lord Boyd Orr. He visualized the need for large-scale global storage of foods in international settings—a kind of world bank in food.

After lengthy negotiations, the revived plan for such international bulk storage was watered down to a pittance. A modest one hundred million dollars were pledged in 1963 in food services and contributions and coupled with development projects in respective countries. No less than half this sum was guaranteed by the United States. Salaries for the execution of various essential undertakings such as the building of roads, irrigation dams and canals, and fertilizer plants, are paid in kind by FAO. Once again the critical protein issue came to the foreground as only very few countries contributed true protein foods and in minimal quantities, such as dried fish, sardines, nonfat milk solids, and similar others. These resources were quickly exhausted and the calorie foods ruled the scene, such as corn, wheat, rice, and sugar.

The size of the total sum devoted to these purposes mirrors in an alarming way the lack of understanding of the true magnitude of the present deficits. The contribution made by the United States—although in absolute terms, as well as relatively, still the largest—is both in global and national terms picayune. It amounts to less than one pro mille of the present food budget of the United States, and yet it is supposed to last on the world scene for a four-year period. It is, however, only fair to draw attention to the fact that the contributions made by the United States are by no means limited to this support. The United States is maintaining and pursuing all the food programs discussed above. They are all of greater dimensions, but it is nevertheless worth keeping in mind that they have never reached such a magnitude that they influenced U.S. consumption. They never constituted more than, at the most, 5 per cent of the U.S. food production—approaching only one-tenth of certain crops' yields in a given year.

Foreign Investments

The United States has to a major extent carried the economic burden of the U.N.'s considerable technical aid to under-developed countries (ETAP—Expanded Technical Assistance Program, as well as its subsequent extension SUNFED—Special United Nations Fund for Education and Development). This impressive and far-reaching program originated with President

Truman and has been supplemented with United States foreign aid. Unfortunately, during latter years this has been given a poorly veiled military emphasis largely favoring projects of a strategic value. The selection of recipient countries has not been made on the basis of relative need, but rather as a means of boosting resistance morale or strengthening governments in strategic areas. Only to a minor degree have these U.S. funds been devoted to providing food, aiding health programs, and so forth.

Looking at the foreign investments abroad, it is striking to see how little the underdeveloped world figures in these dispositions. The United States has invested more in Canada than in all the developing countries of the world. Even in underdeveloped countries, our foreign investments have been more than 85 per cent geared to oil and mining in order to meet our own nation's mounting needs.

Relatively speaking, the United States has larger economic interests in Venezuela than in any other foreign country. The investments there amount to 4 billion dollars of which 3.2 billions is in oil and 400 million in mines. This leaves 400 million for all other purposes. Venezuela's unilateral trade with the United States swallows 550 million dollars annually and places a stifling hand on agriculture and on a series of industrial enterprises which otherwise would develop in that country.

Big International Food Takeover

Even in the direct food field, investment trends divulge that little attention is being paid to the needy world. Most major processing enterprises in the United States, as well as marketing concerns, have gone international on a big scale in the last five or six years (1964). Most of these investments have been made in Western Europe, Australia, South Africa. These endeavors command respect as such, but show little sign of any concern for coping with the vexing intricacies of world feeding. There is, rather, evidence of an unmistakable empire-building by large-scale mergers on the international scene. How the United States food industry has gone international would deserve a chapter of its own. Far more capital has moved out of the United States for these large-scale investments than ever went into supporting desperately needed food industries around the world. Even the value of the international food deliveries shrinks in relative significance when compared with the five to six billion employed in furthering this affluence of the well-provided nations on earth. There is no intention to belittle or downgrade the significance of these U.S. endeavors. On the countrary, these moves are in a major way accelerating progress, rationalizing production and distribution as well as stimulating competition on a high technical level. But these accomplishments should be put in perspective. So far they have made no significant contribution to world feeding nor have they to any substantial degree aided the hundreds of millions faced with the agonies of hunger and deprivation. Going international does not necessarily mean helping the needy. This simplified kind of thinking has for too long distorted our entire discussion of aid. One may even question if the term foreign aid is itself not a misnomer. We need to get back to reality.

The Sugar Question

The Cuban crisis brought to the foreground the question of the world market in sugar as well as how the two major contending world powers were supplied with this commodity. In this case, too, strange anomalies exist. The U.S.S.R. is today the world's leading sugar producer, with sugar beets as the source. It produces two and a half times more than the United States and is thus fairly self-sufficient in sugar, while the United States has considerable shortages which are made up for through importation. Cuba used to be the chief supplier, followed by the outlying territories of Hawaii and Puerto Rico. How closely tied together the United States and Cuba were in relation to sugar is evident from the fact that, on an average, three-fifths of Cuba's export went to the United States during the last three normal years (1958-60) and three-fourths of our entire sugar import came from this island. The shock waves from the Cuban "sugar quake" staged by the Soviet Union, will have worldwide repercussions. The United States has turned to Costa Rica, Taiwan, the Philippines, Mexico and Brazil in order to fill its needs. Again we have here an example of how the present political tensions create economic and nutritional absurdities. Instead of a sound cooperation to the benefit of the hungry, we witness irrational operations as phases of the Cold War.

The U.S.S.R. has signed a long-term agreement with Cuba for substantial sugar deliveries. Presumably the Soviet Union will use some of this sugar for deliveries to satellite countries as well as to supporters among the developing nations. These large purchases presumably also have a dart—pointed toward deviating China, a country which presumably would like to buy the entire crop and needs it.

The Surpluses and the Cold War

There is another and still more valid reason for United States agriculture to concentrate upon the production of the world's most important short-supply commodity, protein. The Soviet wheat production is now considerably larger than that of the United States in terms of both acreage and quantity. The Soviet Union produces on an average three times more wheat than the United States and thereby undeniably possesses a strong potential which, each time there is a good crop year, may be utilized to serve political or economic purposes. Even with a minor improvement in yield (the U.S.S.R., too, enjoys bumper crops, as everybody knows), exportable quantities may arise which in terms of absolute quantities might easily surpass those of the United States.

It is obvious that any major sale of such excess grains on the world market would slow up the speed of improvement in living standard, declared as an immediate and urgent goal for the Soviet peoples. This kind of welfare program is presently very much on their agenda, but such sales would on the other hand no longer cause hunger and, far less, starvation.

As already mentioned, the chances for Soviet record crops are less than for American ones, because of the overall more favorable climate of the United States. Nevertheless, it is not very judicious to compete or to start a race on the grain front. What the world needs basically is not calories and particularly not carbohydrates. They are, by the way, even easier to produce through potatoes or sugar, for example, than through cereals. It is in relationships such as these that one discerns the dominance of agricultural politics over the conceptual thinking, as well as over the planning. Nutritionists and food scientists have not been given a say. A shipload of dried milk carries five to seven times more protein than a grain-filled boat of equal size.

It needs repeating: what the world lacks is protein. In the race or, if you prefer, the battle which goes on between East and West and its two key powers, the United States has the advantage of a food production which is both larger and more dependable. In the surpluses the United States now owns, presently valued at seven to eight billion dollars, it possesses a weapon which in the long run is far more potent than the atom bombs and missiles, and several times more costly.

As things now stand and as the future is shaping up before our eyes, the United States should concentrate its efforts—eventually in cooperation with other countries—and wield its massive protein potential for the benefit of the entire world, irrespective of military advantages or temporary economic gains. Food is the most potent weapon in our great arsenal and an integral part of any peace strategy—peace meaning here not just a world without war or other military operations, but a world where tensions are being reduced below explosive levels. In several ways this development has inadvertently been started by the soybean venture—a major endeavor, as is the manufacture of milk solids. This product can be used as a protein supplement in flour without interfering with established dietary patterns.

But this cannot be done on the frail basis of market speculations. For such a program, long-range protein agreements—preferably on a government level but conceivably also between major enterprises—are required if there is to be a sound economic basis in such ventures. The outmoded way of dividing the world into raw-material-producing countries versus industrialized nations charged with upgrading these commodities, needs to be thoroughly revised. There is every reason to believe that U.S. agriculture with its food-producing potential will emerge within the near future as the nation's most important economic asset. Conversion industries which could mass-produce such items as cheap yeast, dried milk, and soybean products, as well as meat, egg, and poultry factories of modern streamlined design, would have their place in such a development. These commodities would be exchanged for cheap cars, metal ores, artificial fibers, aluminum products, and so on. A new, more realistic approach is required, throwing overboard conventional economic patterns which are not only outdated but also serve the world poorly.

The Fifties—A Turning Point

The 1950's marked a turning point in the history of the United States, as the country by then had used up its natural resources to the degree that it had become in this respect a "have-not" nation. More raw materials for industry had to be bought from abroad than the country itself could produce. This fact forces upon us a reorientation as well as a modification of our thinking. Our food-producing potential will increasingly become the most important branch of economic activity and should therefore be soundly advanced through rational care.

Against this background the United States has every reason in the world to carry out a more cautious population policy. The country is no longer limitless—the last frontier has not only been reached but has been bypassed. Now the era of economizing, good management, and true housekeeping takes over. Only a small minority has so far recognized this inescapable fact.

Thomas Jefferson, in his First Inaugural Address, in 1801, described Americans as "possessing a chosen country with room enough for our descendants to the thousandth and thousandth generations."

Now, not more than five generations later, there is not space enough for a people which desires to live on such a big scale as we Americans do. Available water is not sufficient. The pollution through industry corresponds to the natural waste from four hundred million people; that is around twice as many as the present inhabitants of the country. These and many other needs threaten to become overwhelming.

If the nutritional belt were tightened as of now, and fewer beefsteaks, ice-cream cones, and eggs were eaten, the margin would not be very impressive. If the United States were willing, for example, to lower its nutritional level to the Soviet Russian standard, the present food resources would be adequate for about 275 million instead of the present 192 million. On the Chinese level, the present agricultural output would satisfy 600 to 700 million people; that is about as many as China has today. If the present rate of population growth in the United States continues, the nation will have reached Chinese dimensions in numbers by the year 2010—seven generations after Jefferson!

The Surplus Crisis—An Episode

When the United States food potentials are projected into the future, it is evident that the sudden mechanization and other steps which contributed to the surplus crisis constitute an episode in the country's history—in addition, a one-time device. This generation has within a period of scarcely one decade drawn all the benefits of this mechanical revolution. The next generation cannot expect any similar windfall. Already in the 1980's there will be great difficulties in providing for the nation, especially in proteins. It is hardly likely that the present nutritional level can then be kept up.

In 1975 the population of the United States will amount to 225 millions if the current rate of growth continues. At the present nutritional level and with the improvements that an increased per capita income might provide, an agricultural production 40 per cent higher than the present one will be required and from an acreage which will in all probability have shrunk. By then the yields per acre will have to be increased considerably, demanding major investments and large-scale engineering projects for irrigation, fertilizer plants, and sewage disposal units of entirely new types. They cannot then be allowed to grow as slowly as during the postwar years. This will necessitate a much higher consumption of fertilizers and, above all, water. Water is already the limiting factor in many regions which are fighting insurmountable obstacles in order to meet the steeply climbing needs.

Investment in Peace

Many critical voices have been heard concerning the present storage of current surpluses, now (1964) valued at seven to eight billion dollars per year. Several have spoken indignantly about this squandering of the "taxpayer's money." Rarely, though, have these expenses been compared with the costs of space ventures and much less often to the five-to-six times higher defense budget. Yet basically the investments in the food surpluses are undoubtedly much more sound than the storage of innumerable atom bombs, and also a much more efficient weapon in the Cold War, not to speak of throwing the money into space. If it had been wasted in the sea, there would at least have been the prospect of some return.

It is highly probable that a judicious operating plan for the disposal of the food surpluses in a major war against malnutrition and starvation would in the long run reduce military tensions and antagonistic feelings and lead to much larger savings in defense-spending than the costs for such a program. It was highly encouraging to learn that former President Harry Truman, in the spring of 1964, endorsed the sending of food even to China without attaching any ties but purely on a Christian humanitarian basis.

References

BIRD, A. R. Surplus—the Riddle of American Agriculture. New York, Springer Publishing Company, Inc., 1962, 128 pp.

CLAWSON, M. Uncle Sam's Acres. New York, Dodd, Mead, 1951, 414 pp.

———. Land for Americans. Chicago, Rand McNally, 1963, 141 pp.

ETHYL CORPORATION. Food for America's Future. New York, McGraw-Hill, 1960, 167 pp.

Fortune, The Editors of. America in the Sixties—the Economy and the Society. New York, Harper, 1960, 266 pp.

HIGBEE, E. C. The American Oasis, the Land and its Uses. New York, Knopf, 1957, 262 pp.

———. American Agriculture: Geography, Resources, Conservation. New York, Wiley, 1958, 299 pp.

ORDWAY, S. H., JR. Resources and the American Dream. New York, Ronald Press, 1953, 55 pp.

PETERSON, W. H. The Great Farm Problem. Chicago, Regnery, 1951, 235 pp.

POTTER, D. M. People of Plenty—Economic Abundance and the American Character. Chicago, University of Chicago Press, 1958, 218 pp.

PRESIDENT'S COMMISSION ON NATIONAL GOALS (1960). *Goals for Americans.* Report. New York, Prentice-Hall, 1960, 373 pp.

ROCKEFELLER PANEL REPORTS. *Prospect for America.* Garden City, Doubleday, 1961, 486 pp.

SEARS, P. B. *Deserts on the March.* Norman, University of Oklahoma Press, 1935, 380 pp.

CHAPTER **17**

Cultivation of the Sea
and Its Present
Exploitation

IN the extracts used by Herman Melville as an introduction to his remarkable epic *Moby Dick*, which in condensed form relates the history of mankind, the author describes an episode from Nantucket Island, once the center of a flourishing whaling industry. It is told how, in 1690, people were standing on a high hill, looking out over the ocean where numerous tumbling whales untiringly spouted their water cascades into the air. One pointed toward the sea: "There is the green pasture where our children's grandchildren will go for bread."*

Already, that far back, man was seen in the place of the whale. The whales are forever gone, long ago extinguished by man. Only occasionally does a whale or two now visit these waters. Pollution and heavy fishing, furthermore, have decimated the contribution of these once highly productive waters to the food

* According to Melville this was extracted from *History of Nantucket* by Obed Macy.

374

supply. The Nantucket fishing fleets must now go much farther out to fill their holds.

The New Granaries

Today man stands looking hopefully at the expanses of the seas, wondering if they are perhaps going to be the new granaries which he so badly needs since the limits of what the land surfaces may provide will inexorably be reached. Daily newspapers and popular science writings abound with imaginative expositions about the potentialities of the ocean, the new continent which is going to save mankind. They vie with each other in visionary prospects of how an agriculture of the sea would look: frogmen with artificial lungs will, like subaquatic acrobats, drive tractors, especially built with larvae feet, across the ocean bottom in pairs, each maneuvering one end of a gigantic net or trawl. In another, earlier phase, fishing boats are seen crossing the vast water expanses in orderly battalions along a broad front miles long, catching everything alive by suction or electronic attraction, discarding the non-usuable, keeping the food fish, and returning to the ocean the fry and young fish. The non-usable goes to reduction plants for mass production of poultry feed or hog feed. Other writers speak about huge hanging gardens where large ocean areas have been fenced in with plastic cloth, inside which algae and fish are mass-cultivated. To put it briefly, an effort is made to instill the belief that ocean cultivation is just in the offing. Mankind is being conditioned to take the step from organized hunting in the oceans to regular sea culture, with the implication that fish ranches soon will become a regular feature of the oceans.

The step from individual to organized hunting on a large scale, however, has by and large been taken during the latest half-century and on the whole came as the result of planned research in a number of fields. Oceanography widened man's knowledge about sea currents, about the composition of the sea-water, about light and temperature conditions. Marine biology expanded man's acquaintance with the living world of the oceans and, what is still more important, revealed step by step the laws that govern the productivity of the seas. It further shed light on the life of commercial fish species from the egg clusters through various development stages into large shoals: their feed, their ecological boundaries in salt and temperature, their migration, behavioral patterns, and so forth. Electronics and ultrasonics have provided new technical devices for the search and tracing of fish shoals and the study of their diurnal movements and seasonal migrations. Despite all these impressive advances we still know far too little to make the radical shift to a systematic cultivation of fish. The truth is rather the opposite; increased knowledge has dampened the enthusiasm and given us a more realistic picture of the intricate and complex conditions under which the oceans produce and maintain life.

The Sea—Not Limitless

The immensity of the oceans—covering two-thirds of the earth surface—and the fish abundance in some waters, undoubtedly explain many of the exaggerations and oversimplifications presented about the potentialities of the seas and their fish riches. There is hardly an article or a book on the subject which does not resort to terms like "inexhaustible" or "limitless" in describing the abundance of the oceans. It is important, however, to keep in mind that these words do not exist in Nature's own dictionary. There is in the living world no such thing as limitless and inexhaustible. All life in the oceans is ultimately tied to the primary production, in the top layer, of seaweeds and phyto-plankton with cells containing plant pigments capable of trapping the sunlight energy penetrating into the upper regions of the water masses (generally termed the photic layer, meaning where light reigns).

Technical devices, however ingenious they may be, do little to free the waters and their living organisms from this dependence. The base for their existence is ultimately these pigment-carrying plant organisms, spread to the limit of light's penetration, down to a depth of one hundred feet, occasionally more. Here the creative processes take place which produce the organic matter that sustains life. Even the bottom animals, which may live thousands of feet below the surface, feed from the "manna" raining down from above. This consists of plankton remainders, animal excretions, dead bodies, and other waste. Sometimes part of this organic matter is caught by other scavengers on its way down and may be cycled once or several times by being converted into living matter again before it reaches the large depths. But all this is regulated by the unchangeable fundamental law of the biological world: All flesh is grass.

The Sea as Protein Provider

There is a great deal of loose talk about the sea contributing less than 2 per cent of the world's food production. It was explained in chapter 2 that this kind of reasoning is based upon a superficial thinking about calories, which is both fallacious and misleading. The ocean contributes at present close to one-fifth of the global consumption of animal protein. The world's total meat production is only one and a half times this figure and the milk production about three times. In reality the ocean fisheries correspond as meat producer to about 850 million cattle, almost equivalent to the total number of cattle on earth, according to available statistics. Compare also the discussion in chapter 2 of the true role of the fisheries as protein supplier in countries such as Japan, Norway, England, and Holland. The chart (Fig. 45)

FISH BALANCE IN MILK

(INCREASE IN MILK PRODUCTION REQUIRED
TO COMPENSATE FOR FISH)

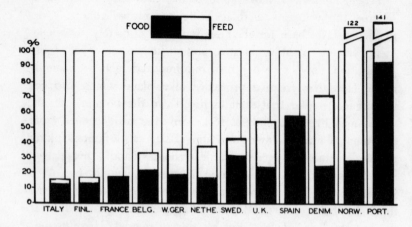

FISH BALANCE IN MILK

(INCREASE IN MILK PRODUCTION REQUIRED
TO COMPENSATE FOR FISH)

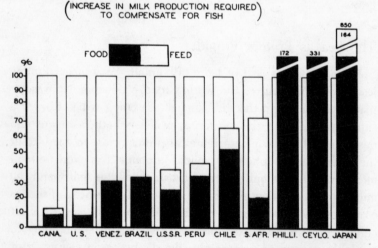

FIG. 45 Fish in dairy terms. The increase required in dairy production to provide an amount of protein equal to that obtained from fish and shellfish.

reveals the relative standing of fisheries in relation to the dairy production of a number of selected countries. This substantiates further the remarkable significance of fisheries in several key nations.

Sea Cultivation Differs Radically from Agriculture

Cultivation of the seas differs radically from crop and livestock production from the land. The different steps of conversion from the stage when the plants catch the sun energy until it has been ultimately converted into edible animal protein is considerably longer in the sea than on land. The feeding chains of the oceans are much longer than those on land, and comprise several more links (Fig. 46). There are among ocean fish few direct counterparts to the ruminants such as cattle and sheep. Only some sardines and the menhaden seem to belong to this category. Around five hundred pounds of feed in the form of phytoplankton yields at the best only one hundred pounds of zooplankton. This is the name for the small, almost microscopic shellfish and other invertebrates which possess the ability to feed on the even smaller, mostly microscopic, phytoplankton (plant plankton), largely unicellular algae. Four-fifths are lost in this conversion process, meaning that they are metabolized or wasted in the growth processes of the grazing zooplankton. In subsequent conversion stages more is lost each time—at least nine-tenths of the input. This happens throughout the other feeding chains of the oceans. The hundred pounds of zooplankton therefore yields a maximum of ten pounds of herring and this in turn will give only one pound of mackerel. From one pound of mackerel only an ounce and a half of tuna is produced. A tuna fish weighing about one hundred pounds thus requires half a million pounds of phytoplankton for its production. Something similar is true about the cod, but one more link is involved in his chain, which totals five. Consequently one pound of cod re-

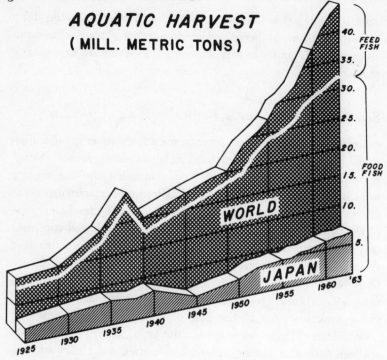

AQUATIC HARVEST
(MILL. METRIC TONS)

FIG. 46

quires a primary production of fifty thousand pounds of phyto-plankton.

The herring has sometimes been called the hog of the sea. This is a lame comparison. It would be more correct to compare the herring to an animal which feeds on a plant-eating insect, for instance on locusts. No such livestock animal exists, unless domesticated anteaters are counted in this category, but they are held not for food production but as an aid in insect control.

These causal relationships explain why, when adding up everything that is caught, for example, in the North Atlantic— one of the world's most heavily fished waters—and relating this catch to the total phytoplankton production which, according to plant physiologists and oceanographers, takes place in these waters, one arrives at the conclusion that the fisheries going on here have almost reached the limit of Nature's productivity. These estimates are based on the present composition of the catch as to species: two-fifths herring, two-fifths cod, and one-fifth of other fish. As a matter of fact, relating the primary production of these waters to present catches, not more than three conversion links can be squeezed in between them. On the other hand, it is known, as indicated above, that several codfish species require up to five links. Taking into account the fact that only 18 per cent of these waters are really efficiently fished (basically the shelves), but that the computations have taken in the primary production over the entire area, one can clearly see how small a margin remains for any further expansion of fisheries in these waters.

The Nutritional Chain

Most fisheries are still carried out close to the shores of the continents, with their relatively shallow waters on the so-called shelves. Their bottom fauna are part of the fish feed and become incorporated into the nutritional chains of these fishes. According to estimates, these bottom fauna in the Kattegat on the east part of the North Sea weigh about 8.25 million tons, of which only 1.65 million tons is potential fish feed. This gives in turn an annual yield of 5,500 tons of flatfish and 4,950 tons of codfish.

It can be safely concluded that there is no considerable margin left in these intensely fished waters. If man wants to extract more from these waters, he will have to resort to artificial cultivation. Man has here gone to the limits of what Nature provides.

The limiting factors in the sea are numerous, however. The most crucial is the availability of mineral nutrients. The high-yielding fishing waters of the globe are found in regions where mineral-rich water reaches the surface from the reserves of the ocean bottom, or along coasts where the outflow from great land masses carries with it such life-supporting nutrients. An indispensable prerequisite for any kind of successful cultivation of the sea implies, therefore, a large-scale fertilization of the oceans, outside of what we already have provided by allowing sewage and other organic pollutants to go via rivers or directly into coastal waters. This fertilizing has already had the effect of augmenting the production, noticeably at river mouths such as in the English Channel and elsewhere. The enormous needs of agriculture, far from filled, make highly unlikely, however, an efficient fertilizing of the oceans of the magnitude required. All studies clearly indicate that the returns from such fertilizing would be higher and more reliable on land than in the sea.

Many people will undoubtedly have noticed how sometimes in the summertime ocean bays and other sea areas seem to bloom, marked by red or green colors. This is often followed by the killing of fish and other living organisms on a massive scale. What has happened in these instances is that life has become overabundant. Algae and other kinds of plankton have developed to such an extent that when they die the oxygen in the water becomes depleted in breaking down all this organic matter. Additional oxygen from the air cannot penetrate the water in time and in required quantities. Death by suffocation hits the animals. Sometimes these causal sequences are aggravated by the formation of toxic substances which directly kill off the fish without awaiting a subsequent oxygen depletion. A considerable number of ocean regions along the coasts of California, in the Gulf of Mexico, and around India, for example, are often plagued with such a red cover—so-called red tides—which may often become quite thick. Fish then die off by the millions. This regularly happens when too many mineral nutrients are added to the oceans through heavy monsoon rains carrying mineral-loaded runoff from adjacent land areas—for instance, the Indian subcontinent.

Numerous diseases also take their toll among the fishes of the world, including those of commercial stocks. These calamities also belong in the overall picture. They cause heavy losses to the global household every year. This is a highly neglected subject in fisheries research. It appears to be more than likely that intense fishing weakens the heavily taxed resistance of fish resources. In this way the disease frequency goes up. Far more research is needed here before safe conclusions can be drawn. The alarming increase in number of instances where crippling diseases are reported may be wrongly interpreted and may merely reflect a better acquaintance with fish diseases, better surveillance, and finally more qualified investigations in this field.

Besides, there are the dangers of poisoning. There are many poisonous fish species and their number is particularly high in warm waters. More and more cases become known where otherwise non-dangerous fish species become poisonous by the eating of certain plankton algae. Whether this has anything to do with the growing pollution of coastal waters is difficult to say at this stage.

Competitors Must Be Fought

For each fourth halibut caught in the Pacific, the sea lions take one. The Alaska fur seals eat, according to estimates, twenty times more salmon than is caught by man in those regions. The guano-producing birds outside the coast of Peru consume anchovetas in a quantity corresponding to one-tenth of the total world fish-catch.

The sea is also inhabited by a teeming world of invertebrates among which the jellyfish, the starfish, and sea urchins are best known to laymen. More conspicuous competitors are bears, seals, and birds, which directly eat what would be fit for human consumption. A large sea lion gulps down no less than thirty-five to fifty pounds of salmon, herring, and flatfish daily.

Recently, the fishermen on the island of Sakhalin presented a request to the Soviet government that the hunting restrictions for bear might be revoked. Biological investigations seemed to prove that the bear was an important factor in the decline of the salmon catches. During the salmon spawning in the rivers of northwest America, there used to be enough in earlier times for both Indians, bears, and dogs. In our days, with the continent bulging with human beings, increasingly energetic claims are made for drastic steps against the bears which rob man of too much. However, it seems not unlikely that Nature will take care of this problem without human assistance. The salmon which is now being planted in these waters from hatching stations is not very resistant. A few weeks after it has returned healthy from the ocean it is quite often found infected with intestinal worms, which spread to dogs and bears. These animals in turn frequently succumb to this type of "salmon poisoning."

Taking into account the whole living mass in the seas, nine-tenths thereof consists of animals or organisms which are of no direct use from a human standpoint. In the nineteenth century steps were taken to eliminate all these competitors of man. "Do away with sea birds, starfish, not to speak of seals and walruses . . ." was the battle cry. Man is the merciless tyrant who believes himself to possess divine right to eradicate any other species if he thinks it stands in his way. The cultivation of the sea and its efficient exploitation will make several such experimental actions indispensable. But the problem is to avoid repeating the mistake made in land cultivation where in too many cases Nature has fought back with relentless force. If it were possible to eradicate one-fourth of the animals which snatch what man's favorites—the food fish—feed on, it has been estimated that the standing stock of these food fish could be increased tenfold. But this naturally is a matter of conjecture. Through such a crusade against what man might term ocean pests, man might inadvertently eliminate the feeding base for other fish species which are essential to the overall balance system among the living organisms of the ocean. Another risk involved is that starfish, for instance, might possibly keep other harmful organisms under control, which through our interference might do still greater damage. These alternatives are mentioned to point out that so far our knowledge about the biology of the sea is actually far too scanty to enable us to predict with certainty what the results would be if we carried out this kind of "weeding" or rather "disinfestation."

Pest Control

What one particular starfish species eats in the North Sea would be sufficient for a doubling of the standing stock of plaice. This is the conclusion of a major biological study of these waters. Yet the starfish is only one of many species that rob from man. The future sea-cultivator has been visualized as moving around on the ocean bottom like a farmer on his properties. This presumptive sea farmer would drive huge tractors studded with nails across the bottom, piercing starfish like janitors picking up waste in our parks with pointed sticks. Quite possibly a great number of flatfish (plaice, sole, etc.) would perish in this operation. An alternative almost equally disastrous to the flatfish would be underwater subaquatic motorcycles which would cross the properties, piercing the enemy in the shape of the starfish. These would be gathered in baskets and hoisted up to the surface off and on to be used as feed in conventional agriculture. As a first stage, operations of this kind would probably be carried out on the continental shelves. The North Sea, by the way, is largely one huge underwater plain, the area where once the mighty Rhine and the Thames joined into one great river.

The idea has also been ventured to start chemical warfare in the oceans. This method was recently practiced in fighting back a devastating attack by starfish on oyster beds on the east coast of the United States.

A more reliable recourse would be to reduce the number of links as far as possible in the production chain, and try to eliminate all predatory fish such as tuna, mackerel, and cod, and in lieu of this intricate and less economic production machinery, to create simple systems by arranging protected living conditions for plankton-consuming fish species. Instinctively we have already started along that road. The herring and sardine were always the chief components of world fisheries. In this case we have thus from the very beginning stuck to the base of the production pyramid. The catches of ocean perch, which are important feed fish for several codfishes, have increased considerably during the last two decades. Commentators have been impressed by the fact that in this way man has been able to widen his sphere in the sea by incorporating new fish species, earlier little used; but it has been overlooked that we thereby deprive a series of valued fishes of their feeding base. Generally, those fish which in this way have been deprived of their sustenance basis have been rated as of higher quality as human food.

The sand eel is another case in point. As fry, it constitutes up to 60 per cent of the feed of herring. In the full-grown stage it is an attractive feed for haddock, whiting, cod, and plaice. When the Danes in the North Sea developed large-scale sand eel fisheries for reduction purposes, they actually removed one of the most valuable feed fishes of the ocean. This inevitably affected the stock of traditional feed fishes in spite of the fact that around eleven sand eels are to be found per square foot in the North Sea.

The Whales—Hard to Beat

The whales, however, are unsurpassed when it comes to converting plankton into meat and fat. These animals are truly miraculous. The young blue whale grows approximately 150 pounds per day—the weight of an adult man. The nursing mother must each day sieve and devour around three metric

THE PRODUCTION PYRAMID

SEA

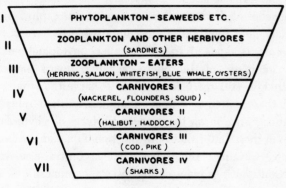

I	PHYTOPLANKTON – SEAWEEDS ETC.
II	ZOOPLANKTON AND OTHER HERBIVORES (SARDINES)
III	ZOOPLANKTON – EATERS (HERRING, SALMON, WHITEFISH, BLUE WHALE, OYSTERS)
IV	CARNIVORES I (MACKEREL, FLOUNDERS, SQUID)
V	CARNIVORES II (HALIBUT, HADDOCK)
VI	CARNIVORES III (COD, PIKE)
VII	CARNIVORES IV (SHARKS)

LAND

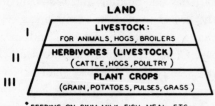

I	LIVESTOCK: FOR ANIMALS, HOGS, BROILERS
II	HERBIVORES (LIVESTOCK) (CATTLE, HOGS, POULTRY)
III	PLANT CROPS (GRAIN, POTATOES, PULSES, GRASS)

*FEEDING ON SKIM MILK, FISH MEAL, ETC.

FIG. 47

tons of so-called krill, a kind of crustacean zooplankton up to two to three inches long. In comparison, the most ingenious catching devices on ships operating in the world's most plankton-rich waters do not yield an acceptable harvest. It takes several hours to catch an amount of plankton adequate to feed even the crew, and then the fuel required to run the ship is not taken into account. Man can hardly compete with the whales in this area of plankton utilization.

Among the phytoplankton of the sea, silicon-encased species (diatoms) dominate. Certain tiny crustaceans, the size of a grass seed, crack open these diatoms, thanks to the special construction of their mouths. They themselves are far more accessible and digestible as feed to a number of marine animals. Many dubious and fallacious statements have been made about the plankton riches of the sea as human food. In fact, phytoplankton is extremely poor food and almost impossible to harvest. Growing attention is devoted to still smaller phytoplankton which seem to dominate this biosphere—so-called dwarf plankton or nannoplankton—still more impossible to harvest. In most cases, however, these statements about plankton as food refer to the tiny creatures grazing on these ocean pastures of phytoplankton. It was upon these latter that both the Kon-Tiki and the Bombard expeditions sustained themselves. They constitute a kind of pelagic counterpart to plant-eating insects, comparable to locusts on land. A truly vegetarian alternative in the sea is offered only by the larger varieties of bottom algae—so-called seaweeds. These are already heavily taxed in many areas on earth for human consumption and also as animal feed and are in addition cultivated in Japan, China, the Philippines, and other places.

In certain respects it is therefore less than correct to speak about sea-farming. What is meant is really large-scale oceanic fish cultivation. It would be possible to concentrate on the cultivation of oysters and mussels, which live directly on phytoplankton, but this would obviously exclude, to a major degree, a concurrent raising of fish. In this area, man has already gone very far, as most oysters and mussels of today are the result of controlled cultivation. Such operations started on a major scale as early as in the nineteenth century.

Fine Ocean Livestock Exterminated

With foolhardy shortsightedness man has subjected many of his real allies in the ocean to extermination. This applies not only to the whales, whose existence is now being threatened. According to desperate appeals by the director of FAO, it appears that the blue whale has moved far into the danger zone. The manatee (the sea cow), which grazed the seaweed pastures of the coastal regions most efficiently, met with destruction in the eighteenth century. There is every indication that this animal might have been a gem in future sea culture. If wisdom and international cooperation would prevail, there still is a chance of saving the green turtle.

On May 1, 1503, Columbus reached two flat islands in the Caribbean Sea, which he named the Green Turtle Islands, later wrongly called the Cayman Islands. He sailed the straits between them. The shores and the water were filled with innumerable huge turtles each resembling, as he describes them, small rock islands. This was the green turtle which was grazing on the wide underwater pastures of seaweeds and related vegetation. Many more episodes are recorded in Columbus's and other travelers' documents about this remarkable animal. Throughout the centuries they were, through their flesh, important protein providers to man in many warm countries. They may be called the buffalo of the Caribbean, where they played a role equal to that of the buffalo on the North American prairie. In times gone by, they were an immense asset to the people living around these fish-poor, shark-infested waters as well as in many other coastal areas or islands with a hot climate. The green turtle has written world history but it is now on its way out through man's brutal taxing. Only isolated specimens are still found and this only occasionally.

Marine-Animal Farms

One form of future sea culture is the marine-animal farm. In many regions in the world they have been tried with considerable success and since time immemorial. Along the lagoon coasts of Indonesia and the Philippines there are many fenced-in sea areas where controlled culture of the milkfish (bango) is carried on, with a return which, measured in protein, by far surpasses that of agriculture. A Scotch fisheries expert recently outlined more drastic steps. Through electronic regulation he planned to divide into plots coastal areas of the oceans, making a kind of fish ranch to which the fish would be directed through electric impulses. The shoals could then be submitted to further electro-shock treatment and harvested. This is a further development of the Soviet catching methods in which fish which have first been attracted by light or electronic impulses are then pumped on board by suction. This method has been successfully practiced in the Caspian Sea and the South Atlantic by Soviet fishing vessels. Nets then became superfluous.

The expanding Soviet and Japanese fisheries and the investments made by these countries in their global exploitation of fish resources in all oceans were discussed in earlier chapters.

The Marine Hemisphere

The immense ocean expanses of the Southern Hemisphere, the marine hemisphere, are still to a large extent awaiting exploitation. These resources may give us a certain breathing spell before the final attack takes place on the Continent of the Seas. In the north Arctic the whales, for all practical purposes, have been extinct for many years and nowadays are of little economic importance. The efforts that have been made to save the whale stock around the Antarctic in order to secure for mankind this indispensable food resource (approximately one-tenth of the world's fat production used to be based on the whales) have been wholly inadequate. The activities of the International Whale Commission were never fully effective. The implementation of the quota caused difficulties, but more serious was the fact that the participating members never could agree on catch limitations which were sufficiently restrictive for full protection.

The two superpowers of modern fishing, Japan and the U.S.S.R., are both on a big scale pushing toward the fishing waters of the Southern Hemisphere, engaging ever larger fishing fleets in these operations. The catching vessels are being supplemented with modern freezing units. Poland, East Germany, and several other countries have already laid the keels for a further expansion of the fishing fleets which are now taking part in the race for this reserve. Poland gave aid to Ceylon during the winter of 1961–62 for the development of its fisheries. Spain, France, West Germany, and England are following suit but on a more moderate scale. This constitutes another phase of the Cold War, which has so far been little noticed.

The Exploitation of the Tropical Atlantic

The tropical Atlantic is at present one such region where exploitation is off to a dramatic start. In the western parts along the African coast, the U.S.S.R. has taken the lead together with Poland and East Germany in extended large-scale fisheries of sardines and mackerels (see also chapter 13). Japan is also operating extensively here, using the Canary Islands as its major operational base but with several facilities for transshipment and processing in many African countries. On the Brazilian side Japan is pioneering large-scale fisheries with modern trawlers both close to the coast for fresh market deliveries, and farther out for tuna.

In the latter case the United States has also entered the scene and now supplements its own tuna needs from these regions. In Puerto Rico, four new canning factories with latest design and equipment are converting this island into a major base for the Atlantic operations of the United States. This is a new phase in the hectic hunt by the United States for more tuna in order to keep up the present per capita consumption (two pounds per year) of tuna for the rapidly increasing population (more than three million per year). The tuna resources of the Pacific are no longer sufficient, even though U.S. seiners have extended their catching operations all the way down to Chilean waters.

The North Atlantic Scene

The coastal shelves off Labrador, Newfoundland, and above all the Davis Strait to the west and south of Greenland, constitute another center for feverish fishing activities. Many tens of thousands of Soviet fishermen operated here during each winter since 1960 with several hundred trawlers, including specialized ships for reconnaissance, storage, transportation home, and those equipped for processing, freezing, canning, and salting. Japan too has appeared on these fishing grounds. The number of Polish and East German trawlers which operate in these regions is steadily increasing. Also, from Western Europe, primarily West Germany, a growing interest is exhibited in the potentially unused fish resources of these waters, especially ocean perch, cod, haddock, and flatfish.

The Canadians show growing concern over these large-scale activities close to their coasts and on other traditional fishing grounds. They are increasingly turning to the resources of their inland waters, lakes, and Arctic bays. They have nonetheless made efforts to put a damper on these developments, through the Northwest Atlantic Fisheries Commission, maintaining that the enormously expanded fishing efforts in these waters are seriously jeopardizing the future of the fish stocks.

Pacific Activities

No less spectacular is the expansion taking place in the Pacific, largely under Soviet leadership in close cooperation with North Vietnam, North Korea, and China. A special Pacific Commission heads up this joint enterprise under the auspices of the Soviet and Chinese science academies.

This is a coordinated planned exploitation covering some of the world's traditionally richest fishing waters: the South China Sea, the Yellow Sea, and the East China Sea. Several Soviet catching fleets have been seen operating in these waters in recent years.

Nor have the Japanese been inactive. Following the Soviet Russian lead, they have especially concentrated on the enlargement of the fishing for the Pacific mackerel-pike (*Cololabis saira*), a fatty fish. To what degree these fisheries undermine more qualified fisheries is so far an open question. This saury is namely a feed fish for several traditional food fishes. The U.S.S.R. has greatly increased its catches of this species and built large canning factories on the former Japanese island of Shikotan for their processing. Huge Japanese floating fish-meal factories (14,000 tons) are sent into the Bering Sea regularly each summer.

Global Research Efforts

Before the next step is taken—the exploitation of the oceans through organized sea culture—a cooperation of global dimensions in development work is mandatory, but also a research effort of dimensions hitherto undreamed of. This will be decisive for mankind's entire future. Large sums are today being spent on ocean research of various kinds, but it is still a modest amount in relation to the needs if the goal really is to be the acquisition of a comprehensive picture of the resources of the sea and the major determinants of its productivity. The number of research vessels needs to be multiplied many times over. Submarines would have to be rebuilt for use in systematic subaquatic investigations.

The Soviet, U.S., and Japanese deep-diving devices, generally termed bathyscaphes, are required in much larger numbers.

Nobody can justly claim that the world cannot afford this. Even a gigantic effort on this front would be inexpensive compared to the enormous sums which are at present appropriated for space adventures. The potentialities for a cultivation on a gigantic scale of the oceans as the last major food resource for mankind are as yet far too little investigated. Therefore no safe predictions can at present be made about prospects and yields. But this much is sure: if the conquest of the last remaining huge continent of our own planet, the sea, is not going to be hampered by as many failures, mistakes, and misjudgments as our conquest of the land surface, a reconnaissance is required of infinitely greater dimensions than at present and with the full use of all the resources of modern science. The world needs a Central Intelligence Agency of the Seas in order to draw from the seas the massive amount of information, data, and experiences required to put together a coherent picture of the functionings of its huge machinery.

"No Man's Property?"

A significant trait in the fisheries efforts of the two super-powers is that primarily both are striving to fill the needs of their own people and are little concerned about the protein-hungry nations along whose coasts they now operate. The U.S.S.R. is even supplementing its catches with purchases from abroad. Japan markets one-third of its catch but largely to the United States, the United Kingdom, and other West European countries; very little reaches countries in need of supplementary protein.

It is most striking to note that the same general attitude is encountered in the large fish-meal bastion created in Peru largely under the technical leadership of the United States and with Western capital. This entire problem is discussed in more detail in chapter 14. The thinking in colonial terms seems still to be very much alive and is especially flourishing in the utilization of the resources of the world oceans, and I am afraid also in the planning of new endeavors. Nobody seems to realize the self-evident fact that non-western peoples also have their rights. This applies as much to West Africa in relation to the fish resources of the Atlantic as it applies to the justified claims of the Andean peoples upon the fish treasures of the Humboldt Current.

This can also be looked upon as a question of efficient utilization. How well is man taking care of the nutritional riches he extracts? Judged in terms of housekeeping, reduction plants are justified only (1) when disposing of waste from evisceration and filleting or (2) when the landed fish cannot be used directly as human food. In a seriously undernourished world these are the only conditions under which this kind of operation conceivably could be accepted.

Unfortunately the anchoveta case is not unique. Still more repulsive to anyone thinking in terms of nutritional economy and utilization efficiency is the fact that no less than one-third of the Atlantic herring catch also is converted to fish meal and this merely because it pays better, chiefly because of the market pattern created by man. Herring is after all one of the finest foods to be had. It has, with certain justifications, even been called a symphony of nutrients. A large portion of the Norwegian catch is utilized this way (see Fig. 48).

Little thought seems to go into exploring new sales channels less offensive to the hungry world. They may not be equally profitable, but should in the long run be more dependable when the squandering game is over. The world's resources have to be wisely used in order to support world progress, not just to over-feed a few privileged groups. Level of profit cannot remain the sole guide to what is "needed." Far more rational action should be urged. We ought to take the initiative in implementing a more equitable distribution of the world's food resources. The concept of common property—*res communis*—has to replace the traditional outmoded *res nullius*—no man's property.

The Ocean's Dwarfish When Facing the Human Giant

Thomas Dekker, the seventeenth-century English author, talked about the sea as an immense fish pond. This is the image which in our days is emerging before our own eyes. Even the

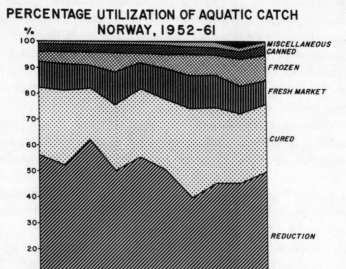

FIG. 48

gigantic ocean, entirely under the reign of man, will constitute
hardly more than a pond when insatiable mankind raises its
demands, and the now starving world tries to fill their protein
needs. The present catch of food fish approaches thirty-five
million metric tons per year. If the sea is to yield a minimum
quantity of protein for the more than sixty million people that
are now being added each year, an additional three to five million tons are required. This means a 10 per cent increase every
year, which corresponds to more than a doubling each decade.
Even if the population explosion abates and the population increase were placed under control, a large-scale exploitation of
the sea is bound to come sooner or later. This will constitute
an undertaking which is infinitely more vital to man's future than

the conquest of space and is equally fascinating and intriguing, if not more so, since at the end of such marine ventures looms the concrete possibility of invaluable benefits to mankind. Everything being done at present along this crucial battlefront in the big struggle for man's survival is deplorably pitiful in the light of the immensity of the challenge, and the high stakes.

INCREASE IN WORLD CATCH FOR NUTRITIONAL IMPROVEMENT

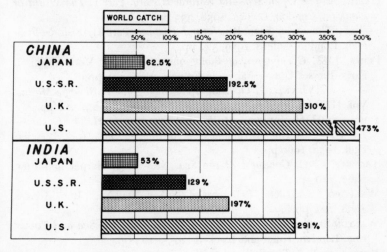

FIG. 49

References

BORGSTROM, GEO. (ed.). *Fish as Food:* Vols. I–IV. New York, Academic Press, 1961–1965.

BORGSTROM, GEO. *Japan's World Success in Fishing.* London, Fishing News, 1964, 320 pp.

BORGSTROM, GEO., and HEIGHWAY, A. (eds.). *Atlantic Ocean Fisheries.* London, Fishing News International, 1961, 380 pp.

CARRINGTON, R. *A Biography of the Sea.* New York, Basic Books, 1960, 286 pp.

CHAPIN, H., and WALTON SMITH, F. G. *The Ocean River.* London, Gollancz, 1953, 325 pp.

COWEN, R. C. *Frontier of the Sea.* New York, Doubleday, 1960, 240 pp.

DANIEL, H., and MINOT, F. *The Inexhaustible Sea.* New York, Dodd, Mead, 1954, 261 pp.

DIETRICH, G., and KALLE, K. *Allgemeine Meereskunde.* Berlin, Bornträger, 1957, 492 pp.

GRAHAM, M. *Sea Fisheries—Their Investigation in the United Kingdom.* London, Arnold, 1956, 487 pp.

HARDY, A. *The Open Sea—Its Natural History,* Part I, *The World of Plankton.* London, Collins, 1958, 335 pp.

———. *The Open Sea—Its Natural History,* Part II, *Fish & Fisheries.* London, Collins, 1959, 322 pp.

PÉRÈS, J.-M. *Océanographie Biologique et Biologie Marine.* Vol. I. Paris, Presses Universitaires de France, 1961, 541 pp.

———, and DEVEZE, L. *Océanographie Biologique et Biologie Marine.* Vol. II. Paris, Presses Universitaires de France, 1963, 514 pp.

SVERDRUP, H. U., JOHNSON, M. W., and FLEMING, R. H. *The Oceans—Their Physics, Chemistry, and General Biology.* New York, Prentice-Hall, 1952, 1060 pp.

TROEBST, C. C. *Conquest of the Sea.* New York, Harper and Row, 1962, 270 pp.

WALFORD, L. A. *Living Resources of the Sea.* New York, Ronald Press, 1958, 321 pp.

WALTON SMITH, F. G., and CHAPIN, H. *The Sun, the Sea and Tomorrow.* London, Hurst and Blackett, 1955, 184 pp.

WILLIAMS, T. I. *The Soil and the Sea.* London, Saturn, 1949, 242 pp.

CHAPTER 18

New Foods
and Synthetic
Nutrients

QUITE frequently, reassuring statements by chemists in different countries appear in the press, claiming that they are the wizards of the future who are going to free mankind from the scourge of hunger. And it is most likely that chemistry, if it continues to develop as it has hitherto, will succeed in synthesizing several, if not most, of the compounds of which our foods are composed, and above all those substances which our body cannot synthesize on its own from other more simple organic molecules. To this category belong, in addition to several vitamins, a series of amino acids, fats, and certain carbohydrates.

But the public discussion about these matters has been grossly oversimplified. It is certainly *not* sufficient to be able to synthesize certain essential substances. They must also be given the special molecular structure which allows them to function in the complicated metabolism of the body. There are for instance, so-called left-rotating and right-rotating molecules respectively.

They are one and the same substance, but in their molecular build-up they have different structure in space. Here they constitute the mirror images of one another. In several critical cases the body can utilize only one of these kinds of molecules. The counterpart may be valueless, may cause metabolic disturbances, or occasionally may be thoroughly harmful. So far, no method is known for the bypassing of this difficulty. Most synthesized compounds are a mixture of these variants of molecules. Methods are available for separation but they are generally costly and complicated.

Synthetic Foods

Despite these complications, there is no doubt whatsoever that future chemists will perform still greater miracles than hitherto. We can place complete trust in their capabilities. There is in principle no limit to the exercise of their talents, copying and outdoing Nature itself. But confidently promising mankind, on this basis, a fifth freedom, namely freedom from dependence upon the plants, borders on hypocrisy and reveals poor acquaintance with the fundamental conditions of man's existence on earth. To envision the future feeding of the world as removed to factories detached from fields, pastures, and the sea, is simply naïve. Even a superficial examination of such an alternative reveals the impracticable nature of these projects.

Let us for a moment assume that we really have mastered all the required techniques and thus are capable of producing in chemical plants all the organic substances man needs. The human body still will always depend on carbon combinations. Consequently, the raw materials we use must contain carbon and, when it comes to proteins, other elements such as nitrogen and sulphur. The only carbon-containing raw materials which could serve this purpose, and which exist outside the constantly renewed products of the soil and the sea, are coal and mineral oils. As is well known, both of these are the basis for our energy supply. Most likely they both are also products of biological synthesis during earlier periods in the history of the earth. We would thus contribute to an even faster depletion of these resources and would be able, at best, to achieve a lease on life of but short duration by such transfer of food provision from the current annual production in the fields, the pastures, and the seas to the coal and mineral oil resources. But this is not the most important drawback.

A much more serious disadvantage is the fact that as soon as these synthetically produced foods are consumed, they will—like all other foods—undergo a metabolic breakdown in the body. Some would be removed as waste. In both cases the coal in this synthetic food would end up as carbon dioxide in the atmosphere. Man is then thrown back upon his dependence on the green plant, which possesses the invaluable talent of being able to trap this dispersed carbon dioxide from the air and thus return it to the great carbon cycle of Nature. Chemistry can certainly not give us the freedom that is promised so highhandedly, because it is only *in cooperation with Nature* that it is capable of making its valuable contribution to the feeding of the world.

Finally, there is a terminological misunderstanding. In far too many cases synthetic foods do not mean what this term really implies. There are extremely few ingredients of food which so far are being made by true chemical synthesis. Vitamins, for instance, are manufactured in rather large quantities, but only an insignificant part is made synthetically in the sense that it is produced from chemicals. In most cases these industries are biological and rely on bacteria and fungi for one phase or other in the manufacture.

Man needs at least 550 pounds of dry matter per year. With the present growth of the world population by more than 60 million people (1964) each year, this means an additional 15.5 million tons each year. The total synthetic organics industry of the United States produces at the present time (1963) 10 million tons, valued at about five billion dollars. In order to create a chemical industry charged with the limited duty to feed merely one year's population increase, this would require an investment of at least eight billion dollars. An additional such installation would be needed each year, and within a decade it would have to be correspondingly larger each year—in 1970 it would be around 20 million tons (10.7 billion dollars). Merely the plants needed today represent in investment seven times more than the total investment so far made in the synthetic organics industry. This illustrates the magnitude of the needs to be filled.

Even the layman no doubt realizes that a chemical industry operates with temperatures, pressures, and other technical attributes which differ considerably from the simple techniques and low temperatures at which Nature works and does so almost complementary to man. This explains why the price for each ton of chemically manufactured substances is many times the amount reached even in agriculture. This is mainly explained by the substantial investments required.

Water

But the key problem is water. It is pointed out in chapter 19 (p. 414) how plants produce organic matter with a water consumption which is 500 to 1,000 times (sometimes even more) as large as the organic dry matter produced. As is well known, this already has created considerable difficulties in many parts of the world. There is simply not enough water available. A synthetic-chemicals industry, however, requires water in quantities which in most cases are considerably higher (see chapter 19, pp. 422–23). This is a costly and limiting factor, even if the water were utilized many times over.

Synthetic Amino Acids

A number of studies have been published on the use of synthetic amino acids for supplementation, and the importance of this procedure to undernourished countries. In this way deficiencies in the aminogram are filled in. Small amounts have what might be called a multiplier effect, far above that of the added amount as the general utilization of the protein is improved. This valuable effect is well documented. What still remains to be established is whether it would be feasible to apply this on a global scale and, perhaps still more essential, whether it is effective under practical conditions.

It is surprising to discover how many civilizations unknowingly have practiced such supplementation by combining foods with proteins in such a way that they fill in each other's deficiencies with respect to the building stones, the amino acids. Conspicuous examples are the beans and corn among American Indians, the Chinese cabbage or soybean with rice in China and Japan. Fish sauces in Southeast Asia are potent sources of such supplementing amino acids. The French hors d'oeuvres, the Scandinavian herring tidbits and smörgåsbord, and the Russian "zakuski" all serve this purpose of providing a rich assortment of supplementary protein.

Consequently, there is the risk that only to a limited degree would this procedure alleviate serious protein shortage. Too little protein still remains the number one issue. We should not be too surprised if the additive effect of synthetic amino acids under field conditions do not give the spectacular results laboratory tests have indicated as possible.

It should also be borne in mind that the distribution of such synthetic additives becomes a crucial issue in all areas when the population still is widely dispersed over the countryside. This is the prevailing pattern in many underfed countries such as China, India, Indonesia, and large parts of Africa and Latin

America. Such supplementing presumably would be a privilege predominantly enjoyed by urban populations.

Finally, it is food for thought that thus far very little effort has gone into implementing any large-scale supplementation as a concrete measure to extend the efficiency of available protein— although it is abundantly clear that protein shortage is the key issue. Once again the beneficiaries are chiefly to be found right in the midst of the well-fed world—surprisingly enough, less among humans and more among our food-producing animals. Our chickens, particularly the broilers, never had it so good and eat more scientifically controlled food than we ever give our own babies. This is supplemented profusely with amino acids.

The Microbes Already Mobilized

As already pointed out, the term synthetic has been given a very wide connotation. In the food field it often implies the application of biological processes and thus embraces the factory-scale production of algae, bacteria, and fungi or the running of fermentative processes where these are involved. Human civilization has for thousands of years leaned upon the microbes, man's most humble servants. They were early utilized in the production of bread, wine, and yeasts. They were used for the clabbering of milk, the maturing of cheese, and for the making of sour cabbage and vinegar. In modern times, industries have been created in which microbes are made to produce enzymes, antibiotics, vitamins, organic acids, alcohol, and blood substitutes such as dextran. Yeasts also early became a highly appreciated source of B-vitamins.

It is therefore quite natural that a microbiological food production has been envisioned as a possibility. No doubt the spokesmen for this course of action have seen a model in the intense activity of the rumen, where bacteria and protozoa convert even the resisting cellulose to acceptable feed for the cow.

Mushroom Cultivation

Mushroom culture was started in Europe in the seventeenth century, maybe earlier. The interest in this kind of cultivation spread over the whole world and is now the basis for a multi-million-dollar industry. The champignon already has the rank of an economic plant but so far it has been almost the only mushroom variety utilized in this manner. Canned mushrooms are a staple article in many countries. The Japanese, Chinese, and some South American Indians did grow a very limited number of other species. There are, however, thousands of mushroom varieties, and it is likely that many more could be brought under cultivation. Factory production of morels has been tested and is technically feasible.

Yeast as Food

In the microbiological field, probably no other group of plants offers greater possibilities than the fungi, and especially the category named yeast fungi. Of the 37,500 kinds of fungi so far known, about two thousand are classified as edible. But only a few have been studied from the commercial point of view. More than twenty-five are generally used as food, but, as already mentioned, hardly more than one or two have become commercially important. One of these is yeast, which can be mass-produced in a short time. Its production efficiency is about 65 per cent in terms of the amount of protein obtained in relation to the quantity of carbohydrates put in by the substance on which it feeds. This is an exceptionally high degree of conversion efficiency. The corresponding figures are: for pork chops, 20 per cent; for milk, 15 per cent; for poultry, 15 per cent; and for beef, 4 per cent. Yeast strains may also be selected for the production of protein, fats, or B-vitamins and can be so fed that a maximum amount results of any one of these constituents.

No wonder that many scientists and technicians have seen yeast as the food of the future. As will be discussed below, the high productivity of yeast can only be utilized economically when the raw materials are at hand in concentrated form. Like all other living organisms, the yeast fungi cannot produce something from nothing. They are even quite demanding with regard to nitrogen sources. In addition to nitrogen salts, all other kinds of mineral nutrients are required. But yeast production is more efficient in this respect. A first-rate phosphate yields through yeast a considerably higher amount of protein than through agriculture. A few figures demonstrate this fact. One metric ton P_2O_5 (anhydro-phosphate) yields approximately the following additional harvest of protein:

TABLE 32

	Metric Tons
Grain	0.6
Peas, beans, etc.	1.5–2.0
Clover, hay	2.0–3.5
Yeast	15

Many raw materials are required, both carbohydrates in the form of sugar, and a number of organic compounds the yeasts are not capable of producing themselves. Such yeast factories, however, require considerable investments. Every homemaker knows that the mushrooms are no cheap food. Only when waste is available in large and fairly concentrated quantities, on which the yeast fungi can grow, is such a production feasible. There are three such possibilities of some importance.

Wooden Steaks

The first source of waste is the sulphite solutions of the pulp factories. They contain a great deal of cellulose which can be converted into sugar. This in turn can be used as feed for fungi. This method is behind all the talk about wooden steaks. The manufacture of yeast from this source is already being applied on a rather large scale in the United States, in West Germany, and in many other countries. A considerable portion of the dried yeast now available in the market originates in such waste.

Curiously enough, if one-third of the paper waste in the United States (i.e., approximately the quantity of paper which is relatively undamaged and therefore can be used this way) were subjected to a similar treatment, a quantity of sugar could be produced which, measured in calories, would take care of about one-third of the daily intake of calories in the United States. If the aim was to produce protein from the same source by means of yeasts, the result would satisfy only a fraction of the U.S. intake.

In Jamaica, in Taiwan, and in other places where large quantities of waste from cane-sugar production are available, yeast factories have been started. They have considerable capacity and yield important protein supplementation. Difficulties have arisen, however, when it comes to getting such yeast into an acceptable form to be employed within the framework of regional dietary patterns. This difficulty will gradually be overcome, of course. Yeast is already an important food and is an ingredient as a protein and B-vitamin additive in the production of such foods as bread, soups, and sausages in many countries.

The third possibility, and the one which in the urbanized countries will achieve greater significance, is a conversion of the sewage of the cities into yeast, among other things. Pond installation for mass-production of algae are also foreseeable. In turn, these algae constitute, after drying and further preparation, a suitable substrate for yeast production. It is evident, nevertheless, that this arrangement would mean an economizing with resources and an immediate return into the consumptional cycles of organic matter, which, although already in circulation, would be upgraded to food again more quickly than if it entered the seasonal cycles of Nature. This could be called a kind of short-circuiting— not the creation of a wider basis, but a more rapid recycling. Such a broadening of man's food sphere is accomplished only by making the cycles convey substantially more matter, whether coal, nitrogen, phosphate, or others capable of feeding additional billions. This is a dubious possibility for reasons which have been analyzed above. Converting sewage into food remains a kind of waste disposal and with inevitable losses but is basically not adding much to the total amount of food within the human biosphere, merely accelerating and shortcircuiting the turnover.

Algae Against Hunger

Popular science articles have abounded in newspapers, especially the Sunday editions, all over the globe, concerning algae as the radical remedy for a starving world. A Swedish scientist went so far as to reassure his readers that they will "solve man's food problem for centuries ahead."

Behind such predictions are experiments with unicellular green algae. These have received special attention because of the large sums which have been spent on similar experiments in space research.

The methods for the experimental culturing of various algae were established several decades ago by plant physiologists. The most recent developments in the field are almost entirely based on these old findings and have resulted in the construction of cultivation vessels for large-scale production. But, as usually is the case, the magnitude of the difficulties has been underrated. Seemingly, very few people have examined the economic conditions for this kind of production.

In the first place, factories for this purpose must be limited to such regions of the world where continuous production is possible. At least one production factor must be obtained without cost, namely, the eternally flowing sunlight energy. If the algae are not to be boiled to death through the abundant energy influx, they require continuous cooling. The plants of the fields take care of this automatically through the daily transpiration and the ensuing evaporation. The field crops would soon "burn" if this built-in mechanism were not there. A prerequisite for a fairly efficient production is that the algae are exposed to optimal illumination. This is possible only through continuous stirring. This means another item demanding energy.

The often quoted yield figures which maintain that algae cultures would surpass the production of the field, do not stand up under close scrutiny. Measured totally, the dry matter production is about the same but only under optimum conditions with respect to light, temperature, nutrients, and so forth. It is further mandatory to continually remove all full-grown cells. In order to obtain maximum yields, aging cells cannot be allowed to consume energy as feed. This involves a third cost in energy— for harvesting by filtering the algal mass at regular intervals. In principle, this procedure is identical to the one employed on a small scale in the repeated harvesting of clover and alfalfa fields and under these conditions the algae yields are of approximately the same magnitude—not higher, as is frequently claimed.

If the energy costs for all these manipulations are added up, it is easy to discover that one is here operating with something which might be compared to a bankrupt bank. In other words, the energy input is larger than the energy output in the form of final algal products. Even this would be acceptable if the aim was to obtain indispensable, precious protein even though the price tag was high. At any rate, one should be aware of the true nature of a venture like this, pay attention to the total balance sheet and register all costs. The day will come when fuel prices no longer are dictated by the West. Then operations like this will be much less favorable or will simply forbid themselves.

Are we actually prepared and even willing to pay any price

for the pleasure of rubbing shoulders with still more human billions? The food prices are already so high that more than half of the world's population cannot afford to pay for even a minimal diet and must depend on subsidies, such as food-stamp plans and aid deliveries. Against this background efforts should be concentrated on undertakings that economically make sense, such as improving the utilization of waste and byproducts from industry (food and other), especially when organic in nature. The hungry and malnourished of the world are now stepping forward and justly demanding their legitimate share. They are also claiming what the privileged few among nations now either discard or allow to go to waste, or regard as cheap enough for use in animal production—such potential food as skim milk, fish flour, brewery yeast, and presscakes of sunflower, peanuts, or palm seed, and extraction residues from copra. This latter group of plant products has revealed an astoundingly high protein quality. Several such items already serve as valuable additives to bread among needy nations. Fish flour has been made odorless and taste-free and is utilized increasingly in crackers, bread, and macaroni, for instance, in tropical Africa, Chile, India, the Philippines, and in several other countries. The fish protein used in animal production in the United States and Western Europe amounts to about one million metric tons. This quantity would be sufficient to provide 100 million people with animal protein on the present Italian dietary level. On the Indian standard it would suffice for 430 millions; in other words, it is equivalent to what the Indian population is consuming in the form of animal products for a whole year.

It was undoubtedly a very strange phase in the annals of world nutrition when the less valuable, but commercially profitable, sugar and fat commodities were extracted—sugar from beets and canes; oils and fats from oilseeds, milk, fish, and slaughter animals—while the protein was discarded almost as waste—such as blood, oilseed cake, skim milk, whey—or at the best marketed as animal food or raw material to the chemical industry. Gradually its value has been recognized but it is still to a major extent utilized in animal feeding! But now the era is dawning when the protein shortage among humans looms as the cardinal problem of world feeding. This might be identified as the third phase.

Nutritionists of the future will be astounded to learn about this formidable wastefulness or prodigality. This large-scale mismanagement will continue for some time but only until the starving nations gain a more commanding say in the matters of the world. Armaments of multibillion-dollar dimensions will in the long run not be able to prevent this shift, unless we, the privileged ones, foolishly prefer to release nuclear annihilation. The inevitable alternative is universal suffocation if the peoples and politicians of the world do not unite in a great crusade for the survival of mankind. Churchill stated in his farewell speech to the British House of Commons that man is facing the ominous choice between Supreme Disaster or Immeasurable Reward.

No statement could be more true, but are the leaders of the world conscious of what is needed in order to realize the second alternative? Today's futile political bickering certainly does not give many indications thereof. One almost gets the impression that the spokesmen of the well-to-do live in the false notion that they have already made the choice in favor of immeasurable reward. No mistake of judgment could be more tragic.

References

ALTSCHUL, A. M. *Processed Plant Protein Foodstuffs*. New York, Academic Press, 1958, 955 pp.

Developments in Industrial Microbiology. Vol. 3. Proceedings of the Eighteenth General Meeting of the Soc. for Industrial Microbiology. New York, Plenum Press, 1962, 398 pp.

DUDDINGTON, C. L. *Micro-organisms as Allies—the Industrial Use of Fungi and Bacteria*. London, Faber, 1961, 256 pp.

HOCKENHULL, D. J. D. *Progress in Industrial Microbiology.* Vol. I-V, New York, Interscience, 1959–64.

JÖRGENSEN, A. *Mikroorganismen der Gärungsindustrie.* Nürnberg, Verlag Hans Carl, 1956, 562 pp.

PRESCOTT, S. C. and DUNN, C. G. *Industrial Microbiology,* 3rd ed. New York, McGraw-Hill, 1959.

UMBREIT, W. W. *Advances in Applied Microbiology,* Vol. I-V, New York, Academic Press, 1959–64, 304 pp.

CHAPTER 19

The Water
Crisis

WATER is indispensable to all stages of food production whether in the fields, in the barns, in slaughterhouses, in processing plants, in dairies, and to some degree in the marketing. For personal use each individual consumes on the average fifty gallons daily, for the following major purposes: one gallon as drinking water; six gallons for laundry; five gallons for personal hygiene; and about eight to nine gallons for the water closet. In addition many persons take, off and on, a twenty-five gallon bath or a shower (five gallons a minute). This totals up to an average of approximately fifty gallons per day. In several West European cities, this amount has already been surpassed. In many United States cities this personal use of water has reached 125 to 150 gallons. Large additional items here are the watering of lawns, frequent use of showers, and air conditioning in the homes.

But this is only a game with figures. The actual amount of water required per individual for his daily life is much larger than these figures indicate. We have not taken into account so far the large quantities used by all the industries manufacturing all we need over a wide register: from cars and artificial fibers to jets, missiles, and housing equipment. We then find that the real consumption in the United States is 1,500 to 2,000 gallons per person daily. According to Soviet Russian estimates, at least 720 gallons are required per person in a modern technical society. When we turn to the production of food we see that this amount is increased approximately tenfold when it includes the water quantities that agriculture utilizes in the production of crops and livestock. In order to produce one single ordinary slice of bread, thirty-five gallons of water are required. This includes the water used by the wheat plant in making the organic matter that goes into the wheat kernel. The following table gives a fairly accurate picture of the water quantities required in agriculture for the production of one pound of organic matter:

TABLE 33

Water Requirements in Food Production

	Pounds of Water per Pound of Organic Matter
Millet	200–250
Wheat	300–500
Potatoes	600–800
Rice	1,500–2,000
Vegetables	3,000–5,000
Milk	10,000
Meat	20,000–50,000

The estimates for meat and milk include the water needed for the production of the indispensable feed. These figures are based upon the conditions in temperate regions. In warmer climates, the evaporation is higher and the amounts of water used up in agriculture increase correspondingly. The average figure for

Australia is no less than 897 tons of water for each ton of wheat kernel.

With improved tilling and thus better soil fertility, the relative water consumption drops somewhat. More dry matter is obtained per ton of water. In other words, the water economy is improved. But usually the yields per acre go up more than the water efficiency improves, so the end result with increasing yields is a greater water use per acre. In other words, the water consumption rises, but the dry matter return is somewhat higher for each ton of water.

Some foods are eaten directly by man. Others are used as feed to give us animal products such as meat, milk, and eggs. To the water needed to produce the feed, we have to add the water the livestock use up in their metabolism in order to retain good health and full productivity. Beef cattle consume about 16 tons of water for the production of each pound of meat. In this estimate is included not merely what is drunk by the meat steers or ingested with their food but also the water that is required in the fields to produce their grass feed and feed grains.

The following approximate figures may be quoted for the actual water intake of the various categories of livestock in temperate regions:

TABLE 34

Water Requirements of Livestock and Poultry

	Gallons Daily
Dairy Cattle* (depending upon yield)	20–25
Hog	4
Horse, Steer or Dry Cows	12
Sheep	2
100 Egg-producing Poultry	4

* 15 to 20 gallons more is needed daily for cleaning of the barns and washing of the milking vessels.

Groundwater Resources Being Tapped

Urbanization swallows ever-increasing quantities of water and is already competing with the green plant, that is, the crops, for the water resources. In 1900 each urban citizen in Sweden used twenty-three gallons of water daily; presently this figure is seventy gallons. At the same time the population grows in number. More significant, however, is the fact that the increased crop yields, in general, demand considerably more water in order to maintain the high level of productivity. The use of refrigeration disposes of rapidly growing quantities; and re-use in this aspect is necessary on an increasing scale if consumption is not going to surpass all other urban needs.

The yield increases of Western Europe since the 1880's takes an additional two to five inches of the rainfall. Therefore less water reaches the groundwater than earlier. The replenishment by Nature is being disrupted by accelerated runoff as well as by the mounting consumption. What used to be added to the groundwater is failing or is drastically diminished. In consequence groundwater levels are falling in many areas, owing to this increased tapping of the resources. The takeout has become larger than the input and on the average this has become a chronic phenomenon. Around major cities like London, Copenhagen, and Hamburg the repercussions are gradually becoming serious, and enormous investments are required to replenish the subterranean reservoirs and prevent them from drying up completely. Considerable sinking has been registered on the Rhine plateau at Basel as well as in the Danube basin around Vienna.

Plant cultivation exacts the highest ransom from the groundwaters when the water is pumped up from wells. Because of the resulting excess take out, an ever-increasing number of holes have to be drilled or they have to be made deeper. At the same time the inflow to the groundwater is steadily reduced. The water level sinks unyieldingly. As a rule, that agriculture which is carried on without such artificially provided water quantities is, in general, if minimum requirements are assured, better adjusted ecologically as to its productive level. Yields are then in better coordination with the availability of water in the cultivated areas. This pumping from groundwater resources, when excessive, gives an erroneous idea of potentialities. The motor-driven pumps of our day know no limitations as to their efficiency. Therefore, the wells can be constantly multiplied in number as well as drilled deeper and deeper, speeding up depletion and desiccation accordingly. Finally the point is reached when these invisible water resources in the ground become exhausted, or when the level has fallen so far down that the costs of pumping are prohibitive. This has happened in Saudi Arabia, in the Negev region in Israel, in the irrigated desert of Texas and Arizona, in California, and in many other places. In Arizona the groundwater level has fallen more than a hundred feet from its earlier regular level and almost as much in Southern California.

Sooner or later one reaches a limit. Exhaustion of the groundwater resources has become especially precarious in dry regions all over the globe, whenever they are tapped to secure food. India alone already irrigates more than twenty-five million acres by pumping from wells, an area almost as large as all the irrigated land in the United States. Since the Union of South Africa was created in 1910, thirty-five thousand wells have been drilled by the government. They were particularly concentrated in the meat-producing parts of the country. After a short time span of twenty-five years, one after the other of these wells dried out as available water became exhausted. Earlier in this century South Africa used to export meat regularly to the United Kingdom.

In California, 53 per cent of the investments for irrigation are placed in wells, and the consequences have proved to be catastrophic. Acre after acre of California's orange- and vegetable-cropping areas have to be taken out of production in order to meet the water needs for the thousands of people who, each year in increasing numbers, invade Los Angeles, already a city of millions. The citrus groves have diminished one-fourth in area and one-sixth in yield because of this development. Salt water is slowly seeping into the continent from the ocean, filling in the space evacuated by the fresh waters. This also contributed to direct loss of cropping land through salinization.

Central Europe has to wrestle with a noticeable and alarming desiccation process which has caused a lively debate about the "steppification" of Europe, particularly the northern plains. This process was started and has further been accelerated through higher yields from the crops as well as by the steeply mounting water needs of modern man for domestic and industrial purposes. Through a similar desiccation process all of southern Texas is in danger of being transformed into a desert despite feverish efforts to bring in more water. But the large-scale industrialization, coupled with the needs for more food, has emptied the water resources at an even greater speed. Recent estimates by the U.S. Geological Survey show that it would take 104 years to restore the groundwater, through natural replenishment, to a reasonable natural level.

Regulating Countermeasures

Strict rationing has been implemented in many places. Before the Second World War, water for domestic household purposes in the Ruhr area of Western Germany was used, on an average, four to five times before it was allowed to continue down this river. The same water was sometimes utilized for industrial purposes up to forty times.

Through drainage and regulations, the water balance in nature is disrupted, often with detrimental effects. Europe offers any number of examples of this kind. The construction of the Kiel Canal between the North Sea and the Baltic had the same effect as a gigantic drainage operation. It lowered the groundwater level in a belt of about five miles on both sides of the canal. The highest figure registered for this drop in groundwater level was sixty feet.

As already mentioned, the groundwater resources around most metropolises are rapidly shrinking, both in Europe and in the United States. Around Baltimore the level has sunk 150 feet since 1916. Investments, frequently very large, are now required in many places in order to avert still greater damages. Recently, an enormous reservoir had to be built near the city of Münster in Westphalia for a total cost of 3.6 million dollars. It was constructed to hold 250 million cubic feet of water. This will amount to a "little" lake of 150 acres, stealing fields, pastures, and forests, as farms are put under water for the creation of this storage dam.

The Ruhr already has storage dams for 6.9 billion cubic feet of water. Nonetheless, it will have to create additional reservoirs, holding 6.5–7.0 billion cubic feet, within the next decade. All these undertakings constitute purposeful efforts to put a stop, if at all possible, to a continued lowering of the groundwater levels, and furthermore, to supply water for sustained increase in the agricultural yields per acre.

In many cases the topographical possibilities of creating new water reservoirs are exhausted. Industrial cities like Mexico City, Madrid, and Magdeburg cannot accommodate more industries and inhabitants without aggravating still more the water shortage. Mexico is radically moving its industries into new cities with better water facilities. In several large Latin American cities such as Rio de Janeiro and Mexico City the water is shut off several hours daily and sometimes for the entire day. Particularly critical examples, especially because of the number of millions of people involved, are Hong Kong and Tokyo. Water had to be provided to Hong Kong through several additional pipelines from mainland China, with which this city has a delivery contract. In the spring of 1964 these resources also were inadequate and water had to be brought in from China in big tankers. Yet, rationing was severe—sometimes as much as four days elapsed between deliveries through the faucets. Tokyo had a similar critical shortage at this time. Usage of water moved so close to the ultimate margins that it is evident that some of these heavily populated areas would not sustain a drought without serious sufferings or a crisis close to catastrophe. There is no buffer any longer. A number of cities in Sweden and distant Denmark (Copenhagen and others) are eyeing Lake Vänern in central Sweden as their only resource to fill future needs. Central Europe is on its way to emptying its only remaining lake of any size, namely Lake Constance. A race is under way to stop the increasing pollution of this last natural reservoir, which threatens its value as a source for drinking water. Water blooms indicating excessive mineral nutrition have already become a regular phenomenon in this big lake. A troublesome consequence of the dwindling groundwater resources is the fact that to a growing degree potable water has to be taken from surface water, involving much greater sanitation hazards and more costly pretreatment in water works. No longer can advantage be taken of the effective filtering which takes place in nature when water trickles down to join the groundwater.

Chlorination and expensive water purification have become increasingly common in order to guarantee the water needs of the cities. In addition, recirculation is becoming a normal arrangement. The water works have become neuralgic spots in a modern society, charged not only with the filtering and refinement of the natural product, contaminated or not, but also with the cumbersome restoration of heavily polluted water to potability.

Constant Withdrawals from the Water Bank, Few Deposits

The account above is intended to throw light on one sector of man's daily life where the costs are rarely acknowledged, far less discussed. It may help the reader to understand why countries which to a considerable degree depend on irrigation often have trouble in making their water resources (surface as well as ground) go far enough. The examples related above may also facilitate an understanding of why proposals for irrigation on a continental scale, based on desalinized water, are loose speculations. They are most unrealistic in not taking into account the magnitude of the water needs for food- and feed-producing crops. Recently such estimates were presented for Texas. Merely for the irrigation of the southern part of the state, 15,000 plants would be required, in effect larger in size than the biggest chemical plants of present-day United States. Besides, the costs for pumping the water around, both up and out over hundreds of miles, would be exorbitant. Despite many impressive technical masterpieces, the huge irrigation projects of the world are serving merely about half of the total irrigated acreage on earth. Irrigation from drilled wells and other local sources is still dominating the scene.

Food Processing Needs Water

The food industry gulps down water in considerable quantities. Canneries, sugar refineries, slaughterhouses, and dairies require huge amounts, flour mills somewhat less. A few gleanings may illustrate the magnitude of these requirements.

TABLE 35

Water Requirements in Food Industries

One Metric Ton	requires in plant processing	Metric Tons Water
Sugar		70
Edible Oil		35
Beer		8
Milk (in the dairy)		4–6

In order to make a slice of bread, as mentioned above, no less than thirty-five gallons of water are used up, counting from the grain fields. Few people give even a thought to this fact when eating a sandwich. We take everything for granted, and—what is worse—we do not get acquainted with the real costs of any of our everyday commodities. The milk we buy bottled and often delivered at our doorstep, the hamburger, and the lowly slice of bread—all represent a world of achievements. If our civilization is going to survive and progress, it is imperative that our youth early in life learn these simple relationships. Aldo Leopold, the great United States writer about Nature, said in one of his essays: "There are two spiritual dangers involved in not owning a farm—one is the fallacy of believing that the breakfast comes from the grocer's store, the other that heat comes from the stove." The world's farmers, who are placed close to the eternal creative forces in plants and animals and in more than one way control this flow, have as a rule a better appreciation of the limiting as well as the creative forces. News media and education have a big mission and a major responsibility in this area.

Water in Industrialization

Even Siberia, developing so fast in recent years, is encountering serious difficulties when it comes to procuring water for its large-scale industrialization. A Soviet technologist recently pointed out that the production of synthetic fibers requires between 80,000 and 115,000 cubic feet of water per ton of fiber while one ton of cotton fabric requires merely 200 cubic feet. Production from plants economizes much more with water than does the chemical industry. A large steam power station may easily gulp up 425 cubic feet of water per second, an enormous lake each year, while hydroelectric dams demand no extra water, outside of what evaporates from the dam.

A few figures may illuminate the water-consuming role of industrial activities:

TABLE 36

Water Requirements in Industry

For the manufacture of one ton of	is required	the following tons of water
Synthetic Rubber		2,500–3,000
Coal		2,250–2,750
Newsprint		900–1,000
Paper Pulp		175–250
Steel		160–260
Gasoline (from coal)		500–900
Oil (refining)		30–60

This represents one facet of the industrialization process which is often overlooked in recommendations to underdeveloped regions. Several among these countries are already utilizing nearly all of their water resources merely to meet basic food needs. The margin for industrial ventures is extremely narrow, as a consequence. The inevitable choice has then to be made between industrial production or food.

The Water Balance of the U.S.

In official surveys the U.S. water needs are presented in the following way:

TABLE 37

U. S. Water Needs

Year	Daily Water Use (billion gallons)	Population (millions)
1900	40	76
1930	92	123
1960	312	180
1975	453	240
1980	592	260
2000	1,000	450

In the above figures, which represent the average daily use, the regular water consumption in agriculture is not included, but merely what is used for irrigation outside of Nature's own contribution. The United States is presently consuming nine times more water than was the case at the turn of the century, and this on top of what the plant crops take directly in Nature and this take-out has also increased considerably.

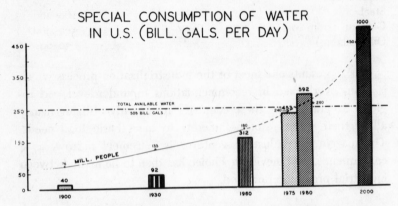

SPECIAL CONSUMPTION OF WATER
IN U.S. (BILL. GALS. PER DAY)

FIG. 50   The U.S. water balance, according to the Paley report. The climb in consumption has been much steeper than anticipated in this report (1955). Sharply increased re-use will be required for all non-consumptive uses. Consumptive uses, such as artificial irrigation for food and feed, will have to be increasingly controlled and all abuses avoided.

The total quantity of water available from all natural sources is about 560 billion gallons. Complete utilization of all available water is for practical reasons not feasible. The re-use of water is therefore becoming increasingly common. The water in the Ohio River basin is already utilized ten times over.

Two-fifths of the United States water consumption (1960) falls into the category of industrial uses; another two-fifths belong to artificial irrigation. This means that the population pressure on the water resources is almost five times larger than the direct pressure represented by the remaining one-fifth—the humans using water for domestic and personal needs. Does anybody believe that China, India, or even Brazil could afford such a water budget! Of special concern, however, is the fact that industry now is taking an increasing share of this available water at the same time that it is multiplying the pressure of pollution on natural waters by dumping growing amounts of waste into them. It is this double grip which is so ominous.

In 1957, restrictions on the use of water in the United States had to be imposed in more than a thousand communities comprising one-seventh of the population. To provide the United States with water during the next twenty years will require investments of between 54 and 74 billion dollars, according to a report recently presented by the Senate.

San Francisco and Los Angeles are now reaching for remaining surface waters available in northern California. The plan is to catch this water through a series of dams and to transport it southward in the gigantic Feather River Project. The estimated cost of this project is two billion dollars—twice that of the Aswan dam. Its completion will take thirty years. Money is being borrowed for the execution of this big project, but it seems unlikely that these loans can be paid back within the stipulated term or within eighty years from now. The *Wall Street Journal* in reporting on this project also warned that a prerequisite for its sound financing would be no inflation during this lengthy period—a fanciful dream to say the least.

Similar facts could be reported from most industrialized countries of the world. The United States has been selected here, as this country is threatened by a water crisis which will have grave repercussions on both agriculture and industry.

The U.S. Geological Survey recently stated publicly that the United States has all but exhausted the exploitation of its major water resources. Nothing remains but to start economizing. All indications are that this was a correct conclusion.

Somebody said once that if forward-looking men had not invented the United States, this continent would by now have been torn by devastating wars between the states along the Rocky Mountains and the states on the West Coast, which are all of them poor in water. This battle is now being launched on the legal plane in the U.S. Supreme Court. It is gradually dawning upon the combatants—and the courts—that there is not much water left. When water is allotted to Los Angeles, another state, city, or region sees itself deprived and its industry and agriculture jeopardized, sometimes to the degree that further development is no longer feasible. The bitterness on both sides is great. Los Angeles, being located on the coast, will be able, however, to procure water through desalinization; but the costs will have to come down still further, preferably below what it costs to regain water from sewage.

Against this background it becomes understandable that the Secretary of Agriculture, Charles F. Brannan, in a speech in 1951, where he expressed himself in highly optimistic words about the capabilities of United States agriculture to meet the rising needs of its growing population as well as to aid the world in this respect, also expressed great concern about the water problem. He considered it highly unlikely that the United States would be able to conjure forth the huge extra quantities of water that would be needed in order to double the agricultural output before the end of this century, which is the order if our present standard is to be maintained in spite of the population growth.

Desalinization

Desalinization of water is by no means limited to ocean water. Over large areas in Australia (see the chapter on that continent) and in many regions of the United States and Israel, pumping over a period of time ultimately yields saline water. Although the current costs are five to ten times as high as purifying water in traditional water works, already many communities find it profitable to desalt water locally, either from the sea (along the coast) or from deep-drilled wells.

The best-known and also the largest desalinization plant in the world is that in Kuwait. This works with a capacity of 3.2 million gallons daily. Kuwait with only 220,000 inhabitants can afford almost any luxury thanks to its income from its oil wells, which it is unwilling to share with its Arabian brothers. The Aruba Island off the Venezuelan coast has a similar plant with a daily capacity of 3.1 million gallons. Most attention has recently been focused on the installation being built to supply the United States base at Guantanamo on Cuba. Five Federal experimental plants are in operation in the United States.

So far, desalinization is not competitive. The energy consumption is ten to a hundred times higher than theoretical estimates had indicated. There is no doubt, however, that the desalinization problem will be solved technically as well as economically. The obstacles encountered are in quite other areas. First, in the field of agricultural production the magnitude of the requirements make the use of desalted water next to impossible for simple practical reasons, not to speak of economic ones. If anything above a limited sprinkling along the ocean coasts of the continents is to be accomplished, then gigantic subterranean tunnels are required. Even pipelines would be wholly inadequate. Open channels would be impracticable. Such costly water cannot be allowed to be lost in evaporation. Furthermore, little thought has been given to the salt mountains which would pile up around the desalinization plants and which would involve heavy disposal costs, to say nothing of the complications involved in keeping all this salt from finding its way to fields and ground-water resources. It is food for thought that the production of one ton of milk would produce more than thirty-five tons of salt.

References

ADDISON, H. *Land, Water and Food.* London, Chapman & Hall, 1955 248 pp.

AGATZ, A., and PALLASCH, D. (eds.). *Wasser—die Sorge Europas.* Dortmund, Ardey, 1951, 178 pp.

BÉNÉZECH, C. *L'eau—Base structurale et fonctionelle des êtres vivants.* Paris, Masson, 1962, 175 pp.

COCANNOUER, J. A. *Water and the Cycle of Life.* New York, Devin-Adair, 1962, 143 pp.

KERR, R. A. *Land, Wood and Water.* New York, Fleet, 1960, 380 pp.

LEOPOLD, A. *A Sand County Almanac.* New York, Oxford University Press, 1949, 226 pp.

MILNE, L. and M. *Water and Life.* New York, Atheneum, 1964, 275 pp.

RODE, A. A. *Das Wasser im Boden.* Berlin, Akademie-Verlag, 1959, 464 pp.

CHAPTER 20

The Dilemma
of Modern
Technology

T HE new big Aswan Dam which is under construction in the upper part of the Nile has been presented in great detail in the newspapers, on TV and radio. This storage dam will be the world's largest artificial lake. It is higher than any other dam which has so far been built. It also influenced world politics. Alternately, it is described as the greatest technical masterpiece of our time and as an example of man's sovereignty over Nature, proving how man can tame huge rivers and govern his own fate. The Aswan Dam has been lauded as a master stroke in the great chess game of human hunger.

Those who speak in these terms would benefit from consulting some library. The British daily newspapers shortly after the turn of the century carried the enraptured descriptions of the first Aswan Dam—in reality the third one—which English and French engineering then created. It was opened in 1902. That dam would bring happiness, it was said, to the people of the Nile Valley; it would chase away hunger from the Egyptian land and restore to this country its glorious past. Such was the theme of the journalistic choir. What was written in those days could be reiterated today, almost word by word, with reference to the fifth dam at present under construction.

Let us look for a moment at the facts on the Egyptian scene. The 1960 census revealed that there were two million more people in the country than had been officially known. The population figure thus jumped from twenty-four to twenty-six million. Aside from these two million, the nation has grown in latter years by half a million people a year or seven million in fourteen years. According to the construction plans for the dam, revised by the Russians, it will not be ready for use in 1970, as originally planned, but in 1975. The irrigation canals will be built by 1972, but the dam cannot be fully filled with water until 1975.

By then, if no catastrophe befalls it, Egypt will have a population of approximately 35 million, that is nine million more than in 1960. As a result of this large project it is estimated that nearly one million acres will be added to the tilled acreage of Egypt. This is about half of the tilled acreage of Wisconsin. Even with bumper crops it would be quite a feat to feed nine million from this acreage. For each one of the newly arrived there would be a little less than one-tenth of an acre. There is a frightening degree of undernourishment among the Egyptian masses in spite of the fact that the present inhabitants have at their disposal an acreage more than twice that amount, or 0.26 of an acre. On top of that, Egypt has a ghost acreage of almost 2.5 million acres, divided almost equally between fisheries and trade (see chapter 5). The 0.26 of an acre is therefore in reality supplemented with 0.085 of an acre. On the present miserable diet level the Aswan Dam, when ready, will supply food for less than one-third of the population addition (1960–1975) or about 2.8 million.

Facts like these justify talk about a dilemma of modern technology. There is nothing wrong with engineering as such. It can and will register greater achievements than ever before in history. Nonetheless, it falls short of the goals. It has grossly underrated the magnitude of the actual needs and its true tasks. On the whole, we can say that technology is an indispensable prerequisite for man's existence and progress. But it has bitten off more than it can chew. This applies to almost every area of its endeavors: plant and animal breeding, feed manufacturing, irrigation, energy supply, mining, forestry, chemistry, highway construction, electro-technology, sewage plants, food preservation, and so on. Do not worry, we have the know-how—this has been the catch phrase, and this overconfidence is encountered even against overwhelming odds.

When may we expect the sobering up? When are we going to return to reality? So far no technology in the world has freed man from his fundamental dependence on water. Rather the opposite is the case, as discussed in the previous chapter. Higher material well-being has only multiplied the water requirements and fortified man's bonds to water. In many areas we are lagging behind in a constantly more critical scale, both in the developing countries we are set to aid as well as right in our own land.

Urbanization

Lewis Mumford, the American sociologist, in his latest monumental monograph paints a fascinating picture of the role of the cities in the development and flourishing of human culture, but also of their mounting critical situation. The megalomania becomes stifling and not infrequently destructive. Our transit systems are facing technical bankruptcy when a large part of the population has to spend one-fourth of the day in commuting back and forth from home to working place, as is the case in many major cities in the United States, Japan, and Western Europe. Several aspects of this nature are analyzed by Mumford, but he leaves out one relationship in many ways far more significant than these questions of convenience and comfort. We will analyze some of these. The urbanization that is changing the entire social structure from a pattern of dispersion to this tremendous agglomeration of millions concentrated in a few pointed regions is revolutionary. The confused discussion about water pollution reveals how little conscious we are of these radical and partly destructive processes which are built into these structures. The high relative proportion of the population concentrated in urban and suburban districts as against the relatively few in rural areas contrasts drastically with conditions a hundred years back and even to a considerable degree with the distribution of the population only thirty to fifty years ago.

The farm population in the United States has been relatively

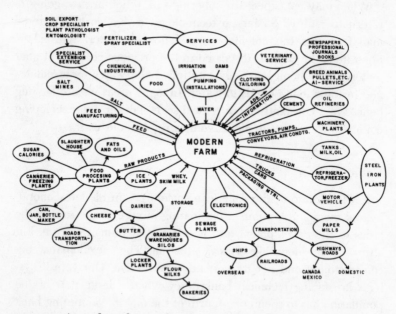

FIG. 51 A modern farmer leaves all food and feed transportation, most of the storage, and almost all processing to outside enterprises. He brings to his farm most fuel, fertilizers and other chemicals; even a substantial part of his own food is purchased. A modern farmer needs the help of a number of nonfarm-employed people in order to be able to produce. Producing food therefore involves far more people than the labor force on the farm.

stable in numbers since 1880—around 20 million. But during the same period population in the cities and suburban regions has zoomed from around 20 to 125 million (1960). In terms of food this means that toward the cities and suburban areas now moves not only a greater proportion of the farm products but also greater loads. What is retained in rural areas has not changed much. The rather simple supplying of foods from the countryside to the towns and cities has in our days taken on big proportions. This has necessitated not only the creation of a powerful distribution system, combined with all kinds of storage, preservation, and packaging issues, but also the creation of a modern highway system capable of carrying the heavy food-laden trucks.

In many West European countries this process has been still more accentuated. The rural population in general, as well as the farm population, has been yet more drastically reduced and the cities have grown in a still more spectacular way—see table:

TABLE 38

Farm and Non-Farm Population in Sweden

	1880 (millions)	1950 (millions)	1960 (millions)
Farm	3	2	1.5
Non Farm	0.8	5	6

This means that in this instance (Sweden) about 7.5 times more foods nowadays leave the farms to feed the non-farm population and only half as much remains on the farms. The efficient distribution of the inhabitants creates few pollution problems. The main rural pollution trouble is that created by silage juice, flowing from forage silos. This juice is loaded with minerals and organic compounds. It is worth noting that this also is caused by a man-induced concentration, in this case of feed.

FIG. 52

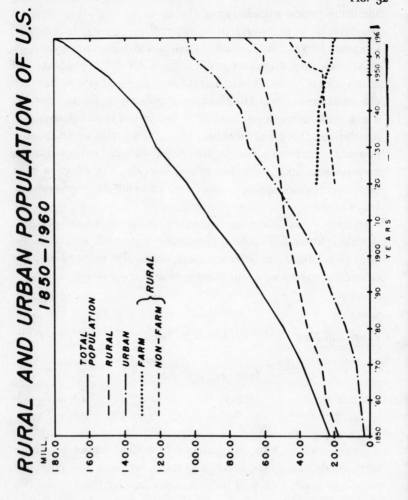

RURAL AND URBAN POPULATION OF U.S.
1850—1960

TOTAL POPULATION
RURAL
URBAN
FARM } RURAL
NON-FARM

MILL.
180.0
160.0
140.0
120.0
100.0
80.0
60.0
40.0
20.0
0

YEARS

1850 '60 '70 '80 '90 1900 '10 '20 '30 '40 1950 60 196

This rapid and extensive urbanization process has had a profound influence upon the supply of minerals in the soil. Among other things, it has induced a depletion of the soils, especially aggravated by the flow of mineral-rich milk to the urban centers. These phenomena constitute one important explanation for the steeply mounting curves in the use of commercial fertilizers. Yet, few countries seem to have reached the point when the amount of nutrients added through artificial fertilizers reaches the quantities that used to be returned to the soils by manure. Not only must old neglect be compensated for, but in addition the increasing tribute which the higher yields remove from the topsoil. The mechanization of agriculture has further increased the need for added mineral nutrients to compensate for the loss of manure.

A heavy two-way traffic flow has emerged, moving between the population centers and the farm regions. The agricultural products later to be refined into foods move out. Back to the soil go many things today (see Fig. 52), but the big volume is represented by the commercial fertilizers. This delivery can no longer be organized during the spring and fall seasons in time for sowing, but the large bulk demands delivery all the year round, with costly storage as a consequence. For the United States the quantity required exceeds seventy million tons. This corresponds to six gigantic freight trains of forty-ton cars, each spanning the entire continent from New York to San Francisco. To organize every year the delivery of all these carloads carrying lime and fertilizers constitutes a major task. Yet in most regions far less is being returned to the soil than it loses. In the long run we will have to strike a balance in order to maintain productivity of the soils and a high-rate quality of the products.

Large-Scale Water Pollution

Part of this dilemma is created by the fact that the return flow in terms of minerals has not yet caught up fully. Much is retained in the cities and part goes to sewage plants. This concentration of human waste ensuing from the food is very much behind the mounting pollution troubles of communities as well as the climbing costs for sewage disposal. So far, U.S. cities have invested more than 25 billion dollars on this account, yet sewage from only half the population is taken care of. The remainder flows into rivers, lakes, and coastal areas. Less than one fourth of the sewage is returned to the soil. More than 13 million tons of mineral nutrients are lost through this channel each year. The sewage industry anticipates the need for an immediate expenditure of around 2 billion dollars and an additional 10.2 billion prior to 1980. This is one area where modern society badly needs the moon-rocket money: for cleaning up the United States and removing the hazards of the presently mounting pollution.

Of the United States population, 135 million are reportedly getting their drinking water from lakes and rivers which are recipients of sewage from cities. Several United States metropolises have, in their suburbs, individual sewage disposal by means of inefficient septic tanks which constitute sanitary hazards. Their overflow seeps into the ground and reaches open ditches, rivers, and lakes. Epidemics, caused by the virus of polio, hepatitis, and others, have in many instances led to judicial measures against development projects for homes.

Four thousand plants, especially built for the disposal of industrial waste, are presently needed to eliminate hazardous pollution of public waters. Such pollution is now causing fish death and other damages. This estimated need merely takes into account currently known cases, but does not take into consideration the constantly growing number of new offenders.

These conditions explain why almost nine-tenths of the people in the United States have to be content with the kind of chlorine cocktail which our faucets furnish in the name of water. The almost universal use of chlorination is our only protection against disease and epidemics. Without this chemical barrier we would be subject to mass infection.

Our water carries another complication, namely the troubles caused by the growing use of detergents. Potable water is containing more and more residues of these compounds. This creates problems for soft-drink manufacturers, breweries, and food-processing industries, which all depend on meticulously clean, first-rate water. The detergents also disturb the biological purification systems based on microbial activities, both those in Nature and those operating in sewage plants. This has raised the demand for bio-degradable detergents which are characterized by being capable of breaking down in these microbial processes. Such new types of detergents have come on the market and are already compulsory in several states in the United States as well as in many West European countries.

The drainage water from fields where certain modern chemicals such as toxaphene, aldrin, DDT, and BHC have been used against insects, may easily build up to toxic levels in neighboring lakes and rivers. This has been confirmed by the experiences from several such incidents reported in the United States. The mass killing of fish in the lower Mississippi (in the spring of 1964) has aroused wide public attention and resulted in congressional hearings. The situation was aggravated by a direct pollution from a plant manufacturing some of these spray chemicals.

Water contamination now takes on such dimensions that pollutants also sneak down to the normally well-protected groundwaters. They are gradually becoming infected both with bacteria and foreign minerals. Remedial measures to clean up the surface waters have almost everywhere been taken too late. A particularly difficult kind of pollution is that caused by oil and gasoline. This frequently spreads through spill, overflow, and leakage from tap station and oil-tank storage areas and finally finds its way down to the groundwater.

Protective sanitary measures are constantly becoming more

comprehensive and complicated. The risks of epidemics are
steadily on the increase. In the postwar period, especially in
Denmark and Central Europe, an increased spread of tapeworms
was noted among both humans and animals, because of polluted
waters. This is causing serious concern. The use of partially
"purified" sewage waters in field irrigation of pastures and crops
may result in widespread infection, sufficient to cause extensive
contamination of both man and livestock.

Mounting Water Needs

The water crisis was discussed in detail in a previous chapter.
Only a few pertinent points will be raised in this context. The
degree of water pollution is often measured in terms of population equivalents—a term similar to that used in appraising
the protein needs. In this case the unit is determined by the
average amount of waste from an adult of standard weight (154
pounds). In this way the organic waste from various industries
may be compared to human sewage as to the strain they are
causing on natural waters and their magnificent cleansing mechanism. Organic matter is then broken down, or degraded. The
amount of oxygen required for this, and the desirable degree of
degradation, can by this method be readily compared to the
strength of the pollution caused by the average waste from
humans and consequently can be calculated in human units
(population equivalents). Estimated according to this method,
the industrial pollution in the United States in 1962 amounted
to 400 million population equivalents. At the turn of the century
the corresponding figure was 15 million! It is estimated that by
1970 it will be above 600 million units. The impact of man upon
Nature is also in this respect considerably larger than sheer population figures would indicate. In other words, we in the United
States have created a kind of civilization which, if all its waste
were disposed of in Nature, would correspond to the direct
waste of a population more than three times as large.

Air Pollution

Man's existence is not threatened merely on the water front. Much pollution is airborne. Besides the voluntary penetration of the lung tissue with cancerogenic substances through cigarette smoking, the smoke- and chemical-filled air of the cities emerges as an involuntary, non-negligible cause of lung cancer. Enormous sums have been invested in various industrialized countries for the battle against the mounting air pollution. But even in this case we do not seem capable of keeping up with the population growth. The dense, killing fog over London in 1952 has frequently been described and discussed in detail by the news media, and in professional journals. It caused four thousand deaths through its high content of toxic agents.

The extensive spreading of radioactive matter from nuclear testings has resulted through fallout in the contamination of almost all food. Most major countries are closely following these developments. The test ban treaty has put a temporary stop to the mounting amounts of strontium-90 in human bones, cesium-137 in flesh, carbon-14 in all organic matter. It is mandatory that this ban be retained, otherwise we are faced with hazardous concentrations of these radionuclides. This has temporarily happened with iodine-131.

Largely through the industrial expansion during the war years, Los Angeles lost its clear and sunny sky, praised throughout its entire earlier history. According to a published report, the daily discharge of particles and chemicals into the air from industry was successfully reduced in 1954 by about 800 metric tons, through the use of special cleansing filters and other devices. During that same year the number of automobiles increased so that they contributed another thousand tons, through exhaust gases. The Los Angeles smog is still a serious matter. Congestion in the lungs, and smarting and watering eyes, are commonplace experiences as soon as the air layers become stagnant and the self-ventilation by Nature through winds and air streams does not suffice. The costs for the protection of the air in Los Angeles had already reached staggering figures by 1960, according to the city authorities. There are many indications that the alarming increase in the frequency of emphysema (a kind of slime accumulation in the lungs) particularly among men can be attributed to the growing prevalence of unclean air for breathing.

Industry Earmarked for Food

Another dilemma of modern technology is the fact that the industrial potential to an increasing degree must be earmarked, directly or indirectly, for food production. Our emancipation from the armies of billions of nitrogen-fixing bacteria and algae involves large amounts of energy on the debit side. We prefer to delete these items from our balance sheets, although we invest in a growing number of nitrogen factories. For each ton of nitrogen produced, an amount of energy equivalent to five tons of coal is needed. This may at the moment not mean much to us with our fuel extravagance, but for countries treading a tight rope economically and for those making sacrifices toward industrialization, this allocation of resources may not be feasible or require priority decisions. With increase in population these requirements will mount considerably. Alternative ways of procuring nitrogen may be advisable, i.e. enhancing the activities of nitrogen-fixing microorganisms. Already Japan, on a regional basis, is mass-cultivating blue-green algae in small village plants to build up the binding of nitrogen in the rice fields.

Coupled with reckless forest devastation, the agricultural methods introduced by Europeans in the course of their worldwide colonization have been among the most costly and destructive acts to which the human household has been subjected. Soil erosion reached global dimensions first in this century, and tens of millions of acres, suitable for tilling, were then lost in all continents. Both the Soviet Union, the United States, and Europe have suffered smarting losses.

Another consequence of the soil erosion is that many of those impressive masterpieces, the world's large irrigation dams, will already within a century become gigantic fortresses of concrete, abandoned in the deserts, or traced only by the marshlands they have created. In the United States alone there are today two thousand such fortresses out of use, filled with silt, sand, and gravel. For the remaining nine thousand reservoirs the estimate is that most of them will reach an average age of fifty years at the most. In South America such dams often have an active lifespan of merely ten, at the most twenty, years. India has thousands of such abandoned storage dams, which are completely filled with silt and gravel.

But modern technology is not only to blame for disregarding this type of indirect devastation. Direct attacks are also made on the food-producing lands by transforming them into airfields, industrial zones, and urban deserts. In the spring of 1953, President Dwight Eisenhower received an appeal by cable from an agricultural region in southern Germany which had been doomed to disappear, in order to leave space for the sterile runs of a concrete military airfield. This appeal not only reflected the understandable reaction of people with a close relationship to and love for the soil, who saw themselves deprived of their livelihood, but it also mirrors a clearer understanding of priorities in a world faced with extreme want.

Since 1938, Denmark has lost 300,000 acres of arable soils for similar purposes. The loss amounts at present to 22,000 acres per year. The most optimistic appraisals conclude that new acceptable land can be found for only another fifteen years at this rate. Furthermore, most of the lost lands are good longtime-cultivated soils, while the new lands will be drained boglands or Seeland with poor fertility. The present plans for residential development in England involve a loss of one-tenth of its tilled acreage. Many Swiss cantons will have been deprived of all cultivated land before the end of this century if the present pace in soil robbery is not slowed down. The skyscraper may in the future become the salvation of the agricultural regions. If not, we will be sawing off the branch on which we sit. As discussed in the chapters on Japan and Australia, we have so far not been able to compensate for the acreage losses through the tilling of new land. This is like the American while falling from the thirty-third floor of a skyscraper who joyfully remarked when passing the thirteenth floor, "This seems to work out fine."

Acute Threats

Aside from this acreage robbery, the water pollution through sewage and industrial waste is most ominous. One menacing sign is the increasing salt content of the Rhine River. The chemical industries are the chief culprits. The salt content is already now so high that the river water can no longer serve for the irrigation of growing crops. In 1898 the chloride content of this water was 40 milligrams per liter. Today it is five times as high.

Holland is now squeezed between two advancing salt fronts which gradually threaten the vegetation. The water in the canals is already being utilized to the degree that the sea water pushes far into the inland and penetrates the soil along the canal beds. In 1949, this salt front reached twenty-eight miles up the Waal River. Simultaneously, the water system of the Rhine dumps thousands of tons of chloride salts daily on the bravely resisting country. The locks at Amsterdam release every day 21,000 metric tons of salt into the Zuider Zee. According to estimates, a quantity of 240,000 metric tons of salt seeps as backlash into the rivers and water systems of Holland daily in dry years. Merely a small portion thereof reverts to the sea. Such a situation is untenable. Our parents' generation reaped the prime benefits from the emancipation of agriculture from the resources of mineral nutrients in the soil through the application of commercial fertilizers. Our generation is now implementing another one-time trick, the emancipation from draft animals. The tractor—the steel horse—in all countries where introduced and used effectively, has freed larger acreages from the duty of providing feed to horses. These acreages are now used to provide food for humans or feed for food-producing livestock. The stables have been replaced by oil tankers and refineries. Oil takes the place of grass as fuel in agriculture. The capital assets are there—in the stored plant products of the oil fields—and we can free ourselves from the duty of producing what we need. When these are exhausted, we bet on new energy sources for which not even atomic power holds out any prospects. There is no way back in this case. If everything that is produced on the tilled lands of the United States at this time would be utilized as fuel, it would not yield enough energy for more than half the number of our cars, much less supply all our machines, trains, and industries.

The use of atomic energy forces mankind to face new, still more serious threats. To dispose of the radioactive waste from the atomic reactors involves difficulties of staggering dimensions. So far, all these issues have been swept under the rug. No conceivable solution is in sight. The costs for the permanent underground vaults protected from radiation, or specially constructed tanks or blocks for disposal in the depth of the oceans, are a minor obstacle compared to the complications raised by the future handling of this waste material. At any rate, it is reported that at this initial stage of the atomic age more radioactive waste has already accumulated than all the oceans of the globe could dilute to non-dangerous concentrations. A great portion of the waste will have to be stored for up to seven hundred years before its radioactivity has tapered off into less dangerous ranges. It is typical of the present attitude, whether indicated by lack of responsibility, poor information, or the pressure of daily chores, that as the only way out of this dilemma it has been proposed that we should launch this waste into space or to other planets, with long-distance missiles. Besides the costs and unwieldy precautionary measures (also against misfirings), this reveals our lack of responsibility for the consequences of such a cosmic contamination. If risks are to be avoided, merely the change of fuel rods in the reactors of the nuclear-powered freight-and-passenger ship *Savannah* will cost from ten to fifteen million dollars, more than the price of an entirely new freighter of conventional design. The construction of the *Savannah* itself amounted to more than 240 million dollars. The leakage of radioactive matter into the sea is far greater than anticipated but still considered at a non-dangerous level. It is hoped that in future ships of this kind constructional improvements would reduce this factor.

The contention is that so far all dangerous waste is under control. But huge sums are being paid for the safety from detrimental radiation. Nevertheless, it remains highly doubtful if we will be capable of keeping up this control if our energy provision is made to rely more heavily on nuclear power. The rivers located in the vicinity of the nuclear experiment stations in New Mexico, from which the surrounding cities obtain water for the inhabitants, recently were found to contain 1.4 to 1.6 times more radioactive substances than the allowed maximum quantity. Off the coast near the Windscale Laboratory in England it was discovered that the sea contains so much radioactive material that the sea algae, which the local inhabitants had been collecting and incorporating in their bread, carried a hazardous level of radioactivity through the accumulation of the radionuclide of ruthenium. Oceanographers of all nations agree that the ocean does not constitute a very safe dumping ground for atomic waste. The water from the depths easily reaches the surface in faraway, unexpected regions.

It is certainly food for thought that man has not managed to control far simpler forms of contamination in spite of extensive administrative efforts and legal precautions. The pollution involved in the global deliveries of mineral oils has become a public nuisance. It has been estimated that approximately a quarter million metric tons of crude oil is being pumped into the sea every year. Death, due to oil, is especially high among the marine birds. Beaches and coastal vegetation are also being ruined by oil, disposed of in the ocean.

Adjustment and Counterattacks

Living nature often fights back when we imagine we have conquered it. The antibiotics, which in the beginning seemed to promise victory over a series of ravaging diseases of humans, animals, and plants, have remained only partially effective. New strains of diseases as well as entirely new diseases have advanced on a broad front when their traditional competitors were eliminated. The staphylococci have become an insidious marauder to which numerous patients in maternity wards and hospitals fall victim, not the least in technologically and hygienically advanced countries like the United States. Ferocious strains of the common fecal microorganism—so-called coli-bacteria—have taken over and now take their toll in human lives. Their viability stems from their resistance to all known antibiotics. This species only rarely was detrimental to man. They existed long before the days of antibiotics but were presumably then held in check by numerous other disease microbes, now removed by these potent remedies.

Malaria is again advancing as a menace to man since the efficiency of the synthetic compounds introduced during the last war has tapered off by degrees owing to new, resistant protozoa. Such microorganisms have been found in Malaya, in parts of Java, Assam, and New Guinea. These strains resistant to synthetic remedies have turned out to be more vicious than the original ones. On the Southeast Asian scene United States military units in the recent struggles there have resorted to the conventional old standby of quinine to cope with malarial infestation. There was also the unpleasant discovery that the insect spray materials used have been circumvented by the disease-carrying mosquitoes. Even the trypanosomes have resisted man's chemical weapons. Consequently, both human sleeping sickness and the corresponding nagana disease of cattle are again on the increase in Africa.

It created almost a sensation when reported a few years ago that some Swedish flies had learned to live with DDT, the well-known fly-killing chemical. Later, DDT-resistant house flies were found in all parts of the globe. The same applies to ticks which spread so many perilous cattle diseases in both Australia and South Africa. Such resistant strains were found in warm areas. A certain fly, pestering cattle, was found to have become arsenic-resistant in 1937, resistant against benzohexachloride in 1948, and against DDT in 1956. Numerous additional examples could be given. This will be sufficient to underline the fact that man's conquests are by no means final. We are engaged in a constantly raging battle in which we have to make our countermoves prudently.

Canning of food (thermal processing) has brought in its trail a series of heat-loving bacteria and owing to these circumstances industry has been forced to revise its cooking times constantly upward in order to be safe from these new intruders. Something similar is the trend in dairies now facing the onslaught of an army of new bacterial strains which presumably built up their forces in the wake of traditional pasteurization. Much higher temperatures are nowadays required to achieve the desired prolongation in the keeping time of the milk, besides killing the pathogens. In a similar way the refrigeration and freezing techniques have favored the appearance of a number of cold-preferring strains and species, capable of growing at the temperature levels of conventional refrigeration, 45°F to 35°F. These circumstances in turn force us to apply even lower temperatures (34°F to 28°F) in order to halt the breakdown and spoilage of food. The conventional refrigerator has therefore become less efficient as a weapon against spoilage. New strains of fungi thrive on benzoic acid in concentrations of far greater strength than is traditionally employed in this preservative, still the leading one in use.

More examples could be related from the fight against plant diseases. The many new spray chemicals have in a surprising way opened up chances for new, or formerly insignificant diseases. The entire disease and pest picture has changed for many crops. Common diseases have been licked—ironically enough, in many cases those against which man already had found rather effective sprays—while new diseases emerged. As a rule these new resistant pests are considerably more difficult to cope with.

We, and especially the spokesmen of our technology, have a tendency to delude ourselves and believe that the chemical barriers which have been built around crops and livestock and as protection for man, are final defense positions, a kind of unassailable Maginot line. But we are in effect involved in a war which has to be waged permanently and relentlessly. Nature fights back and is not willing to yield sovereignty to man. New weapons must continually be forged, and each time victory becomes more difficult and costly. At the same time the existence of additional millions of people depends on the outcome of these efforts. If we really ponder over these facts of our existence and recognize this need for permanent vigilance—how vulnerable we are, how indispensable new weapons are in this relentless fight— we will see that we cannot afford moon travels as long as our existence on earth is in such serious jeopardy. We will realize that we need to meet the new malaria menace, the spread of hepatitis, the advance of wild oats, merely to mention a few examples.

The total annual loss through insect attacks on the growing crops on earth has been estimated at 21 billion dollars. Nobody should believe, however, that this chiefly reflects backwardness. Even in the United States, where all kinds of insect sprays are lavishly used, the annual loss amounts to about four billion dollars. Also in this case, not only are the harmful insect pests destroyed, but also their natural enemies—birds and other insects.

We deprive ourselves of their efficient aid in nature and have to take over all policing in nature ourselves. Experience proves that this is both a costly and a highly hazardous operation.

One of England's leading experts recently pointed out that the locusts used to be a menace to African agriculture only once each decade. By now this threat has become permanent, and several airplane squadrons are involved in constant spraying operations the year around in order to keep this insect under control. The same is true today in all continents (in the Middle East, in India, and elsewhere). A number of airborne units are in permanent headquarters and conduct constant raids.

As is well known, a number of human diseases are spread by insects. A survey concerning Africa proved that if these illnesses could be eliminated, this continent would be capable of feeding two billion people. It goes without saying that such surveys close their eyes to the food problem and merely calculate in terms of national net product and annual salaries. Yet, it demonstrates fairly well the squeeze in which the insects keep the Africans. The protective barrier which was built up by Europeans, Americans, and others for humans and animals by way of vaccines and insect sprays has been seriously disrupted through the postwar national upheavals of this continent. Most epidemics and epizootics have in recent years shown a mounting trend spreading out over new areas and involving thousands of acres of potentially tillable land now ineffectively used because of this debilitating malady.

Balance Indispensable

We register with just pride the fact that we produce so much more per man-hour, but we are inclined to disregard all the factory workers, miners, oil workers, sailors, and engineers of many categories on whom today's farmer depends (see Fig. 52). When we no longer have to produce what we use, but can merely take it out of the bank—from the oil and coal fields—we waste still more. Few farms produce their own energy any longer. The farmer no longer takes care of such activities as the making of butter, the milk delivery to the city, the butchering, brewing, baking, and preserving. These tasks have all been removed to huge new transformation centers. He does not even perform these operations in meeting his own needs. In many cases farmers buy the food for their livestock animals and may in this respect be likened more to an industrial enterprise taking its raw material from external sources. Many a farmer nowadays buys a great deal of food from outside; even bread, meat, milk, and eggs depend on these kinds of producing and processing abilities not to speak of canned, frozen, and dehydrated items.

In order to produce a certain quantity of food we use up more energy today than in earlier, less mechanized times. This constitutes another dilemma—the lack of economic consideration which we thoughtlessly label rationalization. Western technology can justly claim the everlasting honor of having alleviated human drudgery. But we must see to it that the costs are entered into the books and thus decide if we are actually willing to pay the price.

Several important aspects of the dilemma of present-day technology must be left out here for lack of space. Only briefly analyzed here is the long-range deterioration of the soils caused by modern irrigation, particularly when this is permanent and on the very soils which once were made to flourish and produce even lavishly. Large acreages have been transformed into deserts or marshes or have become so impregnated with salt that owing to this interference from man they can no longer be cultivated. This has considerably reduced the net acreage created through irrigation. In this context it is well worth remembering that the large irrigation installations resulting from modern engineering have so far not yielded more irrigated land than the small-scale irrigation measures with ditches, local canals, and drilled wells, such as those which have been created regionally by farmers in the thousands all over the globe. Hydraulic experts hold it unlikely that new gigantic projects will give mankind more than at the most one-fifth of the additional crop harvests required before the end of this century.

Other examples are the rising demands for energy, water, and labor by modern distribution techniques; the inability of modern medicine to cope with death through starvation, which in fact it is worsening by narrowing the scope of its operation; new types of soil deterioration, so-called compaction, caused by heavy agricultural machinery; the strain on plants and animals which follows the heavy yields; many symptoms of deficient quality of final products; and prematurely worn-out animals. The mass-production techniques which allow less and less space for wildlife as an essential element in man's existence are another menace.

Increased Realism A Necessity

In this situation the idea has been launched to go all out and give mankind the fifth freedom, basically through the aid of chemistry. It is proposed that man take over the gigantic synthesis of the forests and the fields and produce everything in factories. Nothing could be more out of touch with reality. Any kind of estimate proves the impracticality of such plans on any important scale. This was discussed in detail in chapter 18.

In all our reasoning and action we still move in a totally misleading time dimension. We speak about the development of the world's few remaining areas such as Alaska, New Guinea, and Siberia, but we forget that if, one day, we will have converted these regions to feeding bastions for the millions, the number of people will by then have grown vastly beyond what these areas will then yield in raw materials and foodstuffs.

Even with an intense development it will undoubtedly take fifteen to twenty years to develop Alaska, which by that time might be able to feed ten million people—less than one-sixth of one year's growth in the world population at the present time. The technical reshaping of the whole of Siberia will take at least twenty to thirty years, and the area may by then offer a livelihood and opportunities to, at the most, five hundred million. At the present time this constitutes less than eight years' net population growth in the world. With the geometric progression at which it is expanding at the moment, it will take less than six years to increase by this amount.

Nor has our gauge for the technical advances been adjusted to the population explosion. The available resources of coal and oil will last at the best two centuries. But this estimate is based upon the assumption that only we, the privileged of the world, are going to maintain our near-monopoly on these resources and satisfy our own accelerated consumption of these commodities. Little thought has been given to the two billion underprivileged in the world who may demand their fair share, the more likely as a considerable part of these deposits are located in their territories.

It is a masterful feat to have weeded with giant bulldozers 15 to 17 million acres of fallow fields in India in one single year. But this acreage brings food merely to one year's added population in that country. The world's largest fertilizer factory, which is located in Sindhri, India, was written up a great deal when it started some years ago. But India would need one such new factory every year, and still nothing would be done to alleviate the accumulated malnourishment among the masses now living in that country.

One sometimes wonders if we, the Westerners, are really sincere in our solemn assurances and manifold plans for technical aid to the underdeveloped countries. Already the task of supplying the present needy with a minimum would put the present world household to a serious test. Public education, research, and world politics certainly need to face reality. There have been periods in human history and developments in various countries, when man prided himself upon knowledge and based his action on the recognition of facts. Our time is more than anything else characterized by a large-scale escapism and a wave of disconcerting antirationalism. We in the western world want to enjoy the full benefits of science and knowledge in our technical development and daily life, but we refuse to pay attention to reality and indisputable facts as soon as they affect our own existence in any detrimental way. This big ostrich maneuver may not only deprive us of our leadership in the world—it may also result in a jolting awakening one day, the day of reckoning, or when the inevitable recognition of reality is enforced by the sheer logic of events.

The Make-Believe Game

The make-believe game will become more costly to us, the chief beneficiaries of the Golden Century that was. The longer we continue pretending in area after area that nothing is happening or has occurred, the greater the damage inflicted upon us. The creation of a number of small countries around the globe as a result of inflammatory nationalism is no solution to the staggering problems of our day, and those issues will all become more acute for every passing year. Greater internationalization is our only chance to progress. Most "isms," be they socialism, capitalism, communism, liberalism, or nationalism, have either completely lost their original meaning or have been forced to revise thoroughly their concepts under the pressure of a revolutionizing technological advancement and when faced with the needs and desperation of the billions. We can already discern a completely new class struggle which is emerging on quite another plane than the earlier one. The present day-to-day political struggle reflects this formidable tension. The choice facing the peoples of the world lies between solidarity or class struggle between the nations of the world. If these contending forces are not heeded and resolved in favor of a serious cooperation, the world is facing a cataclysm of staggering dimensions. If man will eventually survive, civilization may well vanish in this big upheaval.

Suppose . . .

It is astonishing how little human thought has seriously occupied itself with these cardinal problems. The details have enjoyed excessive attention. Has anybody seriously pondered how the world would look today if Malthus had been wrong, as so many economists still allege? If science, as too many pretend, had actually solved all problems and was able to produce unlimited quantities of food? If mankind since his time could have grown outside the biological resources immediately available in each period, unhampered by diseases and malnutrition? The human race would today doubtlessly number at least ten billion. Maybe we ought to be grateful that the earth is not in reality such a cornucopia, even though we, a privileged elite of a few hundred millions, have entertained this fallacy. This has been possible only because we have grabbed from all the corners of the world what we, the white race, could get hold of. In addition, we have reaped the yields of the North American prairie, the Argentine pampas, the South African veld, and the grasslands of Australia.

Do we really intend to continue along this road toward constantly growing billions? Are we going to condition our "have" nations to the thought of eating algal soup, grass pudding, wooden beefsteaks—merely for the dubious pleasure of having still more hundreds of millions thronging an overcrowded globe? Is it not time to make a complete turn around, as has happened earlier in the history of mankind, and be guided by knowledge of

facts, instead of persisting in a make-believe world created by
our concepts, images, and words, hoping for a miracle?

An overwhelming number of scientists, technologists, and
educators from various continents, travel around the globe
preaching, completely contrary to fact, about our unlimited resources and all the technological magic we can muster in areas
like irrigation, fertilizing, and genetics. In lieu of this reassuring
gospel they ought to make mankind aware of its real predicament, familiarize it with all the limiting factors of our existence,
recognize the undisputable fact that man needs water and very
specified carbon molecules to survive, that in the Dictionary of
Nature there exists no such concept as *limitless*, and that we
have gone far beyond the feeding resources of our globe. We
need to declare the Great War for Human Survival—but it is
getting late. Time is running out on us. It is five minutes to
twelve.

Goals Confused with Means

Most people are unable to see our almost terrifying inclination
to confuse means with goals. We are like children, richly endowed with all kinds of toys, and unable to understand that we
deal with realities and facts, not playthings. Instead we need an
overall plan for progress in the world, containing concrete out-
lines for Operation Man's Survival.

The prevailing escapism is of such dimensions that it is bordering on insanity. We enjoy a leisurely existence in a world of
illusion created by our words and fanciful concepts. When
somebody reminds us of reality, we talk ourselves out of it—as
do the insane. This is incidentally the definition given for insanity by Webster's dictionary.

It is necessary to keep in mind that "facts are stubborn things"
as somebody has said. The sooner we accept and adjust to
reality, the better is our chance to save at least part of the values

which western civilization has accumulated over a period of two to three thousand years. If we continue as hitherto, we are heading for inevitable disaster.

This is not the place to analyze the fascinating history of the Idea of Progress. It may merely be established that the traditional distinction in forces friendly and hostile to progress respectively, also has become grossly distorted through this lack of contact with reality. We are getting George Orwell's 1984 on a global scale and to the extent that those individuals who really want progress are labeled reactionary and those hostile to progress are looked upon as the true progressives. This mislabeling is also a dangerous game.

The Great Delusion

One of the great delusions of man throughout the centuries has been the belief that the resources of the earth are inexhaustible. The enormous riches which have overflowed particularly in the western countries, especially after the exploitation of the New World under European management, seemingly confirmed the correctness of this belief. In any case, it helped to lull public opinion at least in the part of the world then industrializing.

A second world war was needed—with its enormous demands on grain resources, forests, livestock, and mineral resources—to awaken a few nations to some understanding of the gravity of the situation. But this newly learned lesson was soon forgotten. If the world is to be able to avert a continued impoverishment and an accelerated depletion of its resources, a vastly improved management must be instituted parallel to an increased production. Science certainly can point out the way to a creative production, in which the world resources are utilized to the maximum without being wasted or used up, leaving future generations destitute. We have to strike a balance and recognize the basic distinction between renewable and non-renewable resources. We also need to recognize the ultimate limits to man's existence. Our spaceship is already getting seriously overcrowded. We have to show prudency and restraint in our future handling of human affairs.

Science and technology have much too often lent themselves to dazzling accomplishments which basically have been nothing but illusions, leaving behind them depleted and destroyed lands. The economists have been apt to occupy themselves largely with the credit side, overlooking the balance. The sums in the debit column have often been considerably larger. An enlightened public opinion could in this context make an important contribution solely by demanding a complete accounting. It is and remains no great feat to empty a filled larder. Our admiration should go to those who fill it. The tremendous values we destroy in return must also be replaced if our legacy to coming generations is not to vanish. To act in such ways that mankind one day stands without fuel, with depleted soils, destroyed forests, emptied mines, and squandered groundwater resources, is not to the credit of science and technology. Their true triumph would be almost the opposite of what now is done, namely the creation of a rich world increasingly filling its coffers to the benefit of future generations. A completely new evaluation is needed, with new guidelines for thought and action. The world needs new kinds of statesmen who pay more attention to the vital issues of mankind than to monkey tricks for the diversion of the masses.

Will the Awakening Come too Late?

In the midst of sweet dreams about new heavens and new earths, society is undergoing a transformation of such a nature as to scare anybody. The modern Frankenstein, the organization monster, emerges in all its paralyzing power. The tools of

destruction are also taking on the guise of inconceivable devilry, not merely through the release of the annihilating power of the atom but also through the destructive force of potent bacteria and the killing effect of their toxins, both mass-produced by microbiologists, or entirely new poison molecules put together by the chemists. They have placed mass-murder of man—genocide—within easy reach.

The worst calamity, however, is that we are being robbed of our biological environment. The artificial, supertechnical world into which we are now moving, which once seemed to give us so generous promises of human happiness and still, if wisely used, could bring just that, is instead threatening to stifle our pursuit of happiness and the fulfillment of humanity. There is good reason to halt and think, when in a country like the United States mental diseases show a steeply rising curve which has already reached the point where more hospital beds are occupied by the mentally disturbed than by people suffering from the diseases of the body.

The pill-eating is another sign of the escapism of our time. Refuge is taken in medicines, not as a cure or remedy but in order to reach a state of euphoria and to remove symptoms. The fireman who believes that he can extinguish a fire by shutting off the alarm clock instead of responding to the signals by dispatching the fire brigade, would be considered crazy. Nevertheless, millions of people react in a similar way. Phenacetin and salicylic acid have become almost daily routine medication. Many resort to tablets in preference to rest, food, and relaxation. The average Swiss above the age of twenty—and he is no worse than others—reportedly consumes ninety pain-relieving tablets per year.

The defense budget of the United States is presently exceeding 52 billion dollars, and the total armament costs of the world are estimated to be above 150 billion dollars per year. Whether one analyzes these staggering sums from the viewpoint of the United

States, the western world, or the world as a whole, this stands out as a clear denunciation of our capability to cope with the world's foremost issues of today: hunger, poverty, and disease. They testify to the failure of human intelligence and prudence. Man has vanished from the picture and the pursuit of happiness has been jeopardized.

This also exhibits in a glaring light the shortcomings of the economic profession as it persists in including in a gauge of prosperity the number of destructive weapons piling up. At the same time the United States food surpluses are described as almost catastrophic, bringing about worldwide disturbances on the food market. Yet, they are minor in relation to the world's needs and have in effect been accumulated over a period of several years. Their value even at the peak did not exceed eleven billion dollars and is presumably (1964) seven billion dollars. There should be ways of coping with these issues, certainly not overwhelming in magnitude or nature. Maybe the world economy has become too important an issue to be handled by the economists—to paraphrase the often quoted statement by Talleyrand about the military men and war.

References

BENHAM, F. *Economic Aid to Underdeveloped Countries*. London, Chatham, 1961, 150 pp.

BROWN, H., BONNER, J., and WEIR, J. *The Next Hundred Years*. New York, Viking, 1957, 193 pp.

COTTRELL, F. *Energy and Society*. New York, McGraw-Hill, 1955, 330 pp.

DE BEUS, J. G. *The Future of the West*. New York, Harper, 1953, 178 pp.

FURNAS, C. C. *The Next Hundred Years—The Unfinished Business of Science*. New York, Blue Ribbon Books, 1938, 434 pp.

HASS, E. *Der Menschenthron wankt*. Munich, F. Bruckmann, 1955, 250 pp.

HIGBEE, E. *The Squeeze, Cities Without Space*. New York, Morrow, 1960, 348 pp.

HYAMS, E. *Soil and Civilization*. London, Thames and Hudson, 1952, 312 pp.

JARRET, H. *Science and Resources: Prospects and Implications of Technological Advance*. Baltimore, Johns Hopkins, 1959, 250 pp.

LABRET, L. J. *Suicide ou Survie de L'Occident?* Paris, Les Éditions Ouvrières, 1958, 402 pp.

MARSH, G. P. *The Earth as Modified by Human Action*, 3rd edition. New York, Scribner, 1885, 629 pp.

MUMFORD, L. *The City in History*. New York, Harcourt, Brace and World, 1961, 656 pp.

ORDWAY, S. H. J. *Prosperity Beyond Tomorrow*. New York, Ronald Press, 1955, 208 pp.

PIDDINGTON, R. A. *The Limits of Mankind—A Philosophy of Population*. Bristol, Wright & Sons, 1956, 153 pp.

VERNON, R. *Metropolis 1985*. Garden City, Doubleday, 1963, 318 pp.

WYLIE, J. C. *The Wastes of Civilization*. London, Faber & Faber, 1959, 160 pp.

CHAPTER **21**

Food

or Moon

Rockets?

"IS it not too early to start playing with the moon? Damned moon! Let us instead get better food. We don't have enough housing or maternity wards. Consumer goods are expensive." These words are picked from a letter to the editor in *Pravda,* the Moscow newspaper, in the spring of 1960.

Communists hold no monopoly on this kind of thought. Vannevar Bush, director of research in several offices in the United States, in a congressional hearing in 1961, labeled operations with manned rockets a publicity stunt, a childish and irresponsible game, and unreasonably costly. Bush, chairman of the commission which mobilized the research resources of the United States during the Second World War, knew what he was talking about.

There are many on both sides of the Iron Curtain, and a still greater number in the great ocean of people outside these two camps, to whom the Cold War lacks meaning, and who observe with justified dismay how the world's resources are squandered in a vain contest to conquer the universe. From the viewpoint of this latter group, the two world wars were fatally wasteful of natural resources and brain power.

It is therefore high time that society, whether represented by the great powers or by small nations, evaluates the basic goals of research. If the present gigantic armament race may be called the great squanderer of millions, space research belongs in the same category and so also to a large degree does atomic research. A single space satellite costs more than the annual budget of a big university, and in many countries involved in this kind of research, much larger sums go to atomic research and space explorations than to the entire cultural budget. Even in the United States, 95 per cent of all federal funds for research are earmarked for these three big items. All other research, as in medicine, public health, biology, biochemistry, and engineering, is competing for the 5 per cent that remains—a frightful misappropriation reflecting a distorted scale of values.

Food for Space Travelers

The detailed attention which is at present devoted to the feeding of the space travelers of the future has a touch of the macabre. For this purpose more research money is often available than for the many unsolved tasks—many of which require urgent and extensive research—which are connected with the control of world hunger, the feeding of the one thousand millions which are now underfed and the additional eight hundred million malnourished. Human imagination and scientific knowledge are being mobilized to find a solution to the nutritional problems in connection with the brief space voyages, which, if they are actually realized, can easily be taken care of through fasting. For the faraway excursions, often described in a very deceptive manner, of fourteen years to Venus and other planets adjacent to the earth, it is easy to calculate the enormous freight trains, loaded with canned goods, oxygen, and water, which would be needed and which would have to be attached to the satellites if enough provisions were to be taken along. In this development work attention is concentrated on algal cultivation on feces, the rearing of fish fry or water fleas, and the raising of quail on board. There are also plans to have large chemical transformation factories built into the space vehicles. Many hope that somehow a way will be found to free man from elementary biological needs. The food on board is only a minor detail in the summons to arms on an enormous scale of the research resources of the world to conquer the universe.

Nobody can deny that behind a great deal of the intense research now going on in this field there are valid scientific questions. But the motivation and the goals set for this work deserve scrutiny and serious questioning. Would we not be more justified in devoting our efforts to our own little spacecraft, the earth, which certainly is well on the way to becoming overpopulated, crowded, and more filled with crucial issues than ever the moon rockets that now occupy the minds of such a large number of our scientists? In spite of all our scientific and technological progress, we have largely failed to master our own situation on earth. We are shocked when we hear that the moon travelers will have to drink their own washing water, but we forget that hundreds of millions on our earth already find themselves literally in this very same predicament. A high proportion of the water molecules which move down the rivers in the densely populated parts of Europe and the United States pass through a human body from ten to forty times before reaching the oceans. Literally, we drink with our dinner what our neighbor sluiced through his water closet in the morning—the same molecules, although in the meantime they have been subjected to purification in water works. The air and water pollution, to say nothing of the radioactive contamination, has in many regions taken on alarming dimensions.

Lack of Proportion

It is high time that responsible scientists sound the alarm. The lacking sense of proportion, and the astounding adaptation which most politicians exhibit, is reason for concern—perhaps they fear that they will not be regarded as progressive or up to date when it comes to voting the hundreds of millions—billions, rather—for atomic and rocket research. The crucial issues involved in providing for the billions of humans on our globe, our spaceship, are largely pushed aside and left to take care of themselves. At any rate this cardinal issue is seriously neglected or constantly belittled. In this context we encounter what would best be termed a demographic as well as a biological illiteracy of frightening dimensions.

If we scrutinize those research projects now under way in various countries, which may be classified as significant contributions to the battle against world starvation and world misery, we will find—even if we are very generous in our appraisal—that the appropriations for this purpose amount to a fraction of the sums used for atomic and rocket research. The economists have established that an annual investment of approximately ten billion dollars is needed for the developing world. This is less than one-tenth of the amount which is at present being used for military purposes, including rocket research. With an investment of that size, it is estimated that a modest increase of, at the most, 2 per cent could be achieved in the gross national product of the developing countries. At present, liberally estimated, two billion dollars annually, or one-fifth of the above-mentioned sum, is invested in the growth of world economy. The overwhelming part of this is used to provide the rich nations with still more oil, machinery, paper pulp, and so forth.

It is further worth noting how very modest the resources are that are available to the special activities of the United Nations:

TABLE 39

1962 Budget of the U.N.'s Specialized Agencies

	Funds Available in 1962 (million dollars)
Food and Agriculture Organization (FAO)	24
World Health Organization (WHO)	30
United Nations Children's Fund (UNICEF)	30
United Nations Economic & Social Council (UNESCO)	44
International Labor Organization (ILO)	15
U.N. Special Fund (SUNFED)	60

Note: The above figures include funds available from the Expanded Program of Technical Assistance in addition to the agencies' own sources.

The total budget of FAO, the Food and Agriculture Organization of the United Nations, is less than what is spent on shoveling snow each year in New York City. It is shameful that UNICEF, for its worldwide food distribution activities among 700 million underfed children, has only 30 million dollars at its disposal annually. and consequently reaches only one-tenth of these children, although even this is a remarkable accomplishment. But there are altogether almost one billion children in the world today, and at least 650 million of these succumb, prior to adulthood. Their voices are not heard through the clamor of our days.

Nine-tenths of the national research appropriations of the technologically developed world are earmarked for military research. It is in itself nothing new in world history that man has willingly staked more on war than on peace. What is new is that it is now being done in the name of science and that the scientists have entered the arena not merely as vouchers but as leaders and promoters. In this connection Hermann Göring's famous antithesis, "Guns or butter," is often quoted. This analogy is false, however, since the scientists now have taken the lead and increasingly identify themselves with the strivings of the politicians to offer grand spectacles. Bread and everyday needs have almost lost out in this process. The astronauts, the gladiators of our era, are not merely the popular heroes. They are also the symbols of modern scientific and technological mastership. Like the declining Roman Empire, we choose spectacles before bread.

Science Enters Politics

Yet, it ought to be evident that science and technology carry a key responsibility for our existence. This is reflected in the newly awakened interest in research which is demonstrated by both individual countries and the politicians of the world. In line with this trend England recently appointed a cabinet member to be solely in charge of research. A proposal for a similar cabinet post was presented in 1959 in the United States by the Academy of Science, and the President has for the last few years had a special advisor on matters of research and science. A similar development may be expected in several other countries. The power position of science and technology has increased enormously in the fifteen years since the end of the Second World War.

In its annual budget the U.S. Government appropriates more than five billion dollars for research and development. The enormousness of this sum is best illustrated by the fact that the total expenditure for these purposes did not reach this amount during the first four decades of this century. This sum is larger than the entire Federal budget a generation ago. The almost whirling rate at which these appropriations climb reflects the high costs of atomic explosions and of space endeavors.

The entire advancement of our society depends upon technological progress, whether we like it or not. It is impossible to launch war successfully, carry on industrial activities, or live a life fairly protected against disease and misery, without the constant protection and vigilance of science and technology. The sad thing is, however, that the politicians and, to an alarming extent, also the scientists and technicians have succumbed to the erroneous belief that only the military war or preparations for it can protect our existence. Consequently, nine-tenths of the huge appropriations for science and technological research are found in the column of military research. In this respect there is no great difference between East and West, or Europe and the United States. It is quite possible that the percentage is still higher, since it is known that money flows to various essential military projects from several other channels, which are never accounted for. A leading American businessman told me in the summer of 1960 that for the expenses of the space agency (National Aeronautics and Space Administration) there is no longer any ceiling. This was confirmed in the gigantic sums which were allocated in the spring of 1961—with practically unanimous political backing—for the staging of moon excursions. The estimated cost for these explorations during the next ten years is in the neighborhood of 34 billion dollars. In view of earlier experiences in the field, the experts hold it likely that this amount will be exceeded considerably. At the same time several leading universities in the United States are semistarved for funds and are not able to take care of their research and teaching obligations. Since this was written an interesting sobering can be discerned, presumably not yet as the result of an overall reevaluation of priorities but in a genuine and immediate concern for the availability of personnel and experts to keep society going.

Huge Underdeveloped Sectors

The historians of the future will discover—if archive material covering this development is available—to their astonishment the disproportion between the funds which in our age were allocated to areas like space and atomic research and those for biology and medicine. This unreasonably lopsided distribution of available means also has indirect repercussions on the recruitment of the young and their choice of profession. They go where the resources are, or they are attracted by the fame to be gained in this overglamorized field. It is already becoming difficult to find qualified applicants for jobs in vital areas such as medicine, agriculture, and sanitation engineering, much less for the training required for a further development of these key disciplines. A number of significant areas of humanistic research are also on a starvation budget. It is at present not even possible to fill the most urgent needs in areas of great importance in the international fields, such as linguistics and anthropology. The world would need more or less a doubling in the number of language teachers, plus a large-scale effort to spread knowledge among the millions. The small percentage of individuals now engaged in international work are poorly trained in languages. The extreme utilitarianism and—it should be willingly admitted—to a certain extent the pressing daily needs, have long been allowed to exclude all sound long-range planning. If we continue along this road we will soon reach the point where the existence of culture itself will be threatened or at any rate seriously undermined.

It must be understood that this analysis in no way should be construed as directed against space research as such. This discipline has its rightful place as a legitimate field for technical and scientific pursuits. But it is used here as a symbol for the present distortion of values and lack of understanding of man's true predicament. The intention is merely to point out that in the competition for funds and personnel there are many other areas which are far more vital to mankind. It must be labeled as almost the peak of insanity that this particular field of research is given larger resources and more money than all other research added together. If we think we should go to the moon, it is not necessarily self-evident that we must go tomorrow. We have managed fairly well without such celestial excursions during several thousand years of human history. There is no reason to be so frightfully overambitious, especially as we desperately need all these resources for tasks which are at least equally intriguing and fascinating and, for the future of mankind, much more urgent and momentous than these space adventures.

The Great Gamble Coming to an End

In order to tackle the great problems of our time we have to rid ourselves of one-eyed technological thinking. We have every reason to admire the scientific knowledge and technical skill which lie behind the space accomplishments of the postwar period, so much more so because this research has widened the boundaries of our knowledge on many important points. But the belief that this is the only way to acquire this information is the tragic mistake of our time. In many cases it is clearly the most expensive way. We have followed the path of least resistance— it is easier to win the ears of the politicians with the new and the fantastic. But the day of reckoning will dawn, and it is probably not so far away, when science and technology will be held responsible before mankind. Men of all nations will then become aware that the spectacular promises given by dam constructors, plant breeders, soil scientists, and chemists have not been fulfilled.

Certainly, we know the technique for desalting of seawater and for irrigation of vast acreages, for the profitable use of fertilizers and for the preservation of foods. But we have constantly been confusing means and goals. We are like Captain Ahab in *Moby Dick*, who in his heart had some glimpse of this: "All my means are sane, my motive and my object mad."

We live and act as if our culture bore a kind of protective seal of immortality. Even when we see evident signs of its decay and the terrifying magnitude of our gamble as verified in cold figures, we refuse to halt and mobilize the brain power of the world for the necessary rescue operation. Nor do we seem to want to create a better civilization in place of the old one, to move from extreme vulnerability to greater safety and assured viability.

Universities of a New Type

The entire basic conceptual thinking about research must be changed. We have largely left it to politicians and social reformers to build the world of mankind. The result is an ugly, assymmetric, and oversized edifice but with individual details of harmony and beauty. Science, technology, and research must move into a completely new dimension. The analysis and study of details is no longer enough. The total picture must be considered, whether in regard to foods, the human body, or the social organism.

We have reaped enormous benefits from our largely analytic approach, but our mistake lay in the belief that by piecing together all the detailed information gained this way we would arrive at a true picture made up of the analytical mosaic pieces. All experience and widened research soon discovered that many mosaic pieces never fitted into any picture of reality.

We have therefore in the field of natural science and technology to engage in synthetic research—large-scale coordinated efforts—to arrive at conclusions valid in reality. In the pursuit of this kind of research new findings will be made that overlook the causal relationships revealed, and completely new natural laws will be laid down.

In order to achieve these aims it is quite possible that universities of an entirely new type are needed. In lieu of single, positive or negative, causal factors, reality confronts us with a multitude of closely interrelated factors mutually affecting each other. What counts in describing reality will in most cases be the limiting factors. Most of our academic teaching has resorted to a simplified scheme of analyzing one factor at a time—a unicausal outlook.

To combat the present, largely irresponsible, optimism—which in the end is nothing but cowardice and escapism—a harsh realism is required which mobilizes the resources of science and technology, not to speed up the bewildering downward race but to organize a battle for our survival, to start climbing again the road of true progress. In order to divert the attention of the masses from our incompetent handling of the earth's problems, we try to hypnotize them with space adventures.

Unfortunately there are too few people who have grasped the fact that man has already outgrown the universe. There is a great deal of glib and cheerful talk going on about how space traffic in the future will ease the pressure on our own planet. Disregarded completely is the vexing humanitarian problem of deciding which thousands shall leave our spaceship in distress, for a hazardous lengthy space trip with questionable destination and risky living. But to return to earth and the present situation—nobody seems to have made the effort to figure out what this would mean technically. Simple calculations show that with the present population growth we would be faced with the overwhelming problem of sending away in spaceships more than 7,500 persons per hour around the clock, month after month, year after year. And ten years from now the number may be ten thousand per hour! The Holy Writ states: "For what does it profit a man, if he gains the whole world and forfeits his soul?" A paraphrase of this biblical text, fit for our time and age would be: "What does it profit man if he gains the universe but loses the earth?"

Peanuts to Essentials

The famous Aswan Dam requires a total investment of nearly one billion dollars. The annual United States budget for space now exceeds 5 billion dollars per year. A first-rate fertilizer plant costs, depending upon size, from 1 to 5 million dollars to build. The designs alone for the moon ship—the Apollo Project—exceed 25 million dollars in costs.

Among the fields which now have to operate on peanuts, compared to the funds for rocket research, are meteorology, climatology, seismic studies, oceanography, fisheries research, industrial microbiology, genetics, research concerning the growing processes of humans, animals, and plants, as well as psychiatry. This is an arbitrary selection. Why should not modern radio telescopes, electronic data machines, accelerators for high-energy studies, and many other expensive instruments be used also for more general fields than space research?

The United States program for oceanographical research has been considerably expanded in the sixties and yet ocean exploration receives a pittance compared to the money resources thrown into space—almost a hundred times greater. There must be something fundamentally wrong with our appraisal that leads to such obviously absurd conclusions.

The Poor and Hungry World—Amazed Spectators

One of the best appeals which this author has read and which undoubtedly expresses the thoughts of millions, not to say billions, of people, was the magnificent address given by the Brazilian chief delegate, Dr. Schmidt, at the opening of the plenary session of the United Nations General Assembly in 1959. But it is indicative of how poor is the understanding of these issues when viewpoints of this kind are not even noticed or considered worth reporting in leading world papers such as the *New York Times*. This paper, which reports what leading politicians say and gives the text of official speeches, did not even mention Dr. Schmidt's pertinent remarks. Among other things, he put the penetrating question of how it could be explained that the Cause of Man has become the most neglected of all present-day issues. "The Golden Age of Mankind still seems to lie in a far-off future," he stated. "In spite of all the dazzling accomplishments by technology, man is not given priority," he said.

To the millions of hungry and diseased living in misery and

poverty, people for whom quite modest amounts of money would often work miracles, it must seem absurd that sums frequently in the billions are channeled to astronautic adventures and to the polishing and further refinement of our means of destruction. These have long ago exceeded what is justified for military efficiency. The world's present stockpiles of atomic bombs seem to the layman to be more than enough for our annihilation. Experts report a shocking overkill capacity.

Is Common Sense Dethroned?

When viewing the world of today, there is good reason to ask the question: Has all common sense been thrown overboard? Is the world so completely devoid of leaders who can speak up on behalf of reason, or are they all under the spell of the cosmic metaphysics? Or have the spokesmen of technology become so hypnotized by this opportunity to play on a really big scale, that they recklessly throw overboard almost all the fascinating projects which the problems of earth offer?

Or is it possibly a question of complete capitulation? The earth is surrendered. It is too perplexing to handle. How can it otherwise be explained that so few, so infinitely few, of the world's leading scientists and technicians have sounded alarm. The space projects seem to be sacrosanct in the East as well as in the West. Is this childish contest for prestige going to be the acme of human strivings? Have we really lost all ambitions in behalf of Mother Earth?

All our ingenuity and brave pioneering efforts are truly needed to make the earth a happy place for mankind. Can we actually afford to ignore so completely the material aspects when the whole world's health, nutrition, and well-being are in the balance? To throw money into the sea of space is a new form of wastefulness, unique in the history of the world. Naïve parallels are drawn with Columbus' discovery of the rich American twin continent—the unexpected gain of this man's stubborn voyages to an alleged India. His discovery enriched a whole world, not the least on the food front. Such surprises are practically excluded in the conquest of space, which, at the most, may contribute to an acceleration of our impoverishment.

Is the Robot Needed?

We also see the contours of an automatized robot society taking shape, created to relieve human drudgery but which also makes man superfluous. This is a strange goal in a world which has only one surplus, namely that of men. Science and technology direct their efforts toward the task of making man superfluous, and at the same time we allow the majority of humans to live a life of suffering and hunger.

There is not much imagination needed to discern that we are at the present time at one of the great crossroads in human history. Are we really prepared to give up Man and live entirely in the world of abstractions and idle chimeras? We will have to pay dearly for this flight from reality. Day-to-day politics constantly reminds us how unreasonable it is to believe that the two categories—the "have" nations and the "have-not" nations—are either instituted by God or are merely the result of differences in education and skill. We refuse to see that the European peoples have stolen a march on the world and have helped themselves to a disproportionate part of the globe's natural resources in forest, soil, and minerals. There is no question but that we, the western nations, have been greatly favored in human history.

The Victory Crown

Nothing less is required than a thorough revision of the priority lists of mankind and a complete reorientation as to what we consider essential to Man's future. Such a shift may be necessary too in order to supersede the Cold War and attain a world condition which better deserves the epithet peaceful. A common battle against starvation, disease, and misery, and above all against ignorance, requires a radical change in the goals of world science. The victory in the fight for world supremacy may not go to the one who has accomplished the most spectacular celestial fireworks but rather to the party which does something efficient to alleviate the distress among the peoples on earth. In reality, these unfortunates in their suffering care little if their saviour labels himself capitalist, communist, or liberal. The victory crown will go to the one who takes the lead in what today is the most essential task: to mobilize the resources of the globe, not for continued multiplication of human distress, with still more billions desperately short of everything, but for the noble task of striking a balance and making us recognize the very obvious limitations of our own spaceship and to act accordingly.

References

ARDANT, G. *Le Monde en Friche*. Paris, Presses Universitaires de France, 1959, 307 pp.

BERNAL, J. D. *World Without War*. New York, Monthly Review Press, 1959, 308 pp.

BORGSTROM, GEO. "Back to Reality," *Minimizing International Tensions*, Social Science Series, No. 11. East Lansing, Michigan State University Press, 1962, 180 pp.

BRINTON, C. *The Fate of Man*. New York, Braziller, 1961, 532 pp.

BROWN, H. *The Challenge of Man's Future*. New York, Viking, 1954, 290 pp.

CLARK, C. *The Conditions of Economic Progress*. London, Macmillan, 1951, 584 pp.

COALE, A. J. and HOOVER, E. M. *Population Growth and Economic Development in Low-Income Countries*. Princeton, N.J., Princeton University Press, 1958, 389 pp.

COOK, F. J. *The Warfare State*. New York, Macmillan, 1962, 376 pp.

HEILBRONER, R. L. *The Future as History*. New York, Harper, 1960, 217 pp.

————. *The Great Ascent*. New York, Harper and Row, 1963, 192 pp.

HOFFMAN, P. G. *World Without Want*. New York, Harper and Row, 1962, 144 pp.

JASPERS, K. *Die Atombombe und die Zukunft des Menschen*. Munich, Piper, 1956, 500 pp.

KVATCH, J. W. *Human Nature and the Human Condition*. New York, Random House, 1959, 211 pp.

LABORIT, H., and MORAND, P. *Les Destins de la Vie et de l'Homme*. Paris, Masson, 1959, 249 pp.

MEIER, R. L. *Science and Economic Development: New Patterns of Living*. New York, Wiley, 1956, 266 pp.

MUDD, S. (ed.) *The Population Crisis and the Use of World Resources*. The Hague, W. Junk, 1964, 565 pp.

PROCHNOW, H. V. *World Economic Problems and Policies*. New York, Evanston, and London, Harper & Row, 1965, 382 pp.

ROSTOW, W. W. *The Stages of Economic Growth—A Non-Communist Manifesto*. Cambridge, Cambridge University Press, 1960, 179 pp.

SHONFIELD, A. *The Attack on World Poverty*. London, Chatto & Windus, 1960, 244 pp.

STALEY, E. *The Future of Underdeveloped Countries*. New York, Harper, 1954, 410 pp.

WILSON, H. *The War on World Poverty*. London, Gollancz, 1953, 232 pp.

Index

INDEX

Italic page numbers refer to figures or tables.

Y